A Natural History of the Butterflies and Moths of Shropshire

I send you wildflowers

This book is dedicated to John Norton M.B.E., F.G.S., F.R.E.S. in recognition of his contribution to the study of natural history in Shropshire.

The publishers wish to acknowledge with thanks financial help which has made the publication of this book possible.

Those who have contributed are the Field Studies Council, Butterfly Conservation Trust Ltd., Caradoc and Severn Valley Field Club, Wildlife Trust's Leighton Fund and an anonymous source.

You never know, you might find it here
On Black Country Rock

David Bowie, 1970

A Natural History of the Butterflies and Moths of Shropshire

Adrian M. Riley F.R.E.S.

Department of Entomology and Nematology, Arable Crops Research Institute, Rothamsted Experimental Station, Harpenden, Hertfordshire, AL5 2JQ.

SWAN HILL
PRESS

First published in the UK in 1991 by
Swan Hill Press

A catalogue record for this book is
available from the British Library.

ISBN 1 85310 249 0

Printed in England by Livesey Ltd., Shrewsbury.

Swan Hill Press

An Imprint of Airlife Publishing Ltd.
101 Longden Road, Shrewsbury SY3 9EB, England.

Contents

Foreword

Introduction

Shropshire — The County   1
    The Oswestry Uplands
    Morraines, Mosses and Meres
    The North-eastern Plain
    The Wrekin Spur
    Welsh Border Vales
    The West Central Hills
    The Clun Forest Uplands
    Ludlow-Wenlock Escarpment
    The Clee Hills Platform
    The Lower Severn Valley

Recording and Conservation in Shropshire   5

Natural History of the species of Macrolepidoptera   13

Appendix I: Inventory of Microlepidoptera recorded
   in Shropshire   143

Appendix II: Distribution maps of the butterflies of Shropshire   170

Acknowledgements and recorders mentioned in the text   181, 182

Gazetteer of localities mentioned in the text   183

References and Bibliography   186

Index of Scientific Names   192

Index of English Names   201

List of Illustrations

Fig. One: Map of Shropshire showing major towns and bordering counties.
Fig. Two: Geographical regions with total numbers of macrolepidoptera recorded from each.
Fig. Three: Moth diversity at the Rothamsted Insect Survey light trap at Preston Montford, 1978–1987.
Fig. Four: Annual totals of brimstone and figure of eight moths at Preston Montford, 1978–1987.
Fig. Five: Annual totals of six-striped rustic and square-spot rustic moths at Preston Montford, 1978–1987.
Fig. Six: Sheet used for collating records for this book.
Fig. Seven: Ordnance Survey 10 km squares with scatter of 2 km tetrads from which records have been received.
Fig. Eight: Tetrads from which butterfly records have been received.
Figs. Nine-Seventeen: Butterfly distribution maps.

Plate One: Llanymynech Rocks
Plate Two: Whixall Moss
Plate Three: Prees Heath
Plate Four: Middletown Hill
Plate Five: Hinkshay
Plate Six: Clun Valley
Plate Seven: Ashes Hollow
Plate Eight: A meadow on Wenlock Edge
Plate Nine: Brown Clee
Plate Ten: Wyre Forest
Plate Eleven: Moths which may now be extinct in Shropshire
Plate Twelve: Some unusual varieties found in Shropshire
Plate Thirteen: Small skipper
Plate Fourteen: Dingy skipper
Plate Fifteen: Wood white
Plate Sixteen: Green hairstreak
Plate Seventeen: Purple hairstreak
Plate Eighteen: White-letter hairstreak
Plate Nineteen: Small blue
Plate Twenty: Silver-studded blue
Plate Twenty One: White admiral larva
Plate Twenty Two: White admiral
Plate Twenty Three: Small tortoiseshell
Plate Twenty Four: Comma
Plate Twenty Five: Small pearl-bordered fritillary
Plate Twenty Six: Pearl-bordered fritillary
Plate Twenty Seven: High brown fritillary
Plate Twenty Eight: Dark green fritillary
Plate Twenty Nine: Grayling
Plate Thirty: Gatekeeper
Plate Thirty One: Large heath
Plate Thirty Two: Ringlet

Foreword

I have no qualifications to write a foreword to this wonderful little book except for the fact that, like the butterflies and moths which are its subject, I love plants and I love Shropshire.

Shropshire is a well-worn county, patchworked with small fields, hedgerows and copses where agriculture still holds sway. It also boasts the birthplace of the Industrial Revolution existing cheek to jowl with a new high tech town, within the confines of which nature has done a wonderful job healing old sores and creating new beauty. The same is true of its many canals and disused railway tracks — nature heals sores in a miraculous way. There is also a wealth of more natural things, the meres and rivers, wetlands and water meadows, bogs, heaths, copses and woodlands. Oh, what woodlands, carpeted with mosses and leafy liverworts. Then there are the high spots, complete with cliffs and quarries and mine spoil and the glories of the Stiperstones Natural Reserve by name and nature.

It was on this broad canvas of flower-decked habitat that I first cut my botanical wisdom teeth whilst walking with Frances Rose, Charles Sinker and many others. It is within this same canvas that you can now seek the fragile beauty of the butterflies and moths which still make Shropshire their home.

Like them we depend on plants for the food we eat and the oxygen we breath, please walk with care. If you are not already a member of the Shropshire Wildlife Trust then please join, that is the best way for you to help ensure that all this fragile beauty will be there for your children to enjoy.

David Bellamy
Bedburn, January 1991

Introduction

In 1985 the Shropshire Trust for Nature Conservation published The *Ecological Flora of the Shropshire Region* (Sinker *et al.* 1985). As well as cataloguing the flora of the county it also gave a detailed account of its topography, geology and climate. David Bellamy, in his foreward to the book, said it is ". . . . a Domesday Book for Shropshire against which all future change will be measured."

Naturalists of all disciplines in Shropshire are fortunate to have at their disposal such a valuable reference to the physical and botanical nature of the county. We now have an enviable opportunity, if not a duty, to complement this latter-day Domesday Book with permanent accounts of those groups of fauna and flora within our own fields of expertise so that, from a mosaic of scientific knowledge and experience, a complete picture of Shropshire's natural heritage will emerge.

Since the publication of the Victoria County History in 1908 there has been no attempt to record comprehensively the history and status of the Shropshire Lepidoptera. The present work brings together the knowledge of lepidopterists past and present who have recorded in the county, thereby providing for the first time, a complete history of the 624 species of macrolepidoptera which have occurred here as well as a species inventory of the 639 species of microlepidoptera so far recorded. The records cover almost 200 years and the changes in status of many species over this period often reflect the changes in our own attitudes to, and the effect we have on, our countryside. The Lepidoptera constitute an excellent barometer by which we can measure these changes. This is particularly true of the butterflies as they are conspicuous, easy to identify and their beauty often catches the eye of the layman. Continuous recording of woodland butterflies, such as the white admiral, can show us how well, or badly, woodland fauna are adapting to changing forestry practices. Likewise, monitoring the numbers of gatekeeper butterflies on farmland may provide an early warning system against the removal of too many hedgerows, with the implications this may have for other dependant wildlife.

For such recording and observations to be most useful, a yardstick is required ". . . against which all future change will be measured." The author believes that this book will provide a foundation for future studies on the butterflies and moths of the county of Shropshire.

A.M. Riley

Shropshire — The County

Shropshire is one of the largest inland counties of England, covering approximately 4,400 square kilometers of extremely varied countryside. It lies on the English-Welsh border, surrounded in the north-west and west by Clwyd and Powys and in the north east and east by Cheshire and Staffordshire, and the south by Hereford and Worcester (Fig. One). There is no coastline. The county can be divided into separate regions according to its topography (Fig. Two). Although Sinker *et al.* (1985) have discussed the geography of the county in great depth, the following short description of each area will help to give an overall impression of their basic characteristics. Fig. Two shows the number of macrolepidoptera species recorded from each of these geographical regions.

The Oswestry Uplands (Fig. Two, area A and Plate One)

These consist mainly of high pastures on Carboniferous rocks with low-lying Permotriassic sandstones to the east. The general character is of high undulating hills and valleys, with small woods and ancient established grassland leys. The soils range from shales and boulder clay in the high sheep-grazed hills, to humose, sandy loam and peat in the lowlands.

The area is very sparsely populated. Oswestry is the main market town for the surrounding hill farmers.

The region has a fine historical list of Lepidoptera but, despite the great potential, it has not been well recorded in recent years. Llanymynech Rocks and Llynclys Common are home to pearl-bordered fritillary and brown argus butterflies.

The Morraines, Meres and Mosses (Fig. Two, area B and Plate Two)

This large area includes probably the most interesting features in Shropshire; the meres and mosses. In stark contrast to the last region it is flat and low-lying. The underlying rocks are Triassic and Permotriassic over which lie peat soils in the north and loam in the south.

The ancient woodlands and grasslands around Shrewsbury have given way to modern intensive agriculture, leaving few ecologically interesting sites, though the mixed woodland and heathland on Haughmond Hill still supports such important species as the grayling butterfly.

The peatlands are large flat expanses with deep-cut channels made during peat extraction. Fortunately, the mosses have escaped both wholesale drainage and ecological succession. There is very little disturbance of these habitats as only small scale peat extraction takes place.

Recording in modern times has been mainly on Whixall and Wem Mosses. Many entomologists from all over Britain have visited them as they are sites for several very interesting species including the large heath butterfly and the northern footman moth. Several entomological societies from outside Shropshire, including the Lancashire and Cheshire Entomological Society, regularly visit these fascinating areas to record the Lepidoptera.

North-eastern Plain (Fig. Two, area C and Plate Three)

A flat area of intensive agriculture which stretches from the northern county boundary southwards to the New Town of Telford. The rocks consist mainly of Permotriassic sandstones with occasional drifts of Pleistocene gravels.

Early industrialization in the areas around what is now Telford New Town has left some interesting habitats including the heather-clad pit mounds around Dawley, though these have been drastically reduced since the establishment of the New Town. However, extensive ecologically oriented landscaping in Telford should produce interesting results in future years and these should be closely monitored.

The established centres of relatively high population have been the source of much recording in this region. Several Rothamsted Insect Survey light traps have operated including one at Wellington and one at Stoke-on-Tern. The author lived and recorded in Wellington for many years. The woods around Wellington are home to the small pearl-

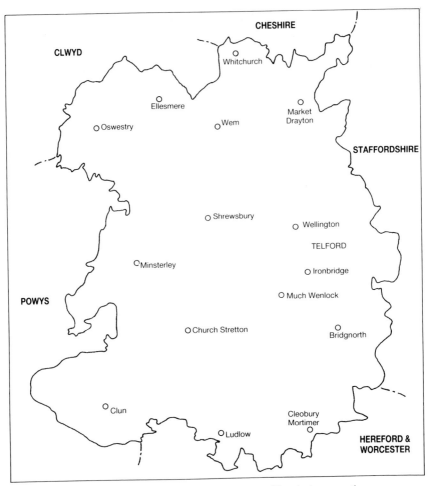

FIG. ONE. Map of Shropshire showing major towns and bordering counties.

bordered and silver-washed fritillary butterflies and alder kitten and Blomer's rivulet moths. Another important species, the white-letter hairstreak butterfly, has suffered badly as a result of Dutch elm disease which has decimated its foodplant in this area.

Welsh Border Vales (Fig. Two, area D and Plate Four)
Upland grazing is the main agricultural practice in this area; leaving the valleys wooded. However some of the lowland flood plains are used as hay meadows. The rock types here are Ordovician dolerite, basalt and Silurian sediments. The attractive speckled yellow moth is fairly common in some of the woodlands but, unfortunately, the area has been relatively poorly recorded.

Wrekin Spur (Fig. Two, area E and Plate Five)
This small area is dominated by the Wrekin hill which rises to 407 m above the North-eastern Plain. It mainly consists of Pre-Cambrian igneous rock with outcrops of Carboniferous limestone.
    There are many ley fields and large areas of mature oak and birch woodland. Important

Lepidoptera species are the white-letter hairstreak and dark green fritillary butterflies and the alder kitten, clouded magpie and scalloped shell moths. Riley, Minshall and Lewis have recorded extensively in this area; otherwise it has been rather surprisingly ignored.

Clun Forest Uplands (Fig. Two, area F and Plate Six)
This area still contains some old-established woodland but it is heavily interspersed with less ecologically valuable coniferous plantations. Fragmented mixed woodland still survives in the valleys which are known locally as Dingles. Most of the hillside slopes are infested with bracken and have little to offer the lepidopterist. Perhaps this explains why this area is so poorly recorded; only Bucknell, in the extreme south-west, has been studied well. The wet upland gley soils are not suitable for arable farming, and grazing is the main agricultural practice on the high leys. The lowland areas are intensively farmed.

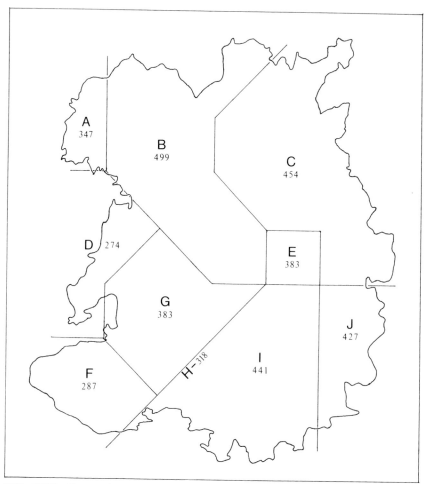

FIG. TWO. Geographical regions of Shropshire showing the number of species of macrolepidoptera recorded in each. **A:** Oswestry Uplands; **B:** Morraines, Mosses and Meres; **C:** North-Eastern Plain; **D:** Welsh Border Vales; **E:** Wrekin Spur; **F:** Clun Forest Uplands; **G:** West Central Hills; **H:** Ludlow-Wenlock Escarpment; **I:** Clee Hills Platform; **J:** Lower Severn Valley.

West Central Hills (Fig. Two, area G and Plate Seven)

The Longmynd, which is the main geographic feature of this area, is a heather and bracken dominated upland on Pre-cambrian Longmyndian rock. It has wet flushes with many fast hill streams. Some old woodlands have survived around Bishops Castle and the region has more old ley grassland than any other in the county.

The Stretton geological fault is a natural corridor along which runs a main road and a railway.

The area has an excellent historical list of Lepidoptera. Church Stretton and the Longmynd were the traditional collecting grounds of Newnham and Harding who published regularly in the entomological journals around the turn of the century. Newnham was the author of the Lepidoptera section of the Victoria County History for Shropshire. The Longmynd is famous nationally for being a former site for the small lappet moth which may now be extinct in Britain. Unfortunately there has been little recording in the area over recent years and perhaps the small lappett is still there, waiting to be rediscovered. In the extreme north of the region is Earl's Hill, a Shropshire Trust for Nature Conservation reserve, which boasts 34 butterfly species.

Ludlow-Wenlock Escarpment (Fig. Two, area H and Plate Eight)

This is a Silurian limestone ridge running south-west to north-east across southern Shropshire. It has been mined in many areas for limestone and this has produced ruderal-type habitats which are very interesting entomologically as continuous re-colonisation can be seen in these areas. The old grasslands are suitable for arable and livestock farming. Undeveloped areas are consequently now few in number but those which have survived are on the popular Wenlock nature trail and so are protected environments.

Clee Hills Platform (Fig. Two, area I and Plate Nine)

The area is dominated by the three Clee Hills of Carboniferous dolerite, coal measures and limestone, surrounded by Old Red sandstone and Silurian Downtonian rocks under Argillic Brown Earths. Clee Hill, Titterstone Clee and Brown Clee ascend in height from south to north with the latter rising to 540 m — the highest point in Shropshire.

Ludlow, which displays much splendid historic architecture, and Cleobury Mortimer are the major centres of population. The main agricultural practices are upland grazing and, in the lowlands, intensive arable farming.

The uplands are mostly bracken-dominated though there are many old grasslands. The climate can be harsh with snow remaining on the high ground until May in some years. There are some interesting entomological sites in this area, mainly in the wooded valleys. One interesting upland site is Boyne Water on the Brown Clee, which is a lake surrounded by a small plantation. Other noteworthy areas in the region are Whitcliffe and Mortimer Forest near Ludlow, where the silver-washed fritillary occurs.

Lower Severn Valley (Fig. Two, area J and Plate Ten)

This region is flat with a comparatively mild climate. It is dominated by the Wyre Forest which is an ancient mixed woodland that straddles the county boundary into Hereford and Worcester. Some very important woodland species are found here, including at least four species of fritillary, the white admiral and wood white butterflies. Other well recorded sites are the mixed woodland at Dudmaston Hall, and Chorley Coppice.

Recording and Conservation in Shropshire

A brief history of recording

Shropshire's Lepidoptera have been relatively poorly recorded in recent years. The bibliography gives a comprehensive list of the various articles regarding individual species noted in the county, and several short lists for small areas of particular interest. These mainly concern the butterflies of regions such as Church Stretton which are popular with tourists.

Three detailed accounts of the Shropshire Lepidoptera have been published to date: The Lepidoptera section of The Victoria County History (V.C.H.) was written by F. B. Newnham and published in 1908. This gave a list of 490 macrolepidoptera species with brief notes on their known distribution in the county at that time. Although the coverage was sparse (the main areas of recording being Church Stretton, Market Drayton, Calverhall and the Wyre Forest) it has provided an important yardstick by which to measure the present distribution and status of many species. This is particularly so with the butterflies as the notes for these were more detailed than those for the moths.

The second list was published by K. G. V. Smith in serial form in the *The Entomologist* between 1952 and 1956. This cited records of 313 species of macrolepidoptera noted between 1921 and 1956. Those species recorded in the V.C.H. were not included.

The third publication was a provisional list published by A. M. Riley in 1980. It contained 479 species of macrolepidoptera which had been recorded, mainly from central Shropshire, between 1965 and 1980 with a brief indication of their relative abundance. This list was greatly enhanced by the work of David Smith who remains the authority on the county's Butterflies, and Rothamsted Experimental Station who operated four light traps in the county during this period. A handful of the species included in this list were insufficiently substantiated and have been omitted from the present work.

In 1950, W. J. Pendlebury completed a list of Shropshire Lepidoptera which consisted mainly of records extracted from the journal of the Caradoc and Severn Valley Field Club *The Record of Bare Facts*. Although this bound manuscript is unique, it was kindly donated to the author by its owner, Mr. Richard Warren, and has proved to be a very valuable source of information.

It is notable that, as time has passed, a much wider area of the county has been worked; a full gazetteer of recorded localities is given at the end of the book. This is mainly due to a greater public awareness of natural history (particularly Lepidoptera) and the environment. This interest is supported at the present time by a wealth of available literature. Most bookshops stock butterfly field guides whereas this was certainly not the case at the turn of the century when entomological literature was both expensive and difficult to obtain. This restricted the pastime to a small, select group of learned (and often wealthy) people.

Increased mobility has also helped recording and comparison with the V.C.H. and the present list illustrates this well. At the turn of the century travel was quite a problem, transport mainly being restricted to either horse or foot. However, this did have some advantages in that the areas being worked were recorded intensively and with great efficiency. Newnham's intimate knowledge of the Church Stretton area and F. C. Woodforde's copious notes on the Lepidoptera of the Market Drayton district are good examples. Nowadays, the motor car enables the enthusiastic recorder to cover many widely separated sites in a single day. Also it is now easy for lepidopterists from outside the county to visit Shropshire's sites of special interest. Whixall Moss and the Wyre Forest are often worked by visiting collectors and recorders.

Organised recording in Shropshire is restricted by the lack of an entomological society such as those which exist in the surrounding counties of Warwickshire (Birmingham Natural History Society) Worcestershire (Worcs. Naturalists Club) and Lancashire and Cheshire (L. & C. Entomological Society). In the early 1900's the Caradoc and Severn Valley Field Club's journal *The Record of Bare Facts* frequently carried Lepidoptera records and was biased towards natural history but, in recent years, that bias has been toward local history and architecture. This vacated niche has yet to be filled which is a great pity as the role played by the *Record of Bare Facts* in recording Shropshire's insect fauna was most valuable.

On a more optimistic note the Shropshire Biological Records Cente (S.B.R.C.), based at Ludlow Museum, has worked hard to accumulate and collate records of the county's Lepidoptera which are submitted by a large number of contributors. Copies of these records are sent to the National Biological Records Centre at Monks Wood Experimental Station in Cambridgeshire to assist in the production of their biological atlases and, perhaps most significantly, the series of books *Moths and Butterflies of Great Britain and Ireland*. When complete these will constitute the standard work on British Lepidoptera.

Also, members of the West Midlands Branch of the British Butterfly Conservation Society (B.B.C.S.) submit butterfly records which are then published in the form of annual species reviews in the Society's newsletter. This is then sent free to Society members and is available to non-members for a nominal price.

The most popular scheme organised by the S.B.R.C. is the butterfly recording project launched in 1985. This was advertised in the local press and through schools and it encouraged many newcomers to become involved in organised biological recording. It has proved to be a valuable source of data on the county's butterflies.

The Field Studies Council's Field Centre at Preston Montford is probably the single most important contributor of records. The staff operate a Rothamsted Insect Survey (R.I.S.) light trap on the site which takes a small sample of nocturnal insects every night of the year. These are sent to Rothamsted Experimental Station in Hertfordshire for identification by A. M. Riley and the results give not only a list of species present but, year by year, an excellent indication of fluctuations in numbers of individuals, species and diversity. The value of such data is considerable and constant reference is made to it throughout this book. The various field courses held by the Field Studies Council at Preston Montford also encourage an awareness of local natural history. Some of these deal specifically with Lepidoptera and so provide further useful data.

Reference collections of Shropshire Lepidoptera are mainly restricted to those owned by a few private individuals. However, Ludlow Museum does have a fairly large collection and also houses those made by several of the more important Shropshire recorders including Shephard and Norton. A collection of the wings of those species caught in the R.I.S. trap at Preston Montford are mounted on cards and used for educational purposes by the Field Studies Council staff.

Unfortunately, many of the historically important collections have either been dispersed (F. B. Newnham's collection was sold at auction in 1923) or have fallen into decay. This means, of course, that records made by these old collectors can no longer be verified. Some of the blame for this must fall on the absence of an active entomological society in the county; collections are often donated or bequeathed to such societies, thus maintaining links with our entomological past. Perhaps the publication of this work will encourage the entomologists of Shropshire to found such a body.

The importance of detailed recording and monitoring

Over the past 40 years expanding urbanisation, large-scale mineral and peat extraction, intensive agricultural practices, re-afforestation with coniferous trees, and the cessation of traditional woodland management techniques such as coppicing have all had a severely detrimental effect on our Lepidoptera. Formerly large habitats have become fragmented and the more sedentary species such as the large heath butterfly (*C. tullia* Müll) are left isolated in small, insular, vulnerable colonies liable to extinction as soon as these sites are altered in any way. Ideally, these areas should be protected as nature reserves and managed according to the ecological needs of the species they contain. In order to do this effectively the butterflies and moths must first be comprehensively recorded and the results sent to the S.B.R.C.

All records received by the S.B.R.C. are catalogued and copies are sent to the National Biological Records Centre at Monkswood Experimental Station in Cambridgeshire. The resulting database can be used by owners of reserves or Sites of Special Scientific Interest (SSSI) to help plan the habitat management strategies used to protect rare or local species. They can also provide valuable data, primarily in the form of species inventories, for the future designation of SSSI's and so help preserve unusual or endangered habitats. However, this is only the first step and further continuous recording and monitoring at these sites is required to reveal trends in the populations of Lepidoptera which reflect the success or failure of management techniques. Careful analysis of the results of monitoring help in the continuous re-evaluation which is desirable for successful habitat management.

Pollard, Hall & Bibby (1986) describe the aims and methods of the national butterfly transect recording scheme and show that changes in habitats are reflected by changes in the relative abundance of butterflies. The scheme involves the methodical recording of butterfly numbers along a set route through an area in order to calculate the relative abundance of species from one generation or year to the next. The use of this technique would be particularly useful for monitoring population trends in those reserves in Shropshire which are managed predominantly for vulnerable butterflies such as the high brown fritillary (*A. adippe* Ver.).

At present the only site in Shropshire which is monitored in this way is the Wyre Forest. Members of B.B.C.S. (per Williams, pers. comm.) have stated that they are prepared to assist with transect monitoring at other sites in the county.

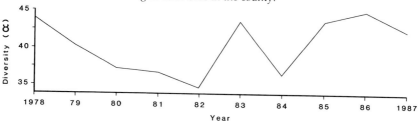

FIG. THREE. Diversity (or log-series ∝) of moth species caught in the R.I.S. light trap at Preston Montford Field Centre, 1978–1987. See text for explanation.

Fig. 3 shows a plot of the diversity of moth species caught in the R.I.S. light trap at Preston Montford Field Centre between 1978 and 1987. Diversity expresses the statistical relationship between the number of species and the number of individuals within a given sample. Unlike the number of species it is independent of sample size and therefore is often a better indicator of species richness in an area. For a more detailed explanation of diversity the reader is referred to Lewis & Taylor (1967). Although data from Preston Montford have yet to be analysed in detail the graph clearly shows a downward trend in moth diversity between 1978 and 1982 and a subsequent recovery to 1987. Certain individual species in the catches show a similar decline and recovery whereas in others these trends are reversed. The two species illustrated in Fig. 4 both feed on a variety of deciduous trees such as hawthorn and the two in Fig. 5 are polyphagous on herbaceous plants such as dock. The trends shown by these species coincide with the removal of scrub from the vicinity of the trap during the period 1978–1982. The habitat temporarily became suitable for herbaceous plants until the trees, which were planted in 1978, developed sufficiently to once again support species such as the brimstone and figure of eight. This example shows how site management can effect moth populations and how management techniques can be monitored by systematic moth sampling.

Habitat management and species conservation in Shropshire

Because of the very large number of species and less concentrated recording our knowledge of moths in Shropshire is generally incomplete and more study is required before all potentially endangered species can be identified and appropriate preservation measures initiated. At the present time efforts should concentrate on recording species and abundance and the protection of prime moth habitats such as Whixall Moss, the upland areas around Church Stretton and the Ercall and Wrekin woodland complex; none of which is currently managed for its Lepidopterous fauna.

Possibly due to a higher public profile, the smaller number of species and more concentrated recording, the status of butterflies in Shropshire is better known. There are five species which require careful protection if they are not to become extinct in the county. They are the wood white (*L. sinapis* L.), high brown fritillary (*A. addipe* Ver.), small blue (*C. minimus* Fuess.), silver-studded blue (*P. argus* L.) and large heath (*C. tullia* Müll).

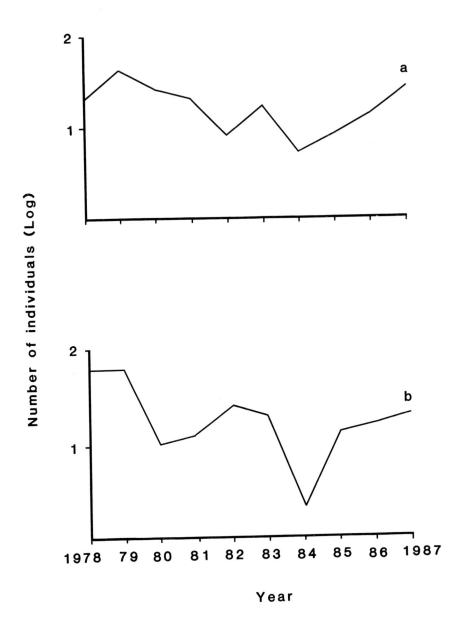

FIG. FOUR. Annual totals ($\log_{10}$ scale) of (a) the brimstone moth (*Opisthograptis luteolata* L.) and (b) the figure of eight moth (*Diloba caeruleocephala* L.) caught in the R.I.S. light trap at Preston Montford Field Centre, 1978–1987. See text for explanation.

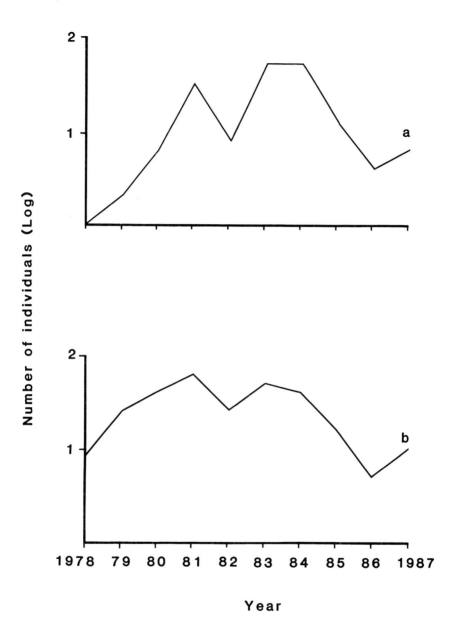

FIG. FIVE. Annual totals (log$_{10}$ scale) of (a) the six-striped rustic moth (*Xestia sexstrigata* Haw.) and (b) the square-spot rustic moth (*X. xanthographa* D. & S.) caught in the R.I.S. light trap at Preston Montford Field Centre, 1978–1987. See text for explanation.

The wood white and the high brown fritillary are woodland species which are restricted in Shropshire to the Wyre Forest (though several strong colonies of the latter have recently been discovered just across the county border into Herefordshire). The latter has declined severely throughout Britain in recent years. Extensive programmes of coppicing and ride management (see Carter & Anderson, 1987) are being carried out in the Wyre Forest by the Forestry Commission and the Nature Conservancy Council. These programmes should benefit both of these species as well as other woodland butterflies. The Forestry Commission hold several other important woodland sites in the county including Haughmond Hill, a historical site for the high brown fritillary and purple emperor (*A. iris* L.). These sites would also benefit from such management regimes. Similar management programmes as well as the replacement of conifers with native broadleaves are being undertaken at Wenlock Edge by the National Trust. These will benefit woodland species found there such as the ringlet (*A. hyperantus* L.) and the silver-washed fritillary (*A. paphia* L.).

The small blue is only known from two sites in the county and one of these is owned by the National Trust where periodic scrub clearance is undertaken to ensure the continued prosperity of kidney vetch on which the larvae feed. Similar removal of successional vegetation for the preservation of grassland, heathland and marshland flora is also being carried out at various sites owned by the Shropshire County Council. It is hoped that these will benefit such species as the small skipper (*T. sylvestris* Poda), large skipper (*O. venata* Brem. & Grey) and, at one site near Ellesmere, the small pearl-bordered fritillary (*B. selene* D. & S.). Conifer clearance is being carried out by the Forestry Commission and the British Butterfly Conservation Society on a small pearl-bordered fritillary site in the Wyre Forest. Once the conifers are removed it is hoped the area will revert to wet grassland and so enhance the habitat for this species.

Heathland preservation is particularly important in Shropshire to the silver-studded blue. The British Butterfly Conservation Society have asked that the name of the only known Shropshire locality for this species is not published here for fear of pressure from collectors and dealers. The site is not currently owned by a conservation organisation and has not yet been designated a SSSI. The habitat is threatened by ecological succession and from encroachment by surrounding agriculture. If this site is not protected and managed as a heathland reserve the silver-studded blue butterfly is in great danger of extinction in Shropshire.

The large heath is restricted to Whixall and Wem Mosses, large raised peat bogs in the north of the county. No conservation management has been undertaken at the former site which, despite being an SSSI, is under threat from peat extraction. At present only small scale mining takes place and the possibility of commercial scale extraction should be removed if this species is to survive. It should be noted that 74 species of Lepidoptera resident on Whixall Moss have not been recorded elsewhere in the county, therefore the area requires conservation for many species in addition to the large heath.

None of the five vulnerable species discussed above should be collected in Shropshire as irreversible damage could be done to their few remaining colonies. However, it should be stressed that the main threat to their survival comes from habitat destruction and not collecting. The Joint Committee for the Conservation of British Insects (J.C.C.B.I.) published *A Code For Insect Collecting* (J.C.C.B.I., 1972; Heath, 1983, pp. 114–116) which gives guidelines for responsible collecting. Providing these guidelines are adhered to, Lepidoptera populations will not be harmed and a valuable reference collection can be compiled. For general naturalists photography is a preferable alternative to collecting but for serious taxonomists and morphological research workers it is not.

An important habitat type not yet discussed is upland moorland. There are several colonies of grayling (*H. semele* L.) and small pearl-bordered fritillary butterfly on the Stiperstones National Nature Reserve which is owned by the Nature Conservancy Council. The upland National Trust areas around Church Stretton are home to many species of moth such as the northern oak eggar (*L. quercus callunae* Palmer) and the common heath (*E. atomaria* L.) which, in Shropshire, are more or less restricted to this habitat. Current management consists of heather cutting and burning every 10–15 years to promote the growth of new shoots for the benefit of grouse. Generally, these techniques should not harm Lepidoptera populations but searches for the small lappet (*P. ilicifolia* L.)

and northern rustic (*S. lucernea* L.) moths should be made on the Longmynd and Stiperstones so that their status can be ascertained and protection afforded.

Essential information required from recorders

Detailed historical information on the Lepidoptera of Shropshire is sparse. Most of the data comes from the labels of collection specimens and the few publications mentioned previously. Although these give us good species inventories, objective information on abundance and distribution is often not available. If we take the small lappet moth as an example, Newnham (1908) states ". . . occasionally found . . . on the Longmynd." However, the seven specimens in the National Collection carry labels which cite Church Stretton as the locality of capture. This illustrates three problems facing conservationists who need an accurate picture of species distribution: "Occasionally found" tells us that the species was considered rare or, at least difficult to find. However, it does not say how many were found by the collector and over what period of time. Such information would give a better picture of abundance. Secondly, the tendency to use the nearest large town as the source locality creates obvious confusion. Finally, the Longmynd is a very large area. This species may still exist there but the chances of confirming it would be far greater if we knew exactly where Newnham originally discovered it.

Some locality names can also be confusing as, with the passage of time, they sometimes fall from use. If they are not included on Ordnance Survey Maps they are often difficult, and sometimes impossible to trace.

O.S. GRID REF.	LOCALITY	DATE	RECORDER	COMMENTS
S 0 4 . . 9 . -	Church Stretton area	c1849	Phillips, J.	Lit ref. Phillips (1849).
S J 4 . . 1 . -	Shrewsbury area	c1883	Harding, M.J.	Lit ref. Harding (1883). A month late due to cold weather
S 0 4 5 . 9 2 -	Cardoc & Ragleth Wood	c1885	Harding, M.J.	Lit ref. Harding (1885) Less common than *A. aglaja*.
S 0 . . . . . -	South Shropshire	11.vii.1887	Hardcourt-Bath, W.	Lit ref. Hardcourt-Bath (1887). utmost profusion... hundreds
S 0 4 . . 9 . -	Woods around Church Stretton	c1901	Newnham, F.B.	Lit ref. Newnham (1901a). Fairly common. Ab. *hemicleodoxa* occasional
S 0 4 7 . 9 4 -	Helmeth Wood	20.vii.1901	Newnham, F.B	Lit ref. Newnham (1901b). ♂ in cop. with ♀ *A. paphia*
S J 6 . . 0 . -	Benthall Edge	1902	Potts, G.	Lit ref. V.C.H.
S 0 7 . . '6 . -	Wyre Forest	c1902	Newnham, F.B.	Lit ref. V.C.H.
S 0 4 . . 9 . -	Tiger Hall, Church Stretton	c1902	Newnham, F.B.	Lit ref. V.C.H. more sparing
S 0 4 7 . 9 4 -	Helmeth Wood	c1902	Newnham, F.B.	Lit ref. V.C.H. more sparing
S 0 4 5 . 9 2 -	Ragleth Wood	c1902	Newnham, F.B	Lit ref. V.C.H. Especially common including ab. *intermedia* Tutt.
S J 2 . . 2 . -	Oswestry district	c1907	Pendlebury, M.	Lit ref. Kec Bare Facts, 1908.
S 0 4 . . 9 . -	Church Stretton area	1913	Pendlebury, M.	Lit ref. Kec Bare Facts, 1914
S J 4 . . 1 . -	Shrewsbury	1919	Ingrams, W.S.	Lit ref. Kec Bare Facts, 1920
S J 2 . . 1 . -	Breidden Hill	1924	Hignett, J.	Per Shropshire Biological Records Centre (SBRC).
S J 6 . . 0 . -	Benthall Edge	11.vii.1925	Potts, G.	Per SBRC
S 0 5 . . 7 . -	Ashford Manor, Ludlow	c1939	Bretherton, R.F	Per Biological Records Centre, Monkswood (BRC).
S J 5 4 . 1 4 -	Haughmond Hill	1947	Platts,	Lit ref. Kec Bare Facts, 1947
S 0 7 3 3 7 8 3	Wyre Forest	c1960	Smith, W.	Per BRC.
S 0 7 4 3 7 6 3	Wyre Forest	1960	Scott, D.W.	Per BRC
S 0 7 . . 7 . -	Wyre Forest	4.iii.1964	B'ham Nat. Hist. Soc.	Per SBRC
S 0 7 0 8 7 0 2	Chorley Covert	1968-1975	South Staffs. Nat. Soc.	Per H.G. Blunt

Argynnis adippe Denis & Schiffermüller   High Brown Fritillary   1606

See reverse for full lit references.

FIG. SIX. Sheet used for collating records for this book.

Recording sheets such as the one in Fig. 6 were used by the present author to collate the historical data and all recent records. This example illustrates some of the problems outlined above. In some cases only the 10 km square is known and in one instance the only available information concerning the locality is "South Shropshire". Further, often only the year of the record is known. This makes phenological comparisons almost impossible.

In order to obtain and maintain an accurate picture of the distribution and abundance of the Lepidoptera, recording must be regular and as detailed as possible. Formal butterfly recording cards which ask for specific information are supplied on request by the S.B.R.C. at Ludlow Museum. However, it is important to emphasise that any form of recording is valuable providing the following basic information is given.

i. The name of the species, preferably English and Latin.
ii The date of the sighting.
iii The locality of the sighting, including an Ordnance Survey grid reference.
iv An indication of abundance (e.g. one, two, several, common etc.).
v The name of the recorder and identifier.

All records should be sent to the S.B.R.C. at least once a year but sightings of unusual species should be reported as soon as possible.

Identification

There are many useful books available on butterflies. Probably the best pocket guide for identification in the field is the *RSNC Guide to Butterflies of the British Isles* (Thomas, 1986). This illustrates all the British species and shows clearly how to distinguish those in the more difficult groups. The *Complete Guide to British Butterflies* (Brookes & Knight, 1983) has excellent photographs of the early stages and is very useful for identifying larvae.

Small field guides which cover only the more common species of moth should be avoided as their omissions make them unreliable. *A Colour Identification Guide to Moths of the British Isles* (Skinner, 1984) has excellent colour photographs of all the species of British larger (macro) moths with many useful diagnostic drawings of the more difficult groups.

The microlepidoptera are less well represented in the literature though guides are available for some families. *British Pyralid Moths* (Goater, 1986) and *British Tortricoid Moths* (Bradley, Tremewan & Smith, 1973 & 1979 (2 Vols.)) contain excellent colour illustrations of the Pyralidae and Tortricidae and the text of both is very helpful. Some of the remaining families are described in Volumes One and Two of *Moths and Butterflies of Great Britain and Ireland* (Heath, 1976 & 1985). Taxonomy of most microlepidoptera groups, where many species measure only three or four millimetres across the wings, is bound to be a specialist occupation, though very rewarding for anyone prepared to provide the commitment. The larvae of some species of microlepidoptera create translucent mines by feeding between the upper and lower leaf surfaces of the foodplant. The form of these mines is usually characteristic to each species and are much easier to identify than the adult moths. "Minology", as it is popularly known, is discussed by A. M. Emmet in Heath (1983). Those who decide to study this subject in detail will undoubtedly be rewarded by finding many valuable records for the county.

Natural History of the Species of Macrolepidoptera occurring in Shropshire between 1807 and 1990

The category 'V.C.H.' refers to records of species up to the time of the publication of the Victoria County History (Newnham, 1908). A comprehensive search of the available literature has shown that several species were noted in the county prior to this date but were overlooked by Newnham. These are included under this heading. Where no recorders name is given it is assumed that they are attributable to Newnham. All unreferenced records have been extracted directly from the V.C.H..

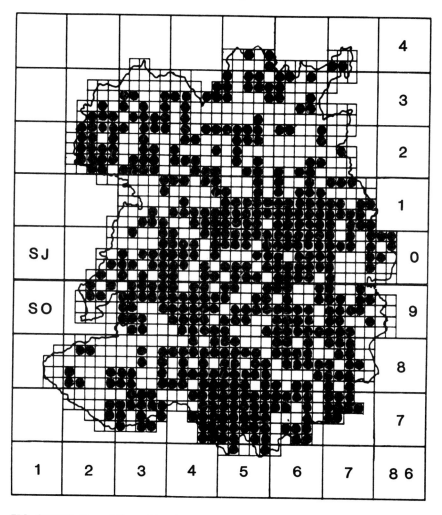

FIG. SEVEN. Map of Shropshire showing the Ordnance Survey 10 km squares and the scatter of 2 km tetrads from which macrolepidoptera records have been received.

Post V.C.H. includes records and observations of all species since Newnham (1908). In the case of common species general observations are made. For very local or scarce species, recorded occurrences are cited as supplied by the various recorders and recording schemes. These are discussed in the section 'Recording in Shropshire'. Unreferenced records originate from B.R.C. at Ludlow and the author's correspondence, collection and observations.

Flight refers to the flight time of the adult insect. Special reference is made to bivoltinism where this is known to occur in Shropshire. This is particularly important as, in the case of several species, it has only previously been noted from southern England.

Larval foodplants (Larval F/p). This section lists the commonly known larval foodplants for each species with reference to alternatives which have been recorded in Shropshire and are not listed in other sources. The vast majority of records for this book have come from light trapping and recording of adult Lepidoptera. Consequently our knowledge of recorded foodplants for Shropshire is incomplete. The lists given under this heading are based on Skinner (1984) and Brookes and Knight (1982) as a guide to future study in the county. **However, where the foodplant in Shropshire is known, the name of the plant is followed by an asterisk.** The floral nomenclature follows that of Sinker, *et al.* (1985).

Under the heading **Notes** varieties which have been noted in the county along with methods of finding some of the more unusual species and other aspects of historical, phenological, taxonomic and behavioural note have been discussed.

The nomenclature conforms with Bradley and Fletcher (1986), as amended by Emmet (1987) and Agassiz (1988). The species numbers agree with Bradley and Fletcher (1979) except where certain species, due to taxonomic revision, have been moved (e.g. *Parastichtis suspecta* 2268 (Bradley and Fletcher (1979)) now follows *Enargia paleacea* 2313 and therefore the number has been changed, for the purpose of the present work, to 2313i). Synonyms used by Skinner (1984) are cross-referenced in the index so that his now standard work on the macrolepidoptera can be referred to more easily.

FAMILY: HEPIALIDAE

14 Ghost Swift *Hepialus humuli humuli* Linnaeus
V.C.H.:   Common throughout.
Post V.C.H.:   Common throughout on wasteground, rough grassland and overgrown lawns.
Flight: June and July.
Larval F/ps: Roots of grasses and many other plants such as nettle and docks. August to May.

15 Orange Swift *Hepialus sylvina* Linnaeus
V.C.H.:   Not uncommon.
Post V.C.H.:   Well distributed and generally common on rough ground and grassland.
Flight: July to September.
Larval F/ps: Roots of herbaceous plants, e.g. docks, bracken and dandelion*. August to May.

16 Gold Swift *Hepialus hecta* Linnaeus
V.C.H.:   In and near damp woods. Recorded from Helmeth and Ragleth Woods (Newnham, 1901a); Gippols, 1903 and 1904 (Allen, per Potts, 1904 and 1905) and Market Drayton, 1907 (H. Pendlebury, per Potts, 1908).
Post V.C.H.:   Recorded from woodlands (Wrekin, Wyre, Wenlock, Shirlett and Iron-bridge), the mosses of Whixall and Wem, and waste ground. It is, however, much more localised than the previous two species and is never as common.
Flight: June and July.
Larval F/p: Stems and roots of bracken*, overwintering twice as a larva.

17 Common Swift *Hepialus lupulinus* Linnaeus
V.C.H.:   Abundant everywhere.
Post V.C.H.:   Very common throughout in most habitats.
Flight: End of May to July.
Larval F/ps: Roots of many wild and cultivated plants including grasses. July to April.

18 Map-winged Swift *Hepialus fusconebulosa* De Geer
V.C.H.:   Very common in the hilly parts among bracken.
Post V.C.H.:   Since publication of the V.C.H. this species has been recorded only very sparsely: Oswestry, 1930 (Hignett, 1931); Donnington, 1949 (Christie); Bromfield, 1963 (Norton); Pontesbury, 1969 (D. Smith); Shirlett, 1970 (Whitney); Bucknell 1972 (Shephard); Hawk Lake, 1985 (Hardwick); Easthope Wood, 1987 and 1988 and Longmynd and Wenlock Edge, 1989 (Coleshaw).
Flight: End of May to July.
Larval F/p: Stems and roots of bracken*, overwintering twice.
Notes: Although this species has not been recorded well in recent years, it is probably found fairly commonly in woods and heathland areas where bracken abounds. Newnham (1901) noted that ab. *gallicus* Lederer was not infrequent in the Church Stretton area. This form lacks forewing markings.

FAMILY: COSSIDAE

161 Leopard Moth *Zeuzera pyrina* Linnaeus

V.C.H.: Recorded only from Bomere, 1907 (H. Pendlebury, per Potts, 1908) and Ellesmere (Peake, 1897; Thompson).

Post V.C.H.: Widespread, recorded mainly as single specimens: Bridgnorth, 1913 (Pitt); Shrewsbury, 1920 (Carless); Cleobury Mortimer, one female 1922 (Woodward, 1922b); Oswestry, 1945 (Hignett); Preston Montford Field Centre, 1968 (Heath); Buildwas, 1969 (Whitney); Pontesbury, 1977 (D. Smith); Bromfield, 1958 & 1978 (Norton); Ludlow, 1979 (Moulton & Norton) and Llanymynech, 22.vii.1989 (Townsend). There are several records from the Wyre Forest (Blunt; Evans; Plant).

Flight: Late June to early August.

Larval F/ps: Inside the stems of many trees and shrubs, including fruit trees, overwintering twice.

162 Goat Moth *Cossus cossus* Linnaeus

V.C.H.: Recorded only from Prees, 1903 (Thornewill); Ellesmere (Peake, 1897) and 1903 (Thompson); Broseley, 1903 (Potts, 1904); Shrewsbury, 1904 (Hughes, per Potts, 1905) and Little Stretton, "a few larvae some years ago".

Post V.C.H.: This scarce insect has only been recorded sparsely since the publication of the V.C.H.: Calverhall, 22.ix.1909, larva (Thornewill); Benthall, 1910 and 1927 (Potts); Shrewsbury, 1919 (Ponsonby) and Oswestry, 1930, ash trees frequently attacked by larvae (Hignett).

Flight: June and July when it occasionally comes to light.

Larval F/ps: The solid wood of many trees, including ash*, overwintering three or four times. The larvae may occasionally be found searching for a pupation site when fully grown. If so it should be kept in a metal container as it may chew through a wooden or cardboard box.

FAMILY: ZYGAENIDAE

163 The Forester *Adscita statices* Linnaeus

V.C.H.: Very local; found in several localities on rough unbroken ground near Stretton (e.g. Ragleth, Ashes Valley and Staley's Cottage). Also recorded from Wyre Forest, 1902 (Rea).

Post V.C.H.: There are no recent records for the Church Stretton area or Wyre Forest but it has been found at Cleobury Mortimer, usually common (Woodward, 1922b); Pennerley, 1970 (Poynton) and Pontesbury, 1978 (D. Smith). It is fairly common at Whixall and Fenn's Mosses. These recent records are unlikely to signify an extension in the distribution of this species since V.C.H. times. Newnham himself thought that it had been overlooked elsewhere in the county. This is almost certainly still the case and *A. statices* is probably awaiting discovery in many suitable localities. It should be looked for flying in the sunshine over damp meadows, wasteground and woodland edges where the larval foodplant grows.

Flight: June and July.

Larval F/ps: Sheep's sorrel and common sorrel. July to April.

169 Six-spot Burnet *Zygaena filipendulae stephensi* Dupont

V.C.H.: Recorded only from Wenlock Edge where it was abundant and Church Stretton where it was uncommon. The paucity of records for the V.C.H. is surprising as we are sure it must have been more widespread than indicated. It's absence from lists sent to him also puzzled Newnham.

Post V.C.H.: Widespread and fairly common though records appear to be more complete in the southern half of the county.

Flight: July and August. Diurnal on rough ground, meadows, woodland rides and flowery roadside verges.

Larval F/p: Common bird's-foot-trefoil*. September to May. Skinner (1984) states that it occasionally overwinters twice.

170 Five-spot Burnet *Zygaena trifolii decreta* Verity

V.C.H.: Unrecorded.

Post V.C.H.: Tick Wood, 1914 (Melvill); Blakeway Coppice, 1952 and The Mounds, near Much Wenlock, 1953 (K.G.V. Smith, 1954); Wyre, 1960 (Scott); Dawley, 1975 (Oram) and Hopton Titterhill, 1982 (Hicks).

Flight: July and August in similar habitats to *Z. filipendulae*.

Larval F/p: Large bird's-foot-trefoil*. August to June. Skinner (1984) states that it occasionally overwinters twice.

Notes: It is possible that the above are mis-identifications for the more common and widespread *Z. lonicerae*. Further investigation is required to determine the true status of *Z. trifolii* in Shropshire.

171 Narrow-bordered Five-spot Burnet *Zygaena lonicerae latomarginata* Tutt

V.C.H.: Widely distributed and fairly common.

Post V.C.H.: Fairly common east of a line from Whixall in the north to Clungunford in the south in similar habitats to *Z. filipendulae*.

Flight: June and July.

Larval F/ps: Meadow vetchling, red clover* and, possibly other species of clover, vetch and trefoil. August to May. Skinner (1984) states that it occasionally overwinters twice.

FAMILY: SESIIDAE

370 Hornet Moth *Sesia apiformis* Clerck

V.C.H.: Ellesmere (Thompson) and Church Stretton where it was less frequent than *S. bembeciformis*. Cited by Stainton (1857. Vol. 1: 102) as common around Shrewsbury.

Post V.C.H.: Unrecorded.

Flight: June and July around mature poplars. Diurnal.

Larval F/ps: At ground level in the roots and trunks of black poplar* and possibly other poplar species. Usually overwinters twice.

Notes: This is an easily overlooked species. However, its presence is indicated by large exit holes of about 8 mm diameter at the base of poplar trees. The adults may be found sitting on poplar trunks during the early morning after emergence from the pupa. They will usually have dispersed by mid-day. It has probably been overlooked since V.C.H. times and searches in suitable localities may prove rewarding.

371 Lunar Hornet Moth *Sesia bembeciformis* Hübner

V.C.H.: Very common around Market Drayton (Woodforde) and Church Stretton. Also recorded from Betton Park, 1907 (H. Pendlebury, per Potts, 1908).

Post V.C.H.: Recorded only from Whixall, 1932 (Hignett); Shrawardine, 1980 (Anon.); Easthope Wood, 15.vii.1985 (a pair *in cop.*) (Coleshaw) and the Ercall Woods, 1986 (Riley).

Flight: July and August. Diurnal, having similar habits to *S. apiformis.*

Larval F/p: Around ground level in the roots and trunks of sallow*. Usually infests larger trees, overwintering twice.

Notes: This is another species which has probably been overlooked as the adults are not often seen by the casual observer. The easiest method of finding it is to search the bases of sallow trees for exit holes which are about the diameter of a pencil. The winter months are the best time to look as the ground level vegetation dies back and permits easier searching.

373 Currant Clearwing *Synanthedon tipuliformis* Linnaeus

V.C.H.: Generally fairly common in gardens where redcurrant and blackcurrant are cultivated.

Post V.C.H.: Widely distributed but not common. Recorded from many localities throughout the county.

Flight: June and July in gardens or allotments where the larval foodplant is grown. Diurnal.

Larval F/ps: Inside the stems of redcurrant*, blackcurrant* and gooseberry. August to May. Its presence can be detected by dark brown frass at the ends of pruned stems in the spring.

374 Yellow-legged Clearwing *Synanthedon vespiformis* Linnaeus

V.C.H.: Recorded only from Wyre Forest, 6.vi.1897 (Rea) and Church Stretton, 23.vii.1901, (Woolley).

Post V.C.H.: Oswestry, Jan. 1933, larvae in oak stump (Hignett, per Pendlebury, 1934) and Whitwell, 1.vi.1952 (K. G. V. Smith, 1954). An apparently rare species in Shropshire.

Flight: May to August. Woodland clearings where oaks have been felled. Diurnal.

Larval F/ps: Under the bark of oak*, preferring freshly cut stumps where coppicing has taken place. Other occasional foodplants are listed as sweet chestnut, beech, walnut, wych-elm and birch (Heath, 1985). August to May. Frass is present on the surface of the bark of infested stumps.

375 White-barred Clearwing *Synanthedon spheciformis* Denis & Schiffermüller

V.C.H.: Recorded only from the Wyre Forest, 6.vii.1897, 11.vi.1899 and 18.vi.1902 (Rea).

Post V.C.H.: This species still exists fairly commonly in the Wyre Forest (Plant, pers. comm.).

Flight: May to July on heathland and in marshy places. Diurnal.

Larval F/ps: Stumps, suckers and young trees of alder* and birch*. Small piles of frass at the bases of such trees and small larval tunnels (2–5 mm in diameter) indicate the presence of larvae.

Notes: Although this species is not included in L. J. Evans' extensive list of Lepidoptera from the Shropshire portion of Wyre Forest it is mentioned as occurring in the Forest by Hickin (1972, p. 182), presumably in Worcestershire.

18

381 Large Red-belted Clearwing *Synanthedon culiciformis* Linnaeus

V.C.H.: Caynton (Paddock); Wyre Forest, 6.vi.1897 (Rea); Market Drayton 1907 (H. Pendlebury, per Potts, 1908) and Church Stretton.

Post V.C.H.: There are no further records from the above localities though it has been found at Oswestry, 1935 (Hignett) and Whixall Moss (Burrows, per Fielding, 1974a), 28.v.1939 (Warren) and 1980 (Watson).

Flight: May and June on heathland and in open woodland. Diurnal.

Larval F/ps: Under the bark of birch*, and possibly alder, trees and stumps. July to April.

Notes: Skinner (1984), states that this species is common over much of England and Wales. It is therefore likely that it has been overlooked in Shropshire. It should be searched for where birch has been felled, small excrescences of brown frass on the tops of birch stumps during autumn and winter indicating the presence of larvae (see Heath, 1985, pp. 383–384).

FAMILY: HESPERIIDAE

1526 Small Skipper *Thymelicus sylvestris* Poda

V.C.H.: Common and widespread.

Post V.C.H.: Common on rough ground throughout the county.

Flight: From the end of June to mid-August.

Larval F/ps: Various soft grasses. August to June.

Notes: Distribution map a. (Fig. 9) and Plate 13.

1531 Large Skipper *Ochlodes venata faunus* Turati

V.C.H.: Common and widespread.

Post V.C.H.: Common on rough ground throughout the county.

Flight: May to the beginning of August.

Larval F/ps: Cock's foot and false brome. July to May.

Notes: Distribution map b. (Fig. 9).

1532 Dingy Skipper *Erynnis tages tages* Linnaeus

V.C.H.: Found on dry banks throughout the county.

Post V.C.H.: Not uncommon on open limestone areas throughout the county. Best known from the Wyre Forest and Earl's Hill (Plant and D. Smith, pers. comm.).

Flight: Mainly May and June with a very occasional partial second emergence during August in hot summers.

Larval F/p: Common bird's-foot-trefoil. June to March or April.

Notes: Distribution map c. (Fig. 9) and Plate 14.

1534 Grizzled Skipper *Pyrgus malvae* Linnaeus

V.C.H.: Local but common where it occurs. Recorded from Market Drayton (Woodforde), Petton Park (Tatton), Broseley, Church Stretton, Hopton Wafers and Shrewsbury.

Post V.C.H.: *P. malvae* is very localised but widespread and not uncommon in suitable localities such as those frequented by *E. tages*. It seems to be most common in the Wyre Forest.

Flight:	May and June, inhabiting rides and new clearings in woods and limestone scrub and grassland.
Larval F/ps:	Wild strawberry, creeping cinquefoil and possibly other *Rosaceae*. June and July.
Notes:	Distribution map d. (Fig. 9).

FAMILY: PAPILIONIDAE

1540 Scarce Swallowtail *Iphiclides podalirius* Scopoli

V.C.H.:	Several adults and larvae of this species were noted at Netley and Longnor between 1807 and 1828 by F. W. Hope and K. Plymley. Allan (1980) gives a full account of these extraordinary records which may be summarised as follows: 1807, one adult; 1822, two adults; 1824, at least one larva on blackthorn and 1828, at least two adults (the recorder states that he was ". . . in quest of <u>them</u> . . ." A specimen labelled "Netley, Salop" is presently held in the Hope Dept. collection at Oxford University.
Post V.C.H.:	Unrecorded.
Flight:	May and June and August and September, usually in, or near, orchards and blackthorn thickets.
Larval F/ps:	Blackthorn and cultivated fruit trees (Riley, N. D. and Higgins, 1970). May to October.
Notes:	This species is a very rare immigrant to Britain and is unlikely to establish itself here as our winters are too cold and wet for its survival.

FAMILY: PIERIDAE

1541 Wood White *Leptidea sinapis sinapis* Linnaeus

V.C.H.:	Phillips (1869, p. 122) states that this species was found at Church Stretton. However, Newnham (1908) had never seen it in the area. His intimate knowledge of this district leads one to doubt the accuracy of Phillips' observation. Newnham was the foremost Lepidopterist in the county at that time and did much of his field work in the Church Stretton area. It is unlikely that he would have overlooked this butterfly. No other records exist for the county up to the publication of the V.C.H.. Noted by Blatch (1868) as more or less abundant in the Wyre Forest.
Post V.C.H.:	First recorded at a wood near Llansantffraid, 1920 (Palmer, per Hignett, 1932). Since 1968 it has been recorded several times from the Wyre Forest and it appears to be maintaining a tentative hold there. The only other Shropshire record is from Chorley Wood, where it was seen in 1977 (B.N.H.S., anon). It is of interest to note that there is a strong colony just over the county border into Herefordshire at Wigmore Rolls.
Flight:	May and June with a partial and occasional second emergence in August. It inhabits wide woodland rides, clearings in woods and disused railway cuttings.
Larval F/ps:	Various vetches including large bird's-foot-trefoil*, meadow vetchling, bitter-vetch and tufted vetch. June and July.
Notes:	Distribution map a. (Fig. 10) and Plate 15.

1543 Pale Clouded Yellow *Colias hyale* Linnaeus

V.C.H.: Westwood, 1900, two in a lucerne field with six *C. croceus* (Pitt, per Potts, 1909).

Post V.C.H.: Cleobury Mortimer, 21.viii.1922 (Woodward, 1922b) and Broseley, ". . . a few years ago . . ." (Broadhurst, per Pendlebury, 1943).

Flight: This species is usually a very rare immigrant to Britain, occurring any time between April and October, and usually noted in the vicinity of clover and lucerne fields.

Larval F/ps: Various clovers and trefoils. June and again in August (South, 1924).

Notes: South (1924) states that this species was plentiful in many parts of the country during the autumn of 1900. This coincides with the first Shropshire records. These occasional increases in the number of sightings are probably due to early immigration resulting in a large home-bred population during August and September. As *C. hyale* is unable to survive British winters it would have to rely on fresh immigrations the following year to maintain its presence here. Such immigrations probably do not occur every year. There has been considerable taxonomic confusion between this species and *C. australis* Verity, and as the above records are no longer confirmable, they must be treated with caution.

1545 Clouded Yellow *Colias croceus* Geoffroy

V.C.H.: Occurs, at times, all over Shropshire.

Post V.C.H.: An infrequent visitor to the county; it is rarely common and in most years it is completely absent. It's most notable years appear to have been 1922, 1941 and 1947 when it was recorded from all over the county (Pendlebury, 1956). Recent records are as follows: 1979 (1 individual), 1983 (6), 1984 (1) and 1986 (2). Prior to these it had not been seen in Shropshire since 1955.

Flight: This immigrant species may arrive in Britain any time between May and September and is usually seen in open country, often around clover fields. It cannot survive our winters.

Larval F/ps: Clovers, trefoils and lucerne. May to July.

Notes: So far as I am aware, the white form of the female (var. *helice* Hübner) has not been recorded in Shropshire.

1546 Brimstone *Gonepteryx rhamni* Linnaeus

V.C.H.: Apparently not common, only recorded from Caradoc (three specimens in 1902) and Church Stretton (one in 1907).

Post V.C.H.: Widespread, found over most of the county, being most common in the Wyre Forest and Wem and Whixall Mosses.

Flight: Late July to autumn and again, after hibernation, from March to June. The adults may fly during the winter in mild weather. It inhabits open woodland, hedgerows and scrubland and is often seen away from its foodplant.

Larval F/ps: Alder buckthorn* and purging buckthorn* June and July.

Notes: Distribution map b. (Fig. 10).

1548 Black-veined White *Aporia crataegi* Linnaeus

V.C.H.: Reported from the Wyre Forest, 20.vi.1851 and 24.viii.1852 in the transactions of the Worcestershire Naturalists Club, 1851, p.10. Also by Hardcourt-Bath (1887a) ". . . many years ago . . ." and Blatch (1886) "Used to be found" at the same locality. Newnham (1908) states that this species is ". . . now almost extinct . . .".

Post V.C.H.: Unrecorded. It became extinct as a British species during the 1920s.

Flight:	Late June to early August in country lanes, woodland rides, orchards and blackthorn thickets.
Larval F/ps:	Plum, apple, hawthorn and blackthorn. September to May.
Notes:	This species is easy to breed and continental stock is often offered for sale by entomological livestock dealers. Such stock is sometimes released by the breeder, either intentionally or not, and recorders should be aware of this practice should a specimen of *A. crataegi* be found.

1549 Large White *Pieris brassicae* Linnaeus

V.C.H.:	Generally well distributed and common throughout the county.
Post V.C.H.:	Recorded from throughout the county. It is usually common though the numbers vary from year to year according to the strength of migrations from the continent. These supplement our resident population.
Flight:	May to September in two broods.
Larval F/ps:	Many species of crucifer, including cabbage*, on which it is sometimes a pest. May to October, occasionally later.
Notes:	Newnham (1908) mentions the occurrence of ab. *chariclea* Stephens, in which the apical patches of the forewings are light brown, throughout the county in the spring. This form is generally smaller than the type. Distribution map c. (Fig. 10).

1550 Small White *Pieris rapae* Linnaeus

V.C.H.:	Common throughout the county.
Post V.C.H.:	Widespread, generally distributed and common.
Flight:	April to September in two or three broods.
Larval F/ps:	Various crucifers, including cabbage*. May to October.
Notes:	Newnham (1901) noted the cream form *novangliae* Scudder (=ab. *metra* Stephens) at Church Stretton. This form has also been noted at Wellington, 25.viii.1973 (Riley). Newnham (1908) also notes the presence of ab. *manni* Mayer, in which the black markings are very heavily defined, and ab. *immaculata* Cockerell, in which the black markings are absent. The latter was stated to be uncommon. Distribution map d. (Fig. 10).

1551 Green-veined White *Pieris napi sabellicae* Stephens

V.C.H.:	Common throughout.
Post V.C.H.:	Widespread, generally distributed and common.
Flight:	April to September in two protracted broods.
Larval F/ps:	Various crucifers, including charlock*, rape, garlic mustard* and cresses. May to September.
Notes:	Newnham (1908) states that ssp. *bryoniae* Hb. was found around Church Stretton. This is an alpine race which is not recognised as British. Potts (1909) also records a very dark *P. napi* caught at Benthall Edge, 2.viii.1908 which appears to approach this form. Higgins and Riley (1970) discuss the status and morphology of this subspecies. The present author visited the Longmynd in 1989 and examined many *P. napi*. Although a few specimens found on the flushes at the summit of the locality were somewhat darker than the type (see Plate 12), the presence of ssp. *bryoniae* could not be confirmed. Newnham also notes the occasional occurrence of ab. *napaeae* Esper. In this form the greenish colour on the veins of the underside of the hindwings is restricted to the basal half. Distribution map a. (Fig. 11).

1552 Bath White *Pontia daplidice* Linnaeus

V.C.H.: Unrecorded.

Post V.C.H.: Pendlebury (1950) notes that this species was reported from several parts of Britain in 1943, including Shrewsbury (Cuthbertson).

Flight: This scarce immigrant is most often recorded in S.E. England during August.

Larval F/p: Mignonette though it is doubtful if this butterfly regularly breeds in the wild in Britain.

1553 Orange-tip *Anthocharis cardamines* Linnaeus

V.C.H.: Common throughout the county.

Post V.C.H.: Common in country lanes, open woodland rides and damp meadows throughout the county.

Flight: May and June.

Larval F/ps: Various crucifers including garlic mustard*, hedge mustard*, cuckooflower* and charlock. Late May to early July.

Notes: Newnham (1901 and 1908) recorded several interesting aberrations from the Church Stretton district: Ab. *turritis* Och., underside of hindwings much whiter than the type (not infrequent in 1902, Church Stretton); Ab. *cinerea* Newnham, underside of hindwing marked with ash grey instead of green (17.v.1886, Little Stretton); ab. *arsenoides* Newnham, female with partial orange tips (16.vi.1887, Church Stretton) and ab. *androgyna* Newnham — a gynandromorph with male markings on the left pair of wings and female on the right (23.v.1888, Church Stretton). He states that in the form most common around Church Stretton, the orange patches on the forewings do not reach the dorsum. Newnham (1894c and 1894d) and Nesbitt (1894) discuss the possibility of a distinct species of Orange-tip in which the discal spot of the male's forewing is placed at the junction between the white ground colour and the orange apical patch rather than inside this patch, as is usually the case. Newnham proposed the name *hesperidis* for this variety which is also smaller than the type. However, it is now considered to be merely a form of *cardamines*.
Distribution map b. (Fig. 11).

FAMILY: LYCAENIDAE

1555 Green Hairstreak *Callophrys rubi* Linnaeus

V.C.H.: Recorded as common from Millen Heath, Calverhall, Petton Park, Church Stretton, Cross Houses and Caradoc.

Post V.C.H.: Widely distributed and sometimes common on scrubland, open woodland and woodland edges where the foodplants occur.

Flight: May and June.

Larval F/ps: Gorse, broom*, dogwood, buckthorn, bird's-foot-trefoil, rock rose and bramble.

Notes: Distribution map c. (Fig. 11) and Plate 16.

1556 Brown Hairstreak *Thecla betulae* Linnaeus

V.C.H.: Recorded only from the Wyre Forest (Edwards) and Petton Park (Tatton) and the neighbourhood of Ellesmere (Peake, 1897).

Post V.C.H.: Unconfirmed records of two individuals near Brown Clee, 1988 and 1989 (per Blunt).

| Flight: | August and September in woodland openings and edges and hedgerows in wooded areas where blackthorn is common. |

Flight: August and September in woodland openings and edges and hedgerows in wooded areas where blackthorn is common.

Larval F/p: Blackthorn. April to July.

1557 Purple Hairstreak *Quercusia quercus* Linnaeus

V.C.H.: Occurs freely wherever there are oak woods.

Post V.C.H.: Often common in woodlands and coppices containing oak throughout the county.

Flight: July and August.

Larval F/p: Oak*. April to early June.

Notes: Although fairly common in suitable localities, this species is easily overlooked as the adults spend much of their time feeding on honey-dew at the tops of oak trees. If present, they can easily be disturbed by throwing a branch into the canopy.
Distribution map d. (Fig. 11) and Plate 17.

1558 White-letter Hairstreak *Strymonidia w-album* Knoch

V.C.H.: Well distributed. First recorded by C. G. Barrett at Benthall Edge in 1866 (Thornewill 1901b).

Post V.C.H.: Up to the mid-1970's this species was quite common in many woodlands and was often abundant in the Ercall and Wrekin Woods (Riley). Although it is still regularly recorded from many parts of the county, decimation of its foodplant by Dutch elm disease has severely effected its numbers (Distribution map a. (Fig. 12)). Two visits to the Ercall Woods, in 1986 and 1987, resulted in only one sighting. Elms are suckering strongly in this and other localities and populations should be closely monitored.

Flight: July and August in woodlands and mature hedgerows where elms occur.

Larval F/ps: English elm and wych elm*. April to early June.

Notes: Newnham (1901 & 1908) found a larva feeding on ash which produced a small adult. Plate 18.

1559 Black Hairstreak *Strymonidia pruni* Linnaeus

V.C.H.: "Scarce in the neighbourhood of Petton Park" (Tatton). Newnham (1908) could not confirm this as Tatton's collection had been dispersed by the time the V.C.H. was being written. Morris (1895) recorded this species only from Oxfordshire, Devon, Huntingdonshire and Northamptonshire — not from Shropshire or any other West Midlands county. Tatton's records must be regarded as dubious.

Post V.C.H.: One unconfirmed record from Breidden, 1941 (E. S. Lewis). This record must also be regarded as dubious.

Flight: End of June and July in old blackthorn thickets and in wooded areas.

Larval F/p: Blackthorn. April and May.

1561 Small Copper *Lycaena phlaeas phlaeas* Linnaeus

V.C.H.: Common all over the county.

Post V.C.H.: Widespread and fairly common on open ground where sorrels and docks grow, such as the edges of fields and wide roadside verges.

Flight: May to October in three broods.

Larval F/ps:	Common sorrel, sheep's sorrel and various docks. August to June in three broods.

Notes: Harding (1906) recorded an aberration approaching ab. *schmidtii* Gerhardt on 8.ix.1906 at Church Stretton in which the copper is replaced by silver. Newnham (1901) states that ab. *caeruleopuncta* Staudinger, which has a row of blue spots along the submargin of the hindwing, was found occasionally at Church Stretton. Other examples of this form were recorded at Meole Brace, 1919 (Melvill, per Ingrams, 1920) and Old Park, 15.viii.1976 (Riley). Newnham (1908) cites an example of ab. *radiata* Tutt, in which the copper bands on the hindwings are replaced by a few minute elongated marks (Church Stretton, Aug. 1907 (Ward)). Seven individuals of ab. *obsoleta* Tutt, in which the copper bands on the hindwings are absent were reported to have been caught in 1908 at Church Stretton by Newnham and Harding (Potts, 1909) and further examples of ab. *radiata* and *obsoleta* were caught at the same locality in 1909 (Potts, 1910). Also recorded are specimens of ab. *aerefimbriata* Newnh. in which the space between the row of black spots and the marginal forewing band is a bright brassy colour (Church Stretton, 1907) and one unnamed aberration which has the left hindwing silvery white (Church Stretton 1.vi.1901). Distribution map b. (Fig. 12).

1569 Small Blue *Cupido minimus* Fuessly

V.C.H.: Recorded by Phillips (1869) from Church Stretton. This could not be confirmed by the V.C.H. author. Also Edge Wood, 1908 (Woodforde).

Post V.C.H.: Very scarce. There are only two confirmed records, from localities in the west of the county in 1986 and central Shropshire in 1988. The recorders have asked that the names of these sites are not published at the present time (D. Smith and T. Coleshaw, pers. comm.). There are unconfirmed records from Ernwood Copse (Wyre Forest), 1960 (W. Smith) (though this seems most unlikely); Wenlock Edge, 1970 (Parr) and Tweedale, 1979 (J. Davis).

Flight: May and June in grassy, usually limestone, areas.

Larval F/p: Kidney vetch. June to April.

Notes: Plate 19.

1571 Silver-studded Blue *Plebejus argus* (*masseyi* Tutt?)

V.C.H.: Recorded as scarce in some dry sandy areas of the Longmynd (Newnham, 1901a & 1908).

Post V.C.H.: This species is resident in one site in north Shropshire and at present is doing well. There are several other old records from the same part of the county. In 1988 a dealer was seen offering for sale some 200 specimens from the known colony at an entomological exhibition. This sort of exploitation cannot be encouraged and so, sadly we do not feel able to publish the exact location of the colony. The relevant conservation bodies know of its existence and whereabouts and hopefully some protection of this species can now be enforced.

Flight: July and August on acid heathland where broom and gorse occur.

Larval F/ps: Mainly gorse, heather and heath. April to early June.

Notes: Newnham (1908) records the capture of a female in which the upperside is
          the same colour as the male. He suggests this may be ab.*bella* Herrich-
          Schäffer. Female specimens from the remaining Shropshire colony also
          show this tendancy towards blue colouration. Many have a blue flush
          covering most of the hindwings and approximately one third of the
          forewings. The males at this site have a much reduced black border around
          all the wings and a series of conspicuous black marginal spots on the
          hindwings. The general colour is much paler, less suffused with black and
          more suffused with white along the forewing costa than the typical *argus*
          subspecies from southern heathland (see Plate 12). Further, the underside of
          the male is much paler. These facts suggest a closer relationship to the now
          extinct subspecies *masseyi* Tutt which formerly occurred in Lancashire and
          Westmorland. This obviously adds considerably to the importance of the
          Shropshire site and strengthens the case for its protection.
          Plates 12 and 20.

1572 Brown Argus *Aricia agestis* Denis & Schiffermüller

V.C.H.:   Haughmond Hill (Harding) and common on some of the hills around
           Church stretton. Newnham (1901a) cites the southern slopes of Caradoc,
           e.g. Rabbit-Bury and the hill between Burway Gate and the reservoir.

Post V.C.H.: Very local and uncommon. Recorded from Shrewsbury, 1910 (Anon.
             B.R.C.); Dawley, 1972 (Riley) (this locality was destroyed during the
             development of Telford New Town); Llanymynech Rocks, 1930, 1939
             (Hignett), 1940 (Thelfall) and 1976 (D. Smith) and Pant, 1985 (Goode).

Flight: May to September in two broods, inhabiting rough grassy calcareous
           hillsides.

Larval F/p: Rock rose. August to April and June and early July.

1574 Common Blue *Polyommatus icarus icarus* Rottemburg

V.C.H.:   Common throughout.

Post V.C.H.: Fairly common on grassland, hillsides and wasteland throughout the county
             where the larval foodplants grow.

Flight: June to September and occasionally October.

Larval F/ps: Mainly bird's-foot-trefoil*. Brookes and Knight (1983) also state lesser yellow
                trefoil, restharrow, prickly restharrow and clovers. June to April.

Notes: Variation in this species is considerable. It is interesting to note that a
           gynandrous specimen with male markings on the left side and female on the
           right was caught by Harding at Church Stretton on 14.ix.1914 (Harding,
           1914). Newnham (1901) also recorded ab. *caerulea* Staudinger (female a
           similar colour to the male) and ab. *thersites* Boisduval (basal spots on
           underside of forewing absent) at Church Stretton. He later (1908) recorded
           ab. *adonides* Newnham (bright blue, without a hint of violet), ab. *icarinus*
           Scriba (basal spots on underside of forewing absent) and ab. *purpurea*
           Newnham (female of a purple tint).
           Distribution map c. (Fig. 12).

1575 Chalkhill Blue *Lysandra coridon* Poda

V.C.H.:   Unrecorded.

Post V.C.H.: Two dozen males were seen on the Longmynd and several were caught by
             Newnham and Harding in August 1916 (Ingrams, 1917) but it is unrecorded
             in Shropshire since.

Flight:	July to early September on chalk and limestone grassland.
Larval F/ps:	Usually horse-shoe vetch but Brookes and Knight (1983) also cite kidney vetch and bird's-foot-trefoil. April to June.

1580 Holly Blue *Celastrina argiolus* Linnaeus

V.C.H.:	Widespread and common.
Post V.C.H.:	Although numbers vary from year to year this species is widespread throughout Shropshire and is not uncommon where holly and ivy grow in close proximity, especially on woodland edges. It is particularly common on western slopes of the Brown Clee Hill. The adult is very mobile and is often seen away from such areas. This is the "Blue" butterfly most often seen in gardens.
Flight:	Double brooded, flying in April and May and again in August.
Larval F/ps:	First brood larvae usually feed on the buds and flowers of holly* and the second brood on those of ivy. However, various alternatives have been recorded outside Shropshire, including dogwood, snowberry, spindle, furze and bramble. May to early July and August and September.
Notes:	Distribution map d. (Fig. 12).

1581 Large Blue *Maculinea arion* Linnaeus

V.C.H.:	Stated by Phillips (1869) to occur around Church Stretton. Newnham (1908) had not seen it there but believed it might be found on the old rough pastures along Wenlock Edge. It was, however, never recorded at that locality.
Post V.C.H.:	Unrecorded. This species is now believed to be extinct in Britain.
Flight:	July. Grassy slopes with short turf where thyme grows.
Larval F/p:	Wild thyme at first and then on the larvae of *Myrmica* ants. July to May.

FAMILY: NEMEOBIIDAE

1582 Duke of Burgundy *Hemearis lucina* Linnaeus

V.C.H.:	Phillips (1896) states that this butterfly occurred in the Church Stretton area. This was the only record for the species in Shropshire at that time.
Post V.C.H.:	Three individuals were seen at Hope Dale by Potts and Powell (Ingrams, 1925) on 30.v.1924 and several more were seen at the same locality on 24.v.1926 (Potts, per Ingrams, 1927). There is an unconfirmed record from Oswestry in May 1985 (Dudley).
Flight:	May and June. Woodland clearings and rides and grazed hillsides and downlands where the larval foodplants grow.
Larval F/ps:	Primrose and cowslip. June and July.

FAMILY: NYMPHALIDAE

1584 White Admiral *Ladoga camilla* Linnaeus

V.C.H.:	Recorded only from Ragleth Wood, 4.vii.1890 (Newnham, 1901a & 1908). Also recorded from Church Stretton by Blatch (1886).

| Post V.C.H.: | Apart from one record from Ticklerton, 25-27.vii.1945 (Hayward) and Pontesbury, 1938 (Leeke, per Pendlebury, 1950) this species is restricted to the south-east corner of the county, principally the Wyre Forest, where it is not uncommon (Distribution map a. (Fig. 13)). It was abundant in this locality in 1987 (Plant, pers. comm.). |

Flight: June to August in woodland clearings and rides.

Larval F/p: Honeysuckle. August to June.

Notes: The larva is figured on Plate 21 and the adult on Plate 22.

1585 Purple Emperor *Apatura iris* Linnaeus

V.C.H.: Regularly recorded from the Yetchleys at Ellesmere (Peake, 1897). Also noted from Haughmond Hill, July 1881 (Harding) and Ragleth Woods, July 1889 and 24.vii.1900 (Newnham, 1901a & 1908).

Post V.C.H.: One record only, of a male near Ludlow in 1985 (Minton). This specimen was not kept for confirmation.

Flight: July and August in large oak woods.

Larval F/p: Goat willow. August to June. Newnham (1908) also cites aspen and black poplar but it is not clear whether he found this to be the case in Shropshire.

1590 Red Admiral *Vanessa atalanta* Linnaeus

V.C.H.: Common most years.

Post V.C.H.: An immigrant species, present every year. Sometimes common. Generally distributed.

Flight: May to October. Often seen in gardens at the flowers of *Buddleia*, *Sedum* and Michaelmas daisy.

Larval F/p: Nettle*. June to September.

Notes: Pendlebury (1950) noted that in 1947 "A black variety of the Red Admiral . . . was seen by Miss Hughes in her garden at Belmont, Shrewsbury on September 4." Newnham (1908) describes individuals, bred by him, which bear a white spot in the red band of the forewing. These appear to conform to ab.*bialbata* Cabeau. He also mentions a specimen in which the red band of the hindwing is ". . . almost white in places." Distribution map b. (Fig. 13).

1591 Painted Lady *Cynthia cardui* Linnaeus

V.C.H.: Widespread. More common in some years than others.

Post V.C.H.: Immigrant. Annual numbers vary but it is present every year. Generally distributed. Often seen in gardens. Also visits the flowers of sallow in early spring.

Flight: April to September.

Larval F/ps: Usually thistles* but occasionally nettle, burdock and mallow.

Notes: Distribution map c. (Fig. 13).

1593 Small Tortoiseshell *Aglais urticae* Linnaeus

V.C.H.: Common throughout. Newnham (1901a) states that ab. *ichnusa* Bon. is met with occasionally.

Post V.C.H.: Widespread, generally distributed and common.

Flight: Throughout the year in two or three generations. Hibernates as an adult and occasionally flies in mild weather during the winter.

Larval F/p: Nettle*. May to September.

28

Notes: A specimen of ab. *semiichnusoides* Pronin. (Russworm, 1978) was caught at Ludlow in 1988 (Minton) and is figured in BBCS News, No. 40, Spring/ Summer, 1988, p.6. Newnham (1908) records the capture at Church Stretton, 23.vii.1907, of a pale specimen in which the normal ground colour is replaced by whitish pink. He calls this form ab. *testudinella* Newnham (= ab. *lutea* Raynor?). Other aberrations recorded by Newnham (1908) are var. (= ab.) *connexa* Butler, in which the median costal spot is joined to that of the hind margin by a black band; ab. *atrebatensis* Boisduval, in which the hindwings are suffused with black (bred by M. J. Harding from larvae collected at Church Stretton, 6.vii.1905); ab. *urticoides* F.d.W., which is a diminutive form, sometimes less than one inch in expanse and an unnamed aberration, bred by M. J. Harding, in which the marginal blue spots of the hindwings extend into wedge-shaped marks, the apices of which almost reach the cell.

Distribution map d. (Fig. 13) and Plate 23.

1594 Large Tortoiseshell *Nymphalis polychloros* Linnaeus

V.C.H.: Uncommon and erratic. Recorded sparingly from Petton Park, Shrewsbury, (Tatton); Ellesmere (Peake); Benthall Edge, 1905 (Potts, 1906) and Church Stretton (Ragleth and Watling Street) and Dudgeley (Newnham, 1901a & 1908).

Post V.C.H.: Extremely rare, probably now extinct in Shropshire. Recorded only from Hope Dale, 24.iv.1926 (Potts); Broseley, ". . . a few years ago . . ." (Broadhurst, per Pendlebury, 1943) and Haughmond and Shrewsbury, 1950 (Rutter).

Flight: July to May, overwintering as an adult in hollow trees etc. Found in large open woods and woodland edges.

Larval F/ps: Elm, sallow, willow and cherry. May and June.

Notes: This is a popular species with amateur butterfly breeders who have a well-intentioned but misguided tendency to release the adults without due consultation. This must be borne in mind by recorders if sightings are made.

1596 Camberwell Beauty *Nymphalis antiopa* Linnaeus

V.C.H.: Rare. Ellesmere, 1872 (Horsefall; Peake, 1897); Tedsmore, near Oswestry, 1872 (Owen); Church Stretton, August 1886 (one) and All Stretton 1887 (two on sallow blossom) (Newnham, 1901a) and Stapleton, August 1900 (one) (per Newnham, 1908).

Post V.C.H.: This rare immigrant has only been recorded three times in Shropshire since 1900: Leebotwood, 3.viii.1909 (Ward); Church Stretton, 1974 and Stiperstones, 1977 (per D. Smith, pers. comm.).

Flight: July to May, overwintering (though this is rare in Britain due to our damp winters) as an adult.

Larval F/ps: Sallow, willow, birch and elm. April to June (South, 1924).

1597 Peacock *Inachis io* Linnaeus

V.C.H.: Common throughout. The diminutive ab. *ioides* Och. occurred occasinally (Newnham, 1901a).

Post V.C.H.: Widespread, generally distributed and common. Often visits garden flowers.

Flight: July to May, overwintering as an adult.

Larval F/p: Nettle*. June and July.

Notes:	A form without the usual eye spots (ab. *belisaria* Ob.?) was bred by Pitt at Bridgnorth in 1917 (Ingrams, 1918). Also an individual with the outer portion of the ocelli white instead of yellow and the costa very bright gold was caught near Buildwas on 26.ix.1920 by Potts (Ingrams, 1921). Distribution map a. (Fig. 14).

1598 Comma *Polygonia c-album* Linnaeus

V.C.H.:	Common in some years and scarce in others.
Post V.C.H.:	Widespread and fairly common throughout. A regular visitor to the garden.
Flight:	Late June to early May in two generations. Overwinters as an adult.
Larval F/ps:	Hop*, elm* and nettle*. May to September in two generations.
Notes:	Harding (1917) noted some interesting aberrations caught at Church Stretton. Ab. *iota-album* Newnham has the comma formed into a straight line and another (un-named) was caught by Newnham which had the comma developed into a complete circle. Newnham (1901a) states that a few specimens of ab. *intermedia* Newnham were caught at Church Stretton in the summer of 1893. This form is described as intermediate between *P. c-album* and *P. egea* Cramer from S.E. Europe, being light fulvous with only a few very small dark spots (= f. *hutchinsoni* Robson?). Distribution map b. (Fig. 14) and Plate 24.

1600 Small Pearl-bordered Fritillary *Boloria selene selene* Denis & Schiffermüller

V.C.H.:	Widely distributed. Recorded from Market Drayton, Ellesmere, Church Stretton and Wyre Forest.
Post V.C.H.:	Widespread but local and mainly restricted to woodlands. In recent years it has been most regularly recorded from the Wyre Forest, Ercall Woods, Pontesbury, Whixall Moss, Earl's Hill and Chorley Wood. (Distribution map c. (Fig. 14.)).
Flight:	June and July with an occasional partial second brood during August and early September.
Larval F/p:	Common dog violet*. July to May.
Notes:	Ab. *obsoleta* Curtis, in which the black spots are absent from all the wings, was recorded by Newnham at Church Stretton on 28.vi.1907 (Newnham, 1908). Plate 25.

1601 Pearl-bordered Fritillary *Boloria euphrosyne* Linnaeus

V.C.H.:	Common in the hilly parts of the county.
Post V.C.H.:	Less widespread than the previous species. Mainly restricted to the larger woods of the south and south-east, most notably the Wyre Forest. The two exceptions are Earl's Hill (per, STNC) and Pant, 1985 (Goode) (Distribution map d. (Fig. 14)).
Flight:	May and June with a partial and occasional second brood in September (Newnham, 1901).
Larval F/p:	Common dog violet. Late June to early May.
Notes:	Newnham (1902b) describes an aberration of this species caught at Church Stretton, 4.vi.1901 ". . . . the posterior wings are almost black above, as in var. *fingal*, but the base of these same wings beneath are light yellow, hind margins orange-red; marginal silver spots reach almost the centre of the wings." He later (1908) gives a fuller description of the specimen which he named ab. *rinaldoides* Newnham. Plate 26.

1606 High Brown Fritillary *Argynnis adippe vulgoadippe* Verity

V.C.H.: Newnham (1908) records this species as common in Ragleth Woods and more sparing at Helmeth, Tiger Hall and the Wyre Forest. Hardcourt-Bath (1887b) described finding it in ". . . the utmost profusion . . ." at an unstated locality in southern Shropshire. He states that he could have caught hundreds had he so desired. There are other odd records from Shrewsbury (Stainton, 1857); Benthall Edge and Abdon Burf, 1902 (Potts, 1903) and Oswestry, 1907 (Pendlebury, per Potts, 1908).

Post V.C.H.: The traditional remaining stronghold in Shropshire for the high brown fritillary is the Wyre Forest. However, Evans (pers. comm.) states that since 1950 its numbers have severely declined and it is now in danger of extinction at this site. On a more optimistic note, several strong colonies have recently been discovered on the Shropshire/Herefordshire border and it is hoped that these and the Wyre Forest populations can be maintained with appropriate site management. Fig. 15 (a-c) shows the dramatic contraction of this species' range in Shropshire.

Flight: Late June to early August in woodland rides and clearings and on woodland edges.

Larval F/ps: Common dog violet. February to early June.

Notes: Newnham (1901a) states that a form, named by him as *hemicleodoxa* (= *intermedia* Tutt), in which the marginal silver spots on the underside of the hindwings are replaced with brownish yellow, is found occasionally with the type around Church Stretton. Newnham (1901b) described finding a male of this species mating with a female *Argynnis paphia* L. at Helmeth Wood, near Church Stretton on 20.vii.1901.
Plate 27.

1607 Dark Green Fritillary *Argynnis aglaja aglaja* Linnaeus

V.C.H.: Found in hilly parts of the county — not necessarily in woodlands. Most noted from Church Stretton and the Wyre Forest.

Post V.C.H.: Widespread but less common than formerly. Found on large tracts of exposed ground such as heathland, moorland and rough grassland, mainly in the western half of the county. The adults are fond of feeding from thistle blossoms.

Flight: Usually July and August though it has been noted as early as the end of May (Newnham, 1908).

Larval F/p: Common violet. August to May.

Notes: Newnham (1901a and 1902a) mentions a specimen of ab. *nigrans* (*sensu* Newnham) caught near the "World's End", Church Stretton, 21.vii.1897. His description is as follows: "Forewings black, shot with dark green, a few fulvous spots on disc; spots near hind margin very faint. Hindwings almost as in type." He later (1908) refers to this form as ab. *aemilia* Acerb. Distribution map d. (Fig. 15) and Plate 28.

1608 Silver-washed Fritillary *Argynnis paphia* Linnaeus

V.C.H.: Common in the wooded hilly parts of the county. Newnham (1901a) cites Tiger Hall, Helmeth and Ragleth Woods.

Post V.C.H.: Frequently recorded from large woods, mainly in the southern half of the county. Abundant in the Wyre Forest in 1987 and 1988 (Plant).

Flight: Late June to early August in woodland rides and clearings, often feeding at bramble blossom.

Larval F/p: Common violet*. August to early June.

Notes: Newnham (1908) describes the females from Church Stretton as being greener than those found in southern England. This may indicate that a form close to *valezina* Esper occurred there at that time. Blatch (1868) records f. *valezina* Esp. in the Wyre Forest.
Distribution map a. (Fig. 16).

1610 Marsh Fritillary *Eurodryas aurinia aurinia* Rottemburg

V.C.H.:   Local and usually scarce. Recorded from damp meadows at Ragleth, Botvylle, near Ticklerton and the Wyre Forest. There are also records (not published in the V.C.H.) from Ludlow, 1900 (Edwards); Bomere, 7.vi.1919 (Ingrams, 1920) and Breidden, 1946, many (Lewis) (per Pendlebury, 1950). In April, 1884 there was a large swarm of the larvae at Church Stretton. There were so many (". . . countless thousands . . .") that the ground was blackened by the swarm. A full account of this is given by Frohawk (1886 and 1924). The adults were recorded in June of that year, though not in numbers, by Harding (1884).

Post V.C.H.:   Possibly extinct in Shropshire. The last records were from Bomere, 7.vi.1919 (Ingrams, 1920); Breidden, 1946 (E. S. Lewis); Wyre Forest, 1948 (Smith, per Pendlebury, 1950) and the Wrekin, 1952 (Lorimer). However, it is interesting to note that the cocoons of *Apanteles bignelli* Marshall (Hymenoptera), which is a specific parasite of *E. aurinia*, were found at Ratlinghope in 1980 (Littlewood, pers. comm.). The cocoons were identified and confirmed by K. G. V. Smith and G. E. C. Nixon. This may suggest the continued presence of *E. aurinia* in this locality.

Flight: May and June in open areas where the foodplant occurs.

Larval F/p: Mainly devil's-bit scabious* but possibly other scabious and plantain species (Brookes and Knight, 1983).

FAMILY: SATYRIDAE

1614 Speckled Wood *Pararge aegeria tircis* Butler

V.C.H.:   Very local and uncommon. Recorded from Ragleth Wood (Newnham, 1901a) near Church Stretton and Broseley, Calverhall and Shrewsbury.

Post V.C.H.:   Widespread and fairly common in woodlands throughout the county.

Flight: March to September in two broods with an occasional third brood in October and November in favourable years.

Larval F/ps: Various grasses such as couch and cock's-foot. Throughout the year.

Notes: Distribution map b. (Fig. 16).

1615 Wall *Lasiommata megera* Linnaeus

V.C.H.:   Common throughout.

Post V.C.H.:   Fairly common on rough grassland and hedgerows throughout the county.

Flight: May and early June and late July to early September. There is an occasional third brood in late September and October in favourable years.

Larval F/ps: Various grasses, during every month of the year.

Notes: Distribution map c. (Fig. 16).

1616 Large Wall *Lasiommata maera maera* Linnaeus

V.C.H.:   Unrecorded.

Post V.C.H.: Two specimens; one male on 28.viii.1930 and one female on 2.ix.1931 at Shrewsbury. These were exhibited at the Entomological Society of London (now the British Entomological and Natural History Society) in 1931 by N. D. Riley on behalf of W. J. Pendlebury. Both specimens were caught by G. Tanner (Anon., 1931 and Pendlebury, 1932) (See also Howarth, 1973).

Flight: In northern Europe the adult flies in June and July. In the south there is a second brood in August and September.

Larval F/ps: Stated to be various grasses, e.g. *Poa annua* and *Glyceria fluitans*, (Higgins and Riley, 1970) both of which are common in the county (Sinker *et al.*, 1985).

Notes: These two specimens remain the only records of the Large Wall in Britain (Howarth, 1973) and much speculation surrounds them. It seems strange that they would have been caught during the flight period associated with south European populations and the possibility must exist that they were reared and released by a local enthusiast. It is unlikely that they should occur in two consecutive years in the same place as casual vagrants, particularly as it would more than likely have been noted in other parts of the country.

1617 Mountain Ringlet *Erebia epiphron* Knoch

Phillips (1869) recorded this species (var. *cassiope* Fabricius) from the Longmynd but, although the larval foodplant (mat grass) is found in the locality, this record is dubious. This species is only found above 450 m above sea level in Cumbria and parts of Scotland. However, it is interesting to note that Newnham (1908) did not dismiss the possibility that *E. epiphron* could exist in the Stretton area. He states that a colleague of his (W. Ashburner), who was familiar with the species from Cumberland, believed several areas of the Longmynd to ". . . correspond in all respects with the locale of this *Erebia* in the north of England."

1620 Marbled White *Melanargia galathea serena* Verity

V.C.H.: Fairly common in the Ragleth Woods in the early 1890's. Also recorded by Thompson from Ellesmere.

Post V.C.H.: Of very erratic appearance in the county. There were two records in 1976 at Much Wenlock (Whitney) and two during 1986 at Sturt Common, Wyre Forest (Bingham) and a locality near Craven Arms (Stoves).

Flight: July and August. Rough grassland, hillsides and woodland edges.

Larval F/ps: Various grasses, mainly cat's-tail, cock's-foot and sheep's fescue. August to June.

1621 Grayling *Hipparchia semele semele* Linnaeus

V.C.H.: Found on the dry stony hills around Church Stretton. Recorded once from Ellesmere by Thompson.

Post V.C.H.: Very local and generally uncommon. Recorded occasionally from widely scattered localities, mainly in the east of the county (Distribution map d. (Fig. 16)).

Flight: Late July to early September on heathland and rocky, grassy hillsides.

Larval F/ps: Various grasses including couch and sheep's-fescue. August to June.

Notes: Newnham (1908) mentions that a specimen of ab. *leuconeura* Newnham, in which the veins on the undersides of the hindwings are marked in white, was "Taken once some years ago."
Plate 29.

1625 Gatekeeper *Pyronia tithonus britanniae* Verity

V.C.H.: Common throughout.

Post V.C.H.: Common on rough grassland, hedgerows and woodland rides, clearings and edges.

Flight: July to early September.

Larval F/ps: Various grasses such as annual meadow-couch* and cock's-foot. August to June.

Notes: A female specimen of ab. *crassiexcessa* Leeds, in which the forewing spots are enlarged to a rather spectacular degree, was caught in the Ercall Woods, 1977 (Riley). This specimen is figured on Plate 12.
Distribution map a. (Fig. 16) and Plate 30.

1626 Meadow Brown *Maniola jurtina insularis* Thompson

V.C.H.: Common throughout, though it was rare in the Church Stretton area prior to 1900 (Newnham, 1901a & 1908).

Post V.C.H.: Very common in grassy areas throughout the county.

Flight: June to September in one protracted generation.

Larval F/ps: Polyphagous on grasses. August to May.

Notes: Newnham (1908) mentions the occasional occurrence of var. *hispulla* Hübner in which the fulvous patches on the forewings are enlarged and a fulvous band is present on the hindwings. This appears to conform to ab. *postfulvosa* Leeds, which the present author occasionally caught at Dawley in the early 1970's. Newnham (1908) also mentions the presence, in damp localities, of bleached specimens in which the fulvous patches are more or less replaced by greyish white. It is possible that these represent forms approaching ab. *radiata* Frohawk.
Distribution map b. (Fig. 17).

1627 Small Heath *Coenonympha pamphilus pamphilus* Linnaeus

V.C.H.: Common throughout.

Post V.C.H.: Very common in grassy areas throughout the county.

Flight: May to the end of September in two broods.

Larval F/ps: Polyphagous on grasses. Throughout the year.

Notes: Newnham (1901a) records the presence at Church Stretton of var. *lyllus* Esper in which the borders of all the wings are darker than the type and ab. *ocellata* Tutt which has a row of small ocelli on the undersides of the hindwings.
Distribution map c. (Fig. 17).

1628 Large Heath *Coenonympha tullia davus* Fabricius

V.C.H.: Common on Whixall Moss in areas undisturbed by peat cutting. Also recorded from the Yetchleys, Ellesmere (Peake, 1897) where it could be found ". . . any fine day towards the end of June . . ."

Post V.C.H.: Common on parts of Whixall, Fenn's and Wem Mosses. Also recorded from Bomere, 1925 (Pendlebury); Dowles, 1929 (Elliott) (though, owing to the type of habitat, this must be very doubtful) and Whitchurch, 1925 (Joy) and 1954 (Turner) (though these probably came from Whixall Moss (see "Notes")). Blackie (1949) cites a record from the Wrekin in 1907. This is unlikely to be valid as the locality does not appear suitable for *C. tullia*.

Flight: Late June and July on mosses.

Larval F/p: Cotton grass*, cross-leaved heath* and white beak-sedge. July to May.

Notes: The aberration *cockaynei* Hopkins has been recorded from Whitchurch by Joy in 1925 and Turner in 1954 (Howarth, 1984). As Whitchurch is the nearest large town to Whixall Moss it is probable that they were actually caught at Whixall as there are no known suitable localities at Whitchurch itself. Ab. *cockaynei* is now known to occur frequently at all the Shropshire localities (J. Joy, pers. comm.). Many aberrations from Whixall Moss are currently housed in the British Museum (Nat. Hist.).
Plate 31.

1629 Ringlet *Aphantopus hyperantus* Linnaeus

V.C.H.: Widespread and common in most woodlands.

Post V.C.H.: Widespread and not uncommon in wooded areas throughout the county.

Flight: June to August.

Larval F/ps: Various grasses, mainly cock's-foot and annual meadow-grass. August to June.

Notes: Distribution map d. (Fig. 17) and Plate 32.

FAMILY: DANAIDAE

1630 Monarch *Danaus plexippus* Linnaeus

V.C.H.: Unrecorded.

Post V.C.H.: This scarce immigrant has only been recorded twice in Shropshire: Uffington, 1929 (Sequera) and Wellington, 1973 (Riley).

Flight: Most British sightings occur between August and October.

Larval F/p: Milkweed. This is not found in the British Isles.

FAMILY: LASIOCAMPIDAE

1631 December Moth *Poecilocampa populi* Linnaeus

V.C.H.: Generally distributed and fairly common around Church Stretton and Market Drayton, the larvae feeding on ". . . almost every forest tree" (Newnham 1901a).

Post V.C.H.: Widely distributed and fairly common throughout the county.

Flight: November and December, mainly in wooded areas.

Larval F/ps: Many deciduous trees including hawthorn*, oak*, birch*, elm*, ash*, apple* and pear*. April to June.

1632 Pale Eggar *Trichiura crataegi* Linnaeus

V.C.H.: By no means common. Recorded only from Shrewsbury (Stainton, 1857. Vol. 1: 155), Market Drayton, Church Stretton and Wyre Forest.

Post V.C.H.: Widely distributed and frequent throughout the county.

Flight: August and September. Hedgerows, wasteland and woods.

Larval F/ps: Mainly blackthorn*, hawthorn*, willow*, apple* and birch. April to June.

1633 Small Eggar *Eriogaster lanestris* Linnaeus

V.C.H.: Very common around Calverhall (Thornewill), common around Market Drayton (Woodforde), frequent at Church Stretton (Newnham, 1901a).

Post V.C.H.: Found infrequently, mainly in the western half of the county, though there is one record of a larval nest on hawthorn at Lilleshall, (1977, Minshall) in the east.

Flight: February and March on scrubland and along hedgerows.

Larval F/ps: Hawthorn* and blackthorn, in a large ovoid web of whitish silk. Newnham (1908) records larvae on elm but he does not say if they were actually feeding. They were final instar larvae and no web was present. April to early July.

Notes: This species has declined nationally in recent years. In Shropshire this is reflected by the paucity of recent records. It appears from Newnham's comments (1908) that in places it was quite a common insect at the turn of the century. This is certainly not the case now. The adult is rarely noticed, even at light. Probably the best way to find the species is to look for the large conspicuous larval nests along hedgerows.

1634 The Lackey *Malacosoma neustria* Linnaeus

V.C.H.: Not common. Only mentioned from Ragleth Woods, near Church Stretton.

Post V.C.H.: Bridgnorth, 1955 (Darling); Pontesbury, 1970 (D. Smith); Bromfield, 1978 (Norton) and the Wyre Forest, where it is fairly common (Evans, pers. comm.).

Flight: July and August. Open woodlands, hedgerows and gardens.

Larval F/ps: Hawthorn*, blackthorn*, birch*, sallows and wild and cultivated fruit trees such as apple, pear and cherry. April to June.

Notes: The localised distribution indicated by these scattered records is probably a true reflection of the species' status in Shropshire. On a national scale it becomes increasingly more local from the Midlands northwards. It is interesting to note that we have no records from the northern half of the county.

1637 Oak Eggar *Lasiocampa quercus quercus* Linnaeus

V.C.H.: Probably found in all the flat parts of the county. Recorded from Church Stretton (among hawthorn in the valleys), Market Drayton (Woodforde), Ellesmere (Thompson) and Whixall Moss.

Post V.C.H.: The only records of *L. quercus* which can definitely be attributed to ssp. *quercus* are as follows: Church Stretton, 1952 (K. G. V. Smith); Wellington, 1968 and 1979 (Riley) and Whixall Moss, 1984 (Riley).

Flight: July and August.

Larval F/ps: A wide variety of trees and shrubs. Most commonly found on bramble*, sallow, oak and hazel. Recorded on birch at Whixall Moss in 1987 (Langmaid and Pelham-Clinton). September to June, overwintering once.

Northern Eggar *Lasiocampa quercus callunae* Palmer

V.C.H.: Occurs commonly on the high moorlands of the county.

Post V.C.H.: Found throughout the county on heather-clad moorland, heathland and mosses.

Flight: May and June.

Larval F/ps: Mainly heather* but occasionally bilberry from July to the September of the following year.

1638 Fox Moth *Macrothylacia rubi* Linnaeus

V.C.H.: Most frequent where there is either rough, unbroken ground or moorland. Ellesmere (Peake) and the Longmynd where it is often common as a larva (Newnham, 1901a).

Post V.C.H.: Frequently recorded from the western half of the county on moorland, heathland and the mosses of the north.

Flight: May and June.

Larval F/ps: Many plants including heather*, bramble and bilberry. July to March.

1640 The Drinker *Philudoria potatoria* Linnaeus

V.C.H.: Common in the larval state where there are damp hedgebanks and ditches.

Post V.C.H.: Common throughout the county in damp localities.

Flight: July and August.

Larval F/ps: Many species of grasses and reeds. September to June. Where large numbers of fully grown larvae are present one can actually hear them feeding by crouching or lying amongst the foodplant at night.

Notes: Newnham (1892b) cites finding ova on alder.

1641 Small Lappet *Phyllodesma ilicifolia* Linnaeus

V.C.H.: Regarded as a great prize. Occasionally found in the larval state on the Longmynd feeding on bilberry Newnham (1908).

Post V.C.H.: Not recorded since 1889.

Flight: April and May. The earliest and latest dates of emergence noted by Newnham (1908) were 17 and 24 May respectively. Moorland and open woodland.

Larval F/p: Bilberry*. June to August.

Notes: This species has always been scarce in Britain. The Longmynd was one of only a few known localities. It is apparently easily overlooked and may still be present in Shropshire though it has not been recorded from anywhere in Britain since 1965. In the national collection at the British Museum (Nat. Hist.) there are seven specimens from Shropshire. All carry Newnham's labels but only one is dated. This states "21.5.1889 larva found at Church Stretton. F. B. Newnham". The other six are labelled "Church Stretton. Bred by F. B. Newnham." Four of the seven specimens conform to ab. *rufescens* Tutt which has a more ochreous ground colour than the type. Plate 11 shows one of Newnham's original Church Stretton specimens of ab. *rufescens*.

1642 The Lappet *Gastropacha quercifolia* Linnaeus

V.C.H.: Taken a few times as larvae at Church Stretton.

Post V.C.H.: Scarce but widespread: Chetton, 1920 and Morville, 1947 (Bythell, per Pendlebury, 1956); Dothill, 1978 (two) (Riley); Preston Montford Field Centre, 1984 (R.I.S. trap, det. Riley) and Bromfield, 1985 (Norton).

Flight: June to August. Open woodlands, hedgerows and orchards.

Larval F/ps: Hawthorn*, blackthorn and buckthorn. August to May.

FAMILY: SATURNIIDAE

1643 Emperor Moth *Pavonia pavonia* Linnaeus

V.C.H.: Of universal distribution; especially common where there are large tracts of heather.

Post V.C.H.: Fairly well recorded from western and northern parts of Shropshire. There are no records from the south east quarter of the county.

Flight: April and May. The male is diurnal and can be seen flying swiftly over the heather in search of the females which fly at night and occasionally come to light.

Larval F/ps: Most commonly heather*, heath*, hawthorn*, bramble* and meadowsweet*. Also recorded on aspen* (K. G. V. Smith, 1954). May to August.

Notes: Perhaps the easiest way to determine the presence of this species from a previously unrecorded locality is to try to assemble males using a virgin female (Newnham 1892a).
Newnham (1891) mentions the presence of two forms of this species from Church Stretton: ab. *rosacea* Newn. which has a strong pink suffusion (Plate 12) and ab. *infumata* Newn. which has all the wings heavily suffused with dark smoky grey (Plate 12). Two individuals of each of these aberrations are now in the national collection at the British Museum (Nat. Hist.). K. G. V. Smith (1954) mentions the continued presence of ab. *rosacea* at Church Stretton.

FAMILY: ENDROMIDAE

1644 Kentish Glory *Endromis versicolora* Linnaeus

V.C.H.: Was found ". . . some years ago . . ." at the extreme northern part of Ragleth Wood but the site was destroyed around 1901, thus rendering this species extinct there (Newnham, 1901a and 1908). Recorded from the Wyre Forest, 3.iv.1897, 21.iv.1898 and 16.iv.1901 (Carleton Rea).

Post V.C.H.: Only recorded from the Wyre Forest. Last reported there in 1970 when a single specimen was seen. Attempts were made to assemble males to a virgin female in 1986 but they were unsuccessful (Evans).

Flight: March and April in open woodland and moorland where the larval foodplant is present.

Larval F/ps: Birch* and sometimes alder.

Notes: This species has its present-day British strongholds in Highland Scotland and is thought to have died out from most, if not all, of its known English localities. Continuous attempts should be made to determine its presence or absence in the Wyre Forest as it may still be resident at very low density. Every caution should be taken to preserve its habitat in this locality. Newnham (1908) noted that specimens from Ragleth Wood appeared smaller and darker than those from southern counties. This species is figured on Plate 11.

FAMILY: DREPANIDAE

1645 Scalloped Hook-tip *Falcaria lacertinaria* Linnaeus

V.C.H.: Occurs freely where birches abound.

Post V.C.H.: Recorded occasionally from widely scattered localities and from various habitats including woodland, the northern mosses and open countryside.

Flight: May to August in two broods.

Larval F/p: Birch*. June to September.

1646 Oak Hook-tip *Drepana binaria* Hufnagel

V.C.H.: Recorded only from the woods around Church Stretton and once from Market Drayton (Woodforde, 1902d).

Post V.C.H.: Frequent throughout the county wherever birch is common.

Flight: May to August in two broods.

Larval F/p: Oak*. June, July and September.

Notes: The apparently very local distribution of this species at the turn of the century is surprising. Newnham had many correspondents throughout the county, none of whom appeared to include *D. binaria* on their lists. If this was not merely due to oversight on their parts, which is unlikely, then the species must have expanded its range considerably over the greater part of the last century. This theory is supported by Newman (1869, p.208) who states that *D. binaria* was only found in the southern and eastern counties of England at that time. It is now known to occur throughout England and most of Wales (Skinner 1984).

1647 Barred Hook-tip *Drepana cultraria* Fabricius

V.C.H.: Frequent in beech woods around Church Stretton, and probably throughout the county, though no other localities are listed.

Post V.C.H.: Very local; recorded only from Condover, 1920 (Ingrams, 1921); Rodington, 1960 (Briggs); Ironbridge, 1974 (Derry); Shirlett, 1980 (Whitney); Monkhopton, 1985 (Jacques) and the Wyre Forest, 1984 & 1985 (Plant).

Flight: May and June and again in August.

Larval F/p: Beech. June, July and September.

1648 Pebble Hook-tip *Drepana falcataria falcataria* Linnaeus

V.C.H.: Widespread.

Post V.C.H.: Widespread and fairly common where birches are found. Recorded occasionally from many habitat types such as the woodlands around the Wrekin where it is very common and the mosses of Whixall and Wem.

Flight: May and June and again in August.

Larval F/p: Birch*. June, July and September.

1651 Chinese Character *Cilix glaucata* Scopoli

V.C.H.: Reported from nearly all parts of the county.

Post V.C.H.: Widespread and fairly common along hedgerows. Also scrubby openings in woodland, heathland and woodland edges.

Flight: May to August in two broods.

Larval F/ps: Mainly hawthorn* and blackthorn*. June, July, September and October.

FAMILY: THYATIRIDAE

1652 Peach Blossom *Thyatira batis* Linnaeus

V.C.H.: Generally distributed but not abundant.

Post V.C.H.: Found fairly frequently throughout the county, mainly in or near woodlands and coppices.

Flight: May to July.

Larval F/p: Bramble. July to September.

1653 Buff Arches *Habrosyne pyritoides* Hufnagel

V.C.H.: Generally distributed but not abundant. Fairly common at Market Drayton (Woodforde).

Post V.C.H.: Fairly common throughout in similar habitats to the last species.

Flight: June to August.

Larval F/p: Bramble*. August to October.

1654 Figure of Eighty *Tethea ocularis octogesimea* Hübner

V.C.H.: Recorded only from Broseley, June 1896 (Bradburne) and Wyre, 18.vi.1899 (Rea) and June and July 1902 (Woodforde, 1902c).

Post V.C.H.: Recorded regularly, though never commonly, north east of a line from Minsterley to Quatford. Also frequent in the Wyre Forest (Blunt; Evans).

Flight: May to July in the vicinity of poplar or aspen.

Larval F/ps: Poplar* and aspen. July and August.

Notes: So far as I am aware, the melanic form *fusca* Cockayne has only been recorded from Dothill (Riley) where it is rare.

1655 Poplar Lutestring *Tethea or or* Denis & Schiffermüller

V.C.H.: Recorded infrequently from Ragleth Woods, Church Stretton (Newnham, 1908) and the Wyre Forest (Woodforde, 1902c).

Post V.C.H.: Only two records: Shrewsbury, 1913 (Pendlebury & Pendlebury, 1914) and one male in a spider's web in the Wyre Forest in August, 1984 (Plant).

Flight: May to August in the vicinity of aspens or poplars.

Larval F/ps: Mainly aspen but Skinner (1984) states that the English subspecies is occasionally found on poplar. Newnham (1901a) states that this species is often recorded "on or near poplar". July to September.

1656 Satin Lutestring *Tetheella fluctuosa* Hübner

V.C.H.: In 1908 this species was only known from the Wyre Forest where it was fairly frequently caught by Carleton Rea (Potts, 1903; Newnham, 1908). It had been found previously at Ragleth Wood but that site was destroyed in 1901 (Newnham, 1901a).

Post V.C.H.: Still found frequently in the Wyre Forest (Blunt; Evans; Plant).

Flight: June to August in mature woodland.

Larval F/p: Birch. August and September.

Notes: The profusion of the larval foodplant may suggest that this species has been overlooked in Shropshire. However, it is regarded as being a very local species throughout Britain. Therefore the scarcity of records may be a true reflection of its status in the county.

1657 Common Lutestring *Ochropacha duplaris* Linnaeus

V.C.H.: Not at all rare.

Post V.C.H.: Recorded frequently from throughout the county.

Flight: June to August in, or on the edges of, woodlands and wooded areas of heathland.

Larval F/ps: Mainly birch, though occasionally oak and alder (Skinner 1984). August to October.

Notes: The melanic form *obscura* Tutt seems to predominate.

1658 Oak Lutestring *Cymatophorima diluta hartwiegi* Reisser

V.C.H.: Generally distributed. Larvae often obtained.

Post V.C.H.: Apart from the Wyre Forest, where it is fairly common (Evans), it has only been recorded from Shrewsbury, 1950 (J. Smith); Shelton, 1953 (MacKensie); Shirlett, 1977 (Whitney) and Pontesbury, 1973, 1979 and 1981 (D. Smith).

Flight: August and September in oak woodlands.

Larval F/p: Oak*. May to July.

1659 Yellow-horned *Achlya flavicornis galbanus* Tutt

V.C.H.: Common among birch.

Post V.C.H.: Frequent throughout in woodlands or heathland in the vicinity of birches.

Flight: March and April.

Larval F/p: Birch*. May to July.

1660 Frosted Green *Polyploca ridens* Fabricius

V.C.H.: Unrecorded.

Post V.C.H.: Appears to be common only in the Wyre Forest (Evans). There are other records from Quatford, 1960 (D'Arcy); Bucknell, 1971 (Shephard); Stoke-on-Tern, 1976 (Littlewood, R.I.S. trap); Shirlett, 1978 and 1980 (Whitney) and the Ercall Woods, 1980 (Riley).

Flight: April and May in woodlands containing mature oaks.

Larval F/p: Oak. May to July.

FAMILY: GEOMETRIDAE

1661 Orange Underwing *Archiearis parthenias* Linnaeus

V.C.H.: Common at Shrewsbury (Stainton, 1857. Vol. 1: 301); Wyre Forest (Blatch, 1886); fairly common around Market Drayton (Woodforde, 1900 and 1902a); not uncommon at Church Stretton and infrequent near Calverhall.

Post V.C.H.: Widespread and frequent in birch woods and heathlands where birches are common.

Flight: March and April. Diurnal, flying in bright sunshine around the foodplant.

Larval F/p: Birch*. May and June.

1662 Light Orange Underwing *Archiearis notha* Hübner

V.C.H.: Frequent at Market Drayton in 1902 (Woodforde, 1902b).

Post V.C.H.: A single record from the Wrekin, 2.iv.1921 (Graham, per Ingrams, 1922).

Flight: March and April. Diurnal, flying in bright sunshine around aspen trees.

Larval F/p: Aspen. May and June.

Notes: Unfortunately there are no confirmatory specimens. It is possible that Graham's record was of *A. parthenias* which is known to occur in the area. However, aspen is found on the Wrekin so further investigations should be made at this locality and others where the foodplant is present. It should be noted that although aspen is frequent in the Wyre Forest (Sinker, *et al.* 1985, p. 329) *A. notha* has not been recorded there (Evans).

1663 March Moth *Alsophila aescularia* Denis & Schiffermüller

V.C.H.: Fairly common throughout.

Post V.C.H.: Fairly common throughout.

Flight: March and April in most habitat types.

Larval F/ps: Polyphagous on deciduous trees. Recorded in Shropshire on birch and elm. May and June.

1665 Grass Emerald *Pseudoterpna pruinata atropunctaria* Walker

V.C.H.: Infrequent at Market Drayton and in the Church Stretton area.

Post V.C.H.: Recorded fairly frequently on heathland and rough ground such as the old heather-clad spoil heaps around Dawley.

Flight: June to August.

Larval F/ps: Mainly gorse and broom. September to May.

1666 Large Emerald *Geometra papilionaria* Linnaeus

V.C.H.: Fairly common at Market Drayton and Church Stretton where Newnham (1901a) found larvae on birch and alder. Also recorded from Wyre Forest (Blatch, 1886).

Post V.C.H.: Recorded frequently throughout, mainly from wooded areas.

Flight: June to August.

Larval F/ps: Mainly birch*, occasionally alder* and hazel. September to May.

1667 Blotched Emerald *Comibaena bajularia* Denis & Schiffermüller

V.C.H.: Recorded only from the Wyre Forest, 1896 (Rea).

Post V.C.H.: Infrequently recorded from most of lowland Shropshire.

Flight: June and July in and near oak woodlands.

Larval F/p: Oak*. September to May.

1669 Common Emerald *Hemithea aestivaria* Hübner

V.C.H.: Apparently rare. Recorded as scarce around Market Drayton.

Post V.C.H.: Fairly common throughout.

Flight: June and July in open woodlands, scrubland and along hedgerows.

Larval F/ps: Polyphagous on deciduous trees and bushes. August to May.

1670 Small Grass Emerald *Chlorissa viridata* Linnaeus

V.C.H.: Unrecorded.

Post V.C.H.: There is a single unconfirmed record of this species caught at light on 3.vii.1939 at Bayston Hill (Wood-Taylor, 1941). The species is known to occur in neighbouring Worcestershire (Skinner, 1984).

Flight: June and early July on damp heathland and mosses.

Larval F/ps: Heather, birch and creeping willow. July and August (Skinner, 1984).

1673 Small Emerald *Hemistola chrysoprasaria* Esper

V.C.H.: Unrecorded.

Post V.C.H.: Longmynd, 1952 (Bretherton); Shirlett, 1969 (Whitney); Dawley, 1975 (Jacques); Bucknell, 1971 (Shephard); Llanymynech, 22.vii.1989 (five individuals) (Townsend) and Ludlow, 8.ix.1989 (one) (R.I.S. trap, det. Riley).

Flight:	June to early August. Woodland edges and hedgerows where the larval foodplant grows.
Larval F/p:	Traveller's-joy. September to June.
Notes:	The individual caught in the R.I.S. trap at Ludlow on 8.ix.1989 (det. Riley) may represent a partial second emergence for that year.

1674 Little Emerald *Jodis lactearia* Linnaeus

V.C.H.:	Fairly common.
Post V.C.H.:	Recorded frequently from woodland areas throughout the county.
Flight:	May and June.
Larval F/ps:	Polyphagous. Recorded on birch, oak and elm in the Ercall Woods (Riley). August and September.

1676 The Mocha *Cyclophora annulata* Schulze

V.C.H.:	Often seen in the vicinity of maple at Church Stretton.
Post V.C.H.:	Unrecorded since the publication of the V.C.H. (1908).
Flight:	May to August in two broods, inhabiting woodlands.
Larval F/p:	Maple*. July and September.
Notes:	It is possible that this species has disappeared from Shropshire. It was probably always very local and Newnham's comments, I believe, refer only to his 'home patch' of Church Stretton. As he cited no actual localities it is difficult to say how this species has fared since the turn of the century. Nationally, it has a very localised distribution within the southern half of Britain.
	Plate 11.

1677 Birch Mocha *Cyclophora albipunctata* Hufnagel

V.C.H.:	Wyre Forest (Blatch, 1886); not uncommon around Market Drayton (Woodforde, 1901b) and Church Stretton.
Post V.C.H.:	Recorded from only two localities: Wyre Forest, 1970 (Scott) and Whixall Moss, 1980 (Watson), 1985 (Hardwick) and 1986 (Cooper).
Flight:	May and June. In southern Britain there is a partial second brood in August. To my knowledge this has not been recorded in Shropshire.
Larval F/p:	Birch. July and September.
Notes:	Ab. *subroseata* Woodforde has a bright red median band and was common at Market Drayton during the early 1900s (Woodforde, 1901d). The type locality for this aberration is, in fact, Market Drayton.

1679 False Mocha *Cyclophora porata* Linnaeus

V.C.H.:	Wyre Forest (Blatch, 1886) and several from Market Drayton, 1900 (Woodforde, 1900e).
Post V.C.H.:	Recorded once from Monkhopton, 1977 (Whitney).
Flight:	May, June, August and September, inhabiting heathland and woodland.
Larval F/p:	Oak. July, August and September.

1680 Maiden's Blush *Cyclophora punctaria* Linnaeus

| V.C.H.: | Fairly common at Market Drayton in 1901 (Woodforde, 1901b). |
| Post V.C.H.: | Only seven records: Cleobury Mortimer, August 1922 (Woodward, 1922b); Shrewsbury (Wood-Taylor, 1941); Wyre Forest (Wimperhill Wood), 1970 (Scott); Pontesbury, 1978 (D. Smith); Shirlett, 1985 (one) (Whitney) and Buttonoak (Wyre), June, 1987 and 25.vi.1988 (four) (Blunt). |

Flight: May and June and again in August.

Larval F/p: Oak. July and September.

1681 Clay Triple-lines *Cyclophora linearia* Hübner

V.C.H.:   Unrecorded.

Post V.C.H.: Two records only: Cleobury Mortimer, August 1922 (Woodward, 1922b) and the Wyre Forest, 1987 (Plant).

Flight: May to July and possibly again as a partial second brood from August to October.

Larval F/p: Beech. July and August.

1682 Blood-vein *Timandra griseata* Peters

V.C.H.:   Occasional at Calverhall (Thornewill), rare at Market Drayton and once at Cloverley Park (Woodforde).

Post V.C.H.: Common throughout the county.

Flight: May to September in two broods. Found in many habitat types.

Larval F/ps: Mainly dock, sorrel and knotgrass. September to April.

Notes: Newnham (1908) states that he did not find this species near Church Stretton and the comments of his other correspondents would suggest that it was quite a rarity in the county at that time. It has been much more frequently recorded since.

1684 Sub-angled Wave *Scopula nigropunctata* Hufnagel

This species is represented in the list of Lepidoptera caught by H. L. Burrows at Whixall Moss (Fielding, 1974a). However, as there has never been a substantiated record from outside Sussex and Kent (Skinner, 1984) it is probably erroneous.

1687 Lace Border *Scopula ornata* Scopoli

V.C.H.:   Unrecorded.

Post V.C.H.: One record from Rodington, 22.vi.1960 (Briggs).

Flight: May to September in two broods, usually on downland.

Larval F/ps: Thyme and marjoram. September to April and June and July.

1690 Small Blood-vein *Scopula imitaria* Hübner

V.C.H.:   Recorded only as scarce at Market Drayton (Woodforde).

Post V.C.H.: Fairly common throughout.

Flight: July and August on wasteground, in gardens and along hedgerows. A single male was caught at Preston Montford on 3.x.1989 (R.I.S. trap, det. Riley), suggesting a partial second emergence for that year.

Larval F/ps: Probably polyphagous. Skinner (1984) cites privet and Newnham (1908) mentions broom in Shropshire. September to May.

Notes: This species appears to be more common and widespread than it was at the turn of the century.

1692 Lesser Cream Wave *Scopula immutata* Linnaeus

V.C.H.:   Very common around Market Drayton (Woodforde, 1900e).

Post V.C.H.: Widely distributed. Recorded from all over the county in damp localities, though not usually common. Abundant at Whixall Moss in 1990 (Cooper).

Flight: June to August.

Larval F/ps: Common valerian, meadowsweet and probably other low-growing plants. September to May.

1693 Cream Wave *Scopula floslactata floslactata* Haworth

V.C.H.: Generally distributed and fairly frequent in meadows.

Post V.C.H.: Recorded infrequently, mainly from wooded areas, throughout the county.

Flight: May and June.

Larval F/ps: Probably many low-growing plants. Skinner (1984) states that it feeds from July to April in captivity on knotgrass, dock and dandelion.

1694 Smoky Wave *Scopula ternata* Schrank

V.C.H.: Recorded only from Market Drayton where it was fairly common (Woodforde, 1900e).

Post V.C.H.: A very local and uncommon species found mainly on heathland and the mosses of the north. Recorded only from Shrewsbury, 1913 (Pendlebury, 1915); Stow Hill, 1958 (Scott); Church Stretton, 1959 (Knill-Jones); Rodington, 1960 (Briggs); Whixall Moss, 1980 (Watson) and the Longmynd, 1970, 1980 and 1983 (Whitney).

Flight: June and July.

Larval F/ps: Heather and bilberry. August to May.

1698 Purple-bordered Gold *Idaea muricata* Hufnagel

V.C.H.: Unrecorded.

Post V.C.H.: Recorded regularly from Fenn's Moss and Whixall Moss since 1930 and Wem Moss, 4.vii.1963 (Warren).

Flight: June and July. Easily disturbed during the day by tapping the ground cover.

Larval F/p: Marsh cinquefoil. August to May.

Notes: This species has only been recorded from the 10 km square SJ43. However, the larval foodplant is found in suitable places throughout the northwest corner of the county (Sinker *et al.*, 1985). It is possible that searching in such places may uncover new sites for this pretty, but easily overlooked, species.

1702 Small Fan-footed Wave *Idaea biselata* Hufnagel

V.C.H.: Generally distributed throughout the county.

Post V.C.H.: Found commonly throughout.

Flight: June to August. Woods, hedgerows, wasteland and rough ground.

Larval F/ps: Probably many low-growing plants such as dandelion, knotgrass etc. Although the natural foodplant is not known, the larvae feed on the above, plantain and bramble in captivity (Skinner, 1984). August to April.

1705 Dwarf Cream Wave *Idaea fuscovenosa* Goeze

V.C.H.: Unrecorded.

Post V.C.H.: Recorded only twice: Oswestry, August 1930 (Hignett, 1931) and Stoke-on-Tern, 1978 (Littlewood, R.I.S. trap).

Flight: June and July on wasteland, in overgrown gardens and rough meadows.

Larval F/ps: Unknown in the wild but larvae will accept dandelion and bramble in captivity (Skinner, 1984). It probably feeds on a variety of low-growing plants.

1707 Small Dusty Wave *Idaea seriata* Schrank

V.C.H.:   Common around Church Stretton among knotgrass.

Post V.C.H.:   Only recorded from central Shropshire where it is usually fairly common: Donnington, 1949 (Christie); Broseley, 1969 (Whitney); Pontesbury, 1976 (D. Smith); Ercall Woods and Wellington up to 1979 when the recorder left the area (Riley) and Preston Montford Field Centre, (annually at R.I.S. trap, det. Riley).

Flight: June to August in two broods. Wasteland, gardens and rough meadows.

Larval F/ps: Probably many low plants. Skinner (1984) cites ivy.

1708 Single-dotted Wave *Idaea dimidiata* Hufnagel

V.C.H.:   Common.

Post V.C.H.:   Widespread and common throughout in damp places.

Flight: June to August.

Larval F/ps: Burnet saxifrage* and cow parsley*. Newnham (1908) found larvae on the latter at Church Stretton.

1709 Satin Wave *Idaea subsericeata* Haworth

V.C.H.:   Unrecorded.

Post V.C.H.:   Very local and infrequently recorded, mainly from the east: Oswestry, 1928 (Hignett, 1931); Bridgnorth, 1951 (K. G. V. Smith); Stoke-on-Tern, 1975-77 (Littlewood, R.I.S. trap); Shirlett, 1978 (Whitney); Pontesbury, 1978 (D. Smith); the Yeld, 1984 (Denman) and Monkhopton, 1985 (Jacques).

Flight: June and July. Woodland rides and grasslands.

Larval F/ps: Probably many low-growing plants. Skinner (1984) cites dandelion, plantain and knotgrass in captivity.

1711 Treble Brown Spot *Idaea trigeminata* Haworth

V.C.H.:   Unrecorded.

Post V.C.H.:   Very infrequently recorded: Shrewsbury, 1922 (Pendlebury, per Ingrams, 1923); Bridgnorth, 1940 (Darling) and 1970 (Wint); Bucknell, 1972 (Shephard); Monkhopton, 1985 (Jacques); Wyre forest, 1984 (Plant) and 1986 (Blunt) and Ludlow, 1989 (R.I.S. trap, det. Riley).

Flight: June to August, mainly in wooded areas.

Larval F/ps: Many low plants. August to May.

Notes: This species is found in the southern half of England and parts of south Wales. It is close to the edge of its range in Shropshire which probably explains the paucity of records.

1712 Small Scallop *Idaea emarginata* Linnaeus

V.C.H.:   Unrecorded.

Post V.C.H.:   Widely distributed and fairly common in damp areas.

Flight: June to August.

Larval F/ps: Bedstraw and probably many other low-growing plants. Skinner (1984) suggests dandelion as a foodplant for captive larvae. September to May.

1713 Riband Wave *Idaea aversata* Linnaeus

V.C.H.:   Found over the whole of the county. Very common in damp places.

Post V.C.H.:   Common throughout.

Flight:	Skinner (1984) states that *I. aversata* flies from mid-June to mid-August with a partial second generation in September in southern England. It appears from the data collected at Rothamsted Insect Survey traps (Preston Montford, Wellington, Rowton and Stoke-on-Tern) that there is only one generation in Shropshire, flying from the last week of June to the first week of September.
Larval F/ps:	Probably many low-growing plants such as bedstraw, chickweed, knotgrass and primrose. September to May.
Notes:	Ab. *remutaria* L., which lacks the broad median bands, is equally as common as the typical form.

1715 Plain Wave *Idaea straminata* Borkhausen

V.C.H.:	Unrecorded.
Post V.C.H.:	Recorded from Shrewsbury, 1913 (Pendlebury & Pendlebury, 1914); Rodington, 12.ix.1962 (Briggs) and Whixall Moss, 1972 (Rutherford), 1980 (Anon, B.R.C.) and 1985 (Hardwick).
Flight:	July. Heathland and woodland.
Larval F/ps:	Probably many low-growing plants such as dandelion, knotgrass, heather and dock. August to May.
Notes:	This species is easily confused with the last. Whixall Moss may be a suitable habitat for *I. straminata* but great care should be taken when attributing records to this species. Further investigation is needed to ascertain its status in Shropshire.

1716 The Vestal *Rhodometra sacraria* Linnaeus

V.C.H.:	Unrecorded.
Post V.C.H.:	Oswestry, 1946 and 1949 (Hignett); Dothill, 1972 (Riley); Pontesbury, 1973 (D. Smith); Preston Montford Field Centre, 1983 (four) (det. Riley) and Woore, 28.ix.1983 (Holdsworth).
Flight:	This usually rare Shropshire immigrant is most often seen in August and September though it could be found at any time from May or June onwards.
Larval F/ps:	Dock and knotgrass. Throughout the summer. It occasionally breeds in southern England though the early stages have never been recorded in Shropshire.
Notes:	This species sometimes has favourable years such as 1983 when four individuals were recorded at the Rothamsted Insect Survey trap at Preston Montford. One of these was a delightful form which had the forewings suffused with pink.

1719 Oblique Carpet *Orthonama vittata* Borkhausen

V.C.H.:	Meole Brace, 1906 (Melvill, per Potts, 1907); Market Drayton, common but local (Woodforde) and Church Stretton, occasional.
Post V.C.H.:	Infrequently recorded. The regular captures at the Rothamsted Insect Survey trap at Preston Montford Field Centre (two in 1967, four in 1971 and annually since) suggest that it is not uncommon where it occurs. There are other records from Calverhall, 1910 (Thornewill, per Potts, 1911); Shrewsbury, 1913 (Pendlebury & Pendlebury, 1914); Rodington, 1962 (Briggs); Bucknell, 1971 (Shephard); Stoke-on-Tern, 1975 (R.I.S. trap, Littlewood) and Hawk Lake, 1985 (Hardwick).
Flight:	Double brooded, in May and June and August and September, inhabiting wet places such as marshland and riversides.
Larval F/ps:	Bedstraw species. September to April and again in July.

1720 The Gem *Orthonama obstipata* Fabricius

V.C.H.: Unrecorded.

Post V.C.H.: There are only five records of this usually scarce migrant: Culmington, 1967 (Coates); Preston Montford, 1969 and 1971 (R.I.S. trap); Dothill, 1976 (Riley) and Preston Montford, 1984 (R.I.S. trap, det. Riley). All single specimens.

Flight: As a migrant it could be found at any time from spring to autumn. The cited records were from June to October.

Larval F/ps: Probably many low-growing plants such as knotgrass, dandelion and groundsel, thoughout the summer months. The early stages have not yet been recorded in Shropshire.

1722 Flame Carpet *Xanthorhoe designata* Hufnagel

V.C.H.: Generally distributed but not abundant.

Post V.C.H.: Frequently recorded throughout the county from woodland and hedgerows.

Flight: May to August in two broods.

Larval F/ps: Uncertain but probably crucifers. Skinner (1984) states that the larvae will take wallflower and cabbage in captivity and Newnham (1901a) states that this species is common in kitchen gardens where cabbages are grown. July to September.

1723 Red Carpet *Xanthorhoe munitata munitata* Hübner

V.C.H.: Unrecorded.

Post V.C.H.: Recorded only from Shrewsbury, 1913 (Pendlebury & Pendlebury, 1914); Church Stretton, 1925 (Bretherton); Meole Brace, 1928 (Henstock) and Preston Montford Field Centre, 1984 (R.I.S. trap, det. Riley).

Flight: June to August, usually on high moorland.

Larval F/ps: Lady's mantle and possibly other low-growing plants. September to May.

Notes: Although Shropshire is on the southern edge of its range in England, further investigation would probably reveal this species to be resident over a wider area of the hilly south west of the county than the present records suggest. Skinner (1984) states that it is rather local in Derbyshire, Staffordshire and the northern half of Wales.

1724 Red Twin-spot Carpet *Xanthorhoe spadicearia* Denis & Schiffermüller

V.C.H.: Uncommon.

Post V.C.H.: Recorded frequently throughout the county.

Flight: Mainly May and June. The second brood which occurs in southern England has been recorded occasionally in August and early September.

Larval F/ps: Bedstraws and probably other low-growing plants. July and September.

1725 Dark-barred Twin-spot Carpet *Xanthorhoe ferrugata* Clerck

V.C.H.: Common throughout.

Post V.C.H.: Common throughout, ab. *unidentaria* Haworth being profoundly dominant.

Flight: May to August in two broods.

Larval F/ps: Polyphagous on low-growing plants such as lady's bedstraw*, dock*, groundsel* etc. July and September.

1726 Large Twin-spot Carpet *Xanthorhoe quadrifasiata* Clerck

V.C.H.: Unrecorded.

Post V.C.H.: Occasional records only, but from widely scattered localities, preferring woodland: Bromfield, 1948 (Norton); Donnington, 1949 (Christie); Bucknell, 1970 (Shephard); Stoke-on-Tern, 1978 (R.I.S. trap, Littlewood); Preston Montford, 1978 (R.I.S. trap, det. Riley) and Wyre Forest (Evans).

Flight: June and July.

Larval F/ps: Polyphagous on low-growing plants such as bedstraw. August to May.

1727 Silver-ground Carpet *Xanthorhoe montanata montanata* Denis & Schiffermüller

V.C.H.: Universal and common.

Post V.C.H.: Very common throughout.

Flight: May to mid-July. Woodland clearings and rides, heathland, gardens and hedgerows.

Larval F/ps: Polyphagous on low-growing plants. Newnham (1901) cites primrose. August to April.

Notes: Variation in this very common species is extensive, particularly with regard to the form of the central band of the forewings. Ab. *degenerata* Prout and ab. *costimaculata* Rebel (see South, 1939. Vol. 2, p 124) occur in small numbers in the Ercall Woods where the species is abundant.

1728 Garden Carpet *Xanthorhoe fluctuata* Linnaeus

V.C.H.: Abundant throughout.

Post V.C.H.: Abundant throughout.

Flight: May to October in three broods. The third brood stated to occur in October in southern England has been recorded occasionally in Shropshire.

Larval F/ps: Various crucifers. Recorded on shepherd's purse in Wellington, 1977 (Riley) and associated with horse-raddish and cabbage by Newnham (1901). June to October.

Notes: The dark ab. *thules* Prout has, to my knowledge, only been recorded once: Dothill, 1977 (Riley). Pendlebury (1915) recorded ab. *costovata* Haw. at Shrewsbury on 15.vi.1913.

1731 Chalk Carpet *Scotopteryx bipunctaria cretata* Prout

V.C.H.: Unrecorded.

Post V.C.H.: One unconfirmed record from Bridgnorth, 1913 (Pitt).

Flight: July and August.

Larval F/ps: Trefoils and clovers. September to June.

Notes: Skinner (1984) states that this species is locally common in the Midlands. In Shropshire it should be looked for on limestone hills. Its status must be considered unknown at the present time.

1732 Shaded Broad-bar *Scotopteryx chenopodiata* Linnaeus

V.C.H.: Common throughout.

Post V.C.H.: Common throughout. Grassland, heaths, rough ground, woodland clearings and hedgerows.

Flight: July and August.

Larval F/ps: Vetches and clovers, including red clover*. September to June.

1733 Lead Belle *Scotopteryx mucronata umbrifera* **Heydermann**

1734 July Belle *Scotopteryx luridata plumbaria* **Fabricius**

V.C.H.: These two species were collectively known as *Eubalia plumbaria* Fabricius (The Belle), having not been separated as distinct species at that time. Newnham (1908) states "Common on the Longmynd and the valleys in places where broom occurs. Very common on rough ground above Staley's Cottage etc."

Post V.C.H. The taxonomic problems involved in distinguishing the adults of these two
Notes: species make records which are unaccompanied by specimens unreliable in many cases. Of the records given below, those marked thus † have been confirmed. The reader should refer to Skinner (1984, pp. 27–28) for diagnostic characters.

S. mucronata: Bridgnorth, 1918 (Pitt); Meole Brace, 1920 (Pendlebury); Llanymynech, 1930 (Hignett); Preston Montford Field Centre, 1967 (Heath)†; Pontesbury, 1970 (D. Smith); Pennerley, 1970 (Poynton)†; Bucknell, 1972 (Shephard)†; Dawley, 1975 (Jacques); Stiperstones, 1978 (Whitney)† and Ludlow, 1980 (Norton)†.

Flight: Mid-May to mid-June on heathland and moorland.

Larval F/ps: Gorse* and broom*. Petty whin is cited by Skinner (1984) but this is now a rare plant in Shropshire. September to March.

S. luridata: Shrewsbury, 1913 (Pendlebury); Dawley, 1970 (Riley)†; Preston Montford Field Centre, July 1971 (R.I.S. trap, det. Nicklen); Whixall, 1972 (Rutherford)†; Sturt Common, 1972 (Young); Dothill, 1976 (Riley)†; Woore, 1984 (Holdsworth) and Catherton Common, 1985 (Blunt).

Flight: Mid-June to August on heathland and moorland. (Note that this species flies later than *S. mucronata*).

Larval F/ps: Gorse* and possibly petty whin though this plant is very rare in Shropshire. September to May.

1737 Small Argent and Sable *Epirrhoe tristata* Linnaeus

V.C.H.: Appears to have been found only around Church Stretton, mainly on the Longmynd, where it was not uncommon (Thornewill, 1900b; Newnham, 1901a) and Wyre Forest, 1904 (Rea, per Potts, 1905).

Post V.C.H.: Widespread but very localised: Church Stretton, 1925 (Bretherton); Stow Hill, 1968 (Scott); Buildwas, 1969 (Whitney); Bucknell, 1972 (Shephard); Chirk, 1974 (Morgan); Bromfield, 1978 (Norton) and Boiling Well, 1987 (several flying in sunshine) (Coleshaw).

Flight: May to July on high moorland and limestone hills.

Larval F/ps: Heath bedstraw and possibly hedge-bedstraw. Newnham (1901a) notes that it was often found in the vicinity of the latter on the Longmynd.

1738 Common Carpet *Epirrhoe alternata alternata* Müller

V.C.H.: Common throughout.

Post V.C.H.: Common throughout in most habitat types.

Flight: May, June, August and September.

Larval F/ps: Various species of bedstraw including hedge-bedstraw*.

1739 Wood Carpet *Epirrhoe rivata* Hübner

V.C.H.: Shrewsbury and Oswestry, 1907 (Pendlebury, per Potts, 1908). Not recorded by Newnham (1908).

Post V.C.H.: Only three records: Candy Wood, 1930 (Hignett, 1931); Stoke-on-Tern, 1978 (R.I.S. trap, det. Nicklen) and Hopton Titterhill, 1982 (Hicks).

Flight: June to August on woodland edges and along mature hedgerows.

Larval F/ps: Hedge-* and lady's bedstraw. August and September.

Notes: Outside southern England this species is known to be very local. The few records from Shropshire reflect this.

1740 Galium Carpet *Epirrhoe galiata* Denis & Schiffermüller

V.C.H.: Omitted from the V.C.H. but recorded among lady's bedstraw at Church Stretton by Newnham (1901a).

Post V.C.H.: Only six records: Albynes, 1910 (Pitt); Blakeway Coppice, 1953 (K. G. V. Smith, 1954); Whixall Moss (Burrows, per Fielding, 1974a); Polebank, 1987 and 1989 (several) (Coleshaw) and Llanymynech, 1930 (Hignett, 1931) and 22.vii.1989 (Townsend).

Flight: June to August on limestone hills and heathland.

Larval F/ps: Various bedstraw species.

Notes: This species is probably more common than the cited records suggest. It is probably widespread along the limestone escarpment of Wenlock Edge. Its superficial resemblance to many other species such as *Xanthorhoe fluctuata* and *Epirrhoe alternata* may mean that it has been overlooked.

1742 Yellow Shell *Camptogramma bilineata bilineata* Linnaeus

V.C.H.: Common and widespread.

Post V.C.H.: Common throughout, with the exception of the high ground in the south west.

Flight: June to August in most habitat types.

Larval F/ps: Polyphagous on low plants such as dock and chickweed. September to May.

1744 Grey Mountain Carpet *Entephria caesiata* Denis & Schiffermüller

V.C.H.: Found amongst heather on the Longmynd.

Post V.C.H.: Very local. Recorded only from Church Stretton, 1925 (Bretherton), 1959 (Knill-Jones), 1960 (Scott) and 1974 (Wallace).

Flight: June to August on high moorland.

Larval F/ps: Heather*, heath and bilberry. September to May.

Notes: This species is probably found in many more of the high moorlands of the south west than the present records suggest.

1745 The Mallow *Larentia clavaria* Haworth

V.C.H.: Common but local in the Market Drayton area (Woodforde; Potts, 1908), "not rare" in the neighbourhood of Church Stretton. Also recorded from Oswestry (Pendlebury, per Potts, 1908).

Post V.C.H.: A local, though frequently recorded, species. Found mainly in the western half of the county, apparently prefering high ground.

Flight: September and October on rough ground, roadside verges and in gardens.

Larval F/ps: Common mallow* and possibly cultivated hollyhock. April to June.

Notes: The apparent preference for high ground in Shropshire is unusual as the species is not noted for this nationally.

1746 Shoulder-stripe. *Anticlea badiata* Denis & Schiffermüller.

V.C.H.: Well distributed and common.

Post V.C.H.: Fairly common throughout.

Flight: March and April. Open woodlands, hedgerows and rough ground.

Larval F/p: Wild rose*. May to July.

Notes: A pale specimen with straw-coloured forewings and with the usual markings very faint was caught in the Ercall Woods, 29.iii.1978 (Riley). This aberration has not been previously described. The name *obsoleta* is proposed (Riley, in prep.). A specimen of ab. *eckfordii* Smith in which the forewings are glossy brown with few markings, was caught in the Ercall Woods, 24.iv.1978 (Riley).

1747 The Streamer *Anticlea derivata* Denis & Schiffermüller

V.C.H.: Less common than *A. badiata*. Recorded from Calverhall, Market Drayton and Church Stretton.

Post V.C.H.: As widespread as *A. badiata* but not as common.

Flight: April and May in similar habitats to *A. badiata*.

Larval F/p: Wild rose*. June and July.

1748 Beautiful Carpet *Mesoleuca albicillata* Linnaeus

V.C.H.: Found only at Broseley, 1907 (Potts, 1908) and in the woods around Church Stretton.

Post V.C.H.: Widespread but infrequent. Recorded from the Wrekin, 6.vii.1914 and 1922; Monkhopton, 1947 (Pendlebury, 1950); Cleobury Mortimer, August 1922 (Woodward, 1922b); Bromfield, 1953 (Norton); Preston Montford Field Centre, 1967, 1970 (R.I.S. trap) and 1967 (Heath); Willey, 1969 (Whitney); Whixall, 1970 (Hull); Stoke-on-Tern, 1976 (R.I.S. trap, Littlewood); Dothill, 1976 (Riley); Shirlett, 1977 (Whitney); Craven Arms, 1978 (Norton), and the Wyre Forest, 1974 (Barnett) and 1987 (Plant).

Flight: June and July in or near woodland.

Larval F/ps: Bramble* and raspberry*. July to September.

1749 Dark Spinach *Pelurga comitata* Linnaeus

V.C.H.: Scarce. Recorded only from Market Drayton (Woodforde).

Post V.C.H.: One record only: Dothill, 1977 (Riley).

Flight: July and August on wasteground, allotments and gardens.

Larval F/ps: Goosefoot and orache. September and October.

Notes: It is surprising that this species has been so poorly recorded in Shropshire. It is locally quite common throughout England and Wales. Its superficial similarity to *Eulithis populata* and *E. mellinata* may have led to it being overlooked.

1750 Water Carpet *Lampropteryx suffumata* Denis & Schiffermüller

V.C.H.: Generally distributed and fairly common.

Post V.C.H.: Widespread and fairly common.

Flight: April and May. Woodland edges and rides, rough ground and hedgerows.

Larval F/ps: Bedstraw species including hedge-bedstraw*. May and June.

Notes: Two individuals of ab. *porrittii* Robson were recorded at Shrewsbury, 21.iv.1913 (Pendlebury, 1915).

1752 Purple Bar *Cosmorhoe ocellata* Linnaeus

V.C.H.: Recorded only from Market Drayton and Church Stretton.

Post V.C.H.: Widespread and frequent. Found in many habitat types.

Flight: May to Septmber in two broods, the first of which (May and June) is the most common.

Larval F/ps: Bedstraw species including heath bedstraw*. June, July, September and October.

1753 Striped Twin-spot Carpet *Nebula salicata latentaria* Curtis

V.C.H.: Unrecorded.

Post V.C.H.: A very local and easily overlooked species. Recorded only from Breidden Hills, 1935 (Pendlebury, 1936) and Craven Arms, 1978 (Norton).

Flight: May to July, on high moorlands.

Larval F/ps: Bedstraw species. May to September.

1754 The Phoenix *Eulithis prunata* Linnaeus

V.C.H.: Market Drayton, scarce (Woodforde) and Church Stretton, not uncommon.

Post V.C.H.: Widespread and frequently recorded, though never common.

Flight: July and August in gardens and allotments where the larval foodplants are grown.

Larval F/ps: Blackcurrant*, redcurrant* and gooseberry*.

Notes: One might suppose that the increased use of pesticides on fruit crops would have had a detrimental effect on this species. However, this does not seem to be the case (at least in Shropshire) as *E. prunata* appears to be more widespread and common now than it was when the V.C.H. was published.

1755 The Chevron *Eulithis testata* Linnaeus

V.C.H.: Common throughout among poplars and sallows.

Post V.C.H.: Widespread and fairly common on moorland and in open woodland.

Flight: July and August.

Larval F/ps: Sallow*, birch*, aspen and possibly poplar (Newnham, 1901a). May and June.

1756 Northern Spinach *Eulithis populata* Linnaeus

V.C.H.: Fairly common in the Church Stretton area and around Market Drayton.

Post V.C.H.: Widespread and fairly common. Abundant in the Ercall Woods where the larvae are common on bilberry (Riley).

Flight: July and August on moorland and in woodlands where bilberry carpets the ground.

Larval F/p: Bilberry*. April to June.

1757 The Spinach *Eulithis mellinata* Fabricius

V.C.H.: Recorded only from Market Drayton (Woodforde) where it was fairly common.

Post V.C.H.: Recorded frequently from most of lowland Shropshire, mainly in gardens.

Flight: June to August.

Larval F/ps: Redcurrant and blackcurrant. April and May.

1758 Barred Straw *Eulithis pyraliata* Denis & Schiffermüller

V.C.H.: Universal.

Post V.C.H.: Found commonly throughout the county.

Flight: June to August. Gardens, wasteground, woodland clearings and scrubland.

Larval F/ps: Bedstraw species. Common on hedge-bedstraw at Admaston, 1978 (Riley). April to June.

1759 Small Phoenix *Ecliptopera silaceata* Denis & Schiffermüller

V.C.H.: Unrecorded.

Post V.C.H.: Common throughout in many habitat types such as woodland, heathland and gardens.

Flight: May and June. The partial second brood which occurs in southern England has not, to my knowledge, been recorded in Shropshire.

Larval F/ps: Willowherb species. Recorded on rosebay willowherb at Dothill, 1977 (Riley). July.

Notes: Newman (1869) stated that *E. silaceata* was common throughout England at that time. It is unlikely that the species had been overlooked in Shropshire and even less likely that it was absent from the county prior to the publication of the V.C.H. I would suggest, therefore, that its omission from that list was erroneous.

1760 Red-green Carpet *Chloroclysta siterata* Hufnagel

V.C.H.: Not uncommon near woods and in lanes near Church Stretton.

Post V.C.H.: Very local, mainly in the southern half of the county. Recorded only from Candy, 16.ix.1920 (Hignett, 1931); Blakeway Coppice, 1953 (K. G. V. Smith, 1954); Bucknell, 1970 (Shephard); Bromfield and Craven Arms, 1978 (Norton); Woore, 1979 (Holdsworth); Wyre Forest, 1984 (Blunt) and Preston Montford Field Centre, 1987, two (R.I.S. trap, det. Riley).

Flight: September, October and, after hibernation, in April and May. Woodlands.

Larval F/ps: Polyphagous on deciduous trees including birch*. June to August.

1761 Autumn Green Carpet *Chloroclysta miata* Linnaeus

V.C.H.: Unrecorded.

Post V.C.H.: Frequently recorded from woodlands and scrubland, mainly in the southern half of the county.

Flight: September, October and, after hibernation, in March and April.

Larval F/ps: Polyphagous on many deciduous trees including birch* and oak*. June to August.

1762 Dark Marbled Carpet *Chloroclysta citrata citrata* Linnaeus

V.C.H.: Frequent in the Church Stretton area.

Post V.C.H.: Widespread and fairly common in woods (e.g. Ercall) and moorlands such as those around Church Stretton.

Flight: July and August.

Larval F/ps: Sallow, birch*, bilberry* and wild strawberry. April to June.

Notes: This species is easily confused with the next. The acutely angled postmedian lines of both fore- and hindwings help to separate the two. The later flight period of *C. truncata* can also be a useful guide.

1764 Common Marbled Carpet *Chloroclysta truncata* Hufnagel

V.C.H.:   Common throughout.

Post V.C.H.:   Common throughout in many habitat types.

Flight: May and June and again from August to November.

Larval F/ps: Polyphagous. Recorded in Shropshire on birch, hazel, oak and ash. October to May and July and August.

1765 Barred Yellow *Cidaria fulvata* Forster

V.C.H.:   Present wherever wild rose is found.

Post V.C.H.:   Recorded frequently from throughout the county.

Flight: June and July in woods, on rough ground, wasteland and in gardens.

Larval F/p: Wild rose*. May and June.

1766 Blue-bordered Carpet *Plemyria rubiginata rubiginata* Denis & Schiffermüller

V.C.H.:   Local, though not uncommon in Ragleth Woods amongst alder. Also Twemlows and Calverhall (Thornewill) and Market Drayton (Woodforde).

Post V.C.H.:   Widespread, mainly in woodlands but also scrubby wasteland and overgrown orchards, allotments, gardens etc.

Flight: June to August.

Larval F/ps: Many deciduous trees including blackthorn*, alder, birch and apple.

1767 Pine Carpet. *Thera firmata* Hübner.

V.C.H.:   Generally distributed though less common than *T. obeliscata*.

Post V.C.H.:   Very local. Usually uncommon though it occurs most years at the R.I.S. trap at Preston Montford Field Centre (det. Riley). Also recorded as common at Broseley and Shirlett in 1969 (Whitney). Other records: Church Stretton and Shrewsbury, 1913 (Pendlebury & Pendlebury, 1914); Candy, 1928 (Hignett, 1931); Pontesbury, 1972 and 1977 (D. Smith); the Wrekin, 1977 and the Ercall Woods, 1979 (Riley) and Wyre Forest, 1960 & 1961 (Evans) and 1984–88 (Blunt).

Flight: July to November in pine plantations.

Larval F/p: Scots pine*. October to September (Skinner, pers. comm.).

1768 Grey Pine Carpet *Thera obeliscata* Hübner

V.C.H.:   Generally distributed and common. This species was referred to as *T. variata* Schiff. by Newnham (1901a) and should not be confused with *T. variata* D. & S. (= *T. britannica* Turn.), the spruce carpet.

Post V.C.H.:   Widely distributed and common in conifer plantations.

Flight: May to July and September and October.

Larval F/ps: Various conifers including spruce, fir and Scots pine*. October to April and July and August.

1769 Spruce Carpet *Thera britannica* Turner

V.C.H.:   Benthall, 1903 (Potts, per Pendlebury, 1950) but not recorded in the V.C.H.

Post V.C.H.:   Frequently recorded from spruce plantations throughout the county.

Flight: May to July and September and October. A single male was caught in the R.I.S. trap at Ludlow (det. Riley) on 6.ii.1989 (Riley, 1989b). This is extremely early for *T. britannica*.

Larval F/ps: Various spruce species. October to April and June and July.

1771 Juniper Carpet *Thera juniperata juniperata* Linnaeus

V.C.H.: Unrecorded.

Post V.C.H.: Recorded only from Bucknell, 1972 (Shephard); Wyre Forest, 1974 (Barnett); Woore, 1979 (Holdsworth) and Preston Montford Field Centre, 30.x.1987 (R.I.S. trap, det. Riley).

Flight: October and November on limestone hills and gardens where the foodplant is grown.

Larval F/ps: Juniper and probably cypress species. August and September.

1773 Broken-barred Carpet *Electrophaes corylata* Thunberg

V.C.H.: Common at Calverhall (Thornewill) and Church Stretton.

Post V.C.H.: Widespread and fairly common. Woods, hedgerows and scrubland.

Flight: May and June with a partial second brood in some years in August (e.g. Preston Montford Field Centre, 21.viii. (two) and 23.viii.1987 (one) (R.I.S. trap, det. Riley).

Larval F/ps: Many deciduous trees including hawthorn*, oak and birch.

1774 Beech-green Carpet *Colostygia olivata* Denis & Schiffermüller

V.C.H.: Frequent amongst *Galium* at Church Stretton.

Post V.C.H.: Recorded only from Candy Wood, 1948 (Hignett, per Pendlebury, 1950); Ironbridge, 1974 (Derry) and Pontesbury, 1983 (D. Smith).

Flight: July and August in wooded limestone areas.

Larval F/ps: Bedstraw species. September to May.

1775 Mottled Grey *Colostygia multistrigaria* Haworth

V.C.H.: Wyre Forest, 1906 (Edwards, per Potts, 1907); Wrekin, 1907 (Potts, 1908); Market Drayton, fairly common (Woodforde) and Church Stretton.

Post V.C.H.: Found locally throughout the county. Woodland edges and clearings and moorland.

Flight: March and April.

Larval F/ps: Bedstraw species including lady's bedstraw*. May and June.

1776 Green Carpet *Colostygia pectinataria* Knoch

V.C.H.: Found throughout wherever heath bedstraw or hedge-bedstraw is present.

Post V.C.H.: Widespread and common in most types of habitat.

Flight: May to July.

Larval F/ps: Bedstraw species. August to May.

1777 July Highflyer *Hydriomena furcata* Thunberg

V.C.H.: Apparently generally distributed and abundant in some places (e.g. Longmynd).

Post V.C.H.: Very common throughout in most habitat types.

Flight: July and August.

Larval F/ps: Sallow*, hazel*, bilberry* and heather. May and June.

Notes: The form which is found on high moorland, feeding on heather and bilberry, is much smaller than those associated with hazel and sallow. It is interesting to note that both forms occur commonly in the Ercall Woods where hazel is common and bilberry carpets the floor of the wood.

1778 May Highflyer *Hydriomena impluviata* Denis & Schiffermüller

V.C.H.: Generally distributed, with the exception of Market Drayton.

Post V.C.H.: Very local but widespread, occurring only where alders grow. Frequent at Preston Montford Field Centre (R.I.S. trap, det. Riley).

Flight: May to early July.

Larval F/p: Alder*. August to October.

1779 Ruddy Highflyer *Hydriomena ruberata* Freyer

V.C.H.: Unrecorded in the V.C.H. but noted by Blatch (1886) from the Wyre Forest.

Post V.C.H.: Local and scarce. Recorded only from Shrewsbury, 29.v.1913 (Pendlebury, 1915); Pontesbury, 1978 (D. Smith); Woore, 1982 & 1983 (Holdsworth) and Whixall Moss (Fielding, 1974a), 1931 (Hignett) and 1986 (Cooper).

Flight: May and June. Open woodland, mosses and heathland.

Larval F/ps: Sallow species. Skinner (1984) cites eared sallow as the main food. July to September.

1781 Small Waved Umber *Horisme vitalbata* Denis & Schiffermüller

V.C.H.: Unrecorded.

Post V.C.H.: Local and scarce. Recorded only from Bromfield, 1952 and 1978 (Norton); Craven Arms, 1978 (Norton) and Shirlett, 1978 (Whitney).

Flight: May and June and August, in two broods. Hedgerows and scrubland on limestone.

Larval F/p: Traveller's-joy. June and July and September and October.

1782 Fern *Horisme tersata* Denis & Schiffermüller

V.C.H.: Unrecorded.

Post V.C.H.: Recorded once from a shop window in Bridgnorth, 1987 (Riley, 1988) and once at Ludlow, 7.vii.1989 (R.I.S. trap, det. Riley).

Flight: Late June to August on hedgebanks etc in the vicinity of traveller's-joy.

Larval F/p: Traveller's-joy. August and September.

Notes: The larval foodplant is very common in the town of Bridgnorth. The fern is probably well established there.

1784 Pretty Chalk Carpet *Melanthia procellata* Denis & Schiffermüller

V.C.H.: Unrecorded.

Post V.C.H.: Recorded only from Broseley, 1969 (Whitney); Wellington, 1976 (Riley); Preston Montford Field Centre, 1978 (det. Riley); Llanymynech, 1982 (Anon., B.R.C.) and 22.vii.1989 (several) (Townsend).

Flight: June to August in woods and hedgerows on limestone.

Larval F/p: Traveller's-joy*. August and September.

1787 Argent and Sable *Rheumaptera hastata hastata* Linnaeus

V.C.H.: Wyre Forest (Blatch, 1886) and 1902 (Rea, per Pendlebury, 1950) and occasional in birch woods around Church Stretton, Newnham (1901 and 1908).

Post V.C.H.: Found most commonly on the mosses of the north. Otherwise recorded from Cleobury Mortimer, June 1922 (Woodward, 1922b); Bomere, 1922 and 1923 (Ingrams, 1923; 1924); Benthall, 1925 (Potts); Craven Arms, 1978 (Norton) and Wyre Forest, occasional (Blunt; Evans; Plant).

Flight: May and June in the vicinity of birches.

Larval F/p: Birch. July and August.

1788 Scarce Tissue *Rheumaptera cervinalis* Scopoli

V.C.H.:   Market Drayton, locally common (Woodforde, 1902b and 1903a), and Calverhall.

Post V.C.H.: Very local and uncommon: Shrewsbury, 1913 (Pendlebury, 1915; Ingrams, 1923); Pontesbury, 1971 (D. Smith); Preston Montford Field Centre, 1978 (R.I.S. trap, det. Riley) and Ludlow, 1989 (R.I.S. trap, det. Riley).

Flight: April to June. Hedgerows and gardens.

Larval F/p: Barberry, including cultivated varieties. June and July. Wild barberry is widespread in Shropshire but not common (Sinker, *et al.*, 1985).

1789 Scalloped Shell *Rheumaptera undulata* Linnaeus

V.C.H.:   Unrecorded.

Post V.C.H.: Very local and uncommon. Recorded only from Shrewsbury, 1913 (Pendlebury & Pendlebury, 1914); Whixall, 1930 (Hignett, 1931) and 1986 (Cooper); Wrekin (K. G. V. Smith, 1954); Wyre Forest, 1968 (Whitney); Broseley, 1971 (Whitney); Shirlett 1974, 1976 and 1978 (Whitney); Ercall Woods, 1978 (Riley); Wem Moss, 1978 (D. Smith); Woore, 1982 (Holdsworth) and Wyre Forest, 1984–88 (Blunt; Plant).

Flight: June and July. Woodlands and damp scrubland.

Larval F/ps: Bilberry*, sallow and aspen. August to October.

1790 The Tissue *Triphosia dubitata* Linnaeus

V.C.H.:   Fairly common throughout.

Post V.C.H.: Widespread and frequent, though local. Found in a variety of habitats including woodlands, moorland, the northern mosses, gardens and rough ground.

Flight: August and September and, after hibernation, in April and May.

Larval F/ps: Buckthorn and alder buckthorn. May to July.

1791 Brown Scallop *Philereme vetulata* Denis & Schiffermüller

V.C.H.:   Unrecorded.

Post V.C.H.: Recorded only twice: Oswestry, 1948 (Hignett) and Preston Montford Field Centre, 1978 (R.I.S. trap, det. Riley).

Flight: July in the vicinity of buckthorn.

Larval F/p: Buckthorn. May and early June.

1792 Dark Umber *Philereme transversata britannica* Lempke

V.C.H.:   Unrecorded.

Post V.C.H.: Recorded only once from Bucknell by Shephard in 1971.

Flight: July. Woodland edges, hedgerows and limestone hills.

Larval F/p: Buckthorn. May and June.

Notes: This species is known to be local and infrequent in the Midlands. There are, however, several suitable localities in Shropshire such as the limestone outcrops of Wenlock Edge where it may be as yet undiscovered.

1794 Sharp-angled Carpet *Euphyia unangulata* Haworth

V.C.H.:   One record from Oswestry, 1907 (Pendlebury, per Potts, 1908). Not noted by Newnham (1908).

Post V.C.H.: Unrecorded.

Flight: July and August in woodlands and along hedgerows.

Larval F/ps: Chickweeds and stitchwort. August and September.

Notes: This species is easily confused with several other "Carpets" and the above record should therefore be treated with caution. *E. unangulata* is very local and, on the whole, uncommon in the Midlands. It is figured on Plate 11.

Notes on the genus *Epirrita*:

It is unwise to attribute records of this genus to a particular species without examination of the genitalia. The earlier flight period, small size, bold, angular forewing markings and preferred habitat may help to identify *E. filigrammaria* but the other three are often so similar that separation by superficial characters is impossible.

1795 November Moth *Epirrita dilutata* Denis & Schiffermüller

V.C.H.:   Generally distributed.

Post V.C.H.: Widely distributed and common in woodlands.

Flight: October and November.

Larval F/ps: Polyphagous on deciduous trees, e.g. blackthorn*, apple* and hawthorn*. April to June.

1796 Pale November Moth *Epirrita christyi* Allen

V.C.H.:   Unrecorded.

Post V.C.H.: Recorded from only three localities: Nordley, 1970 (Whitney); Ercall Woods, where it is common (Riley) and Preston Montford Field Centre, where it is frequently caught in the R.I.S. trap (det. Riley).

Flight: September to November in woodlands.

Larval F/ps: Polyphagous on deciduous trees. Recorded in Shropshire on wych elm and alder. April to June.

1797 Autumnal Moth *Epirrita autumnata* Borkhausen

V.C.H.:   Unrecorded.

Post V.C.H.: Frequently recorded at the R.I.S. traps at Preston Montford Field Centre (det. Riley) and Rowton (det. Nicklen); local but frequent in the Wyre Forest (Evans). Also recorded from Benthall and Tickwood, 31.viii.1924 (Potts, 1925); Rodington, 1962 (Briggs); Shirlett, 1978 (Whitney) and Woore, 1984 (Holdsworth).

Flight: September and October in woodlands.

Larval F/ps: Birch, alder and possibly larch. April to June.

1798 Small Autumnal Moth *Epirrita filigrammaria* Herrich-Schäffer

V.C.H.:   Frequent amongst bilberry and heath on the Longmynd. Also recorded from Oswestry, 1907 (Pendlebury, per Potts, 1908).

Post V.C.H.: Apart from the Longmynd, where this species still occurs, it has only been recorded at Preston Montford Field Centre (one individual at the R.I.S. trap in 1978, one in 1988 and several in 1989, det. Riley).

Flight: August and early September on high moorland.

Larval F/ps: Heather* and bilberry*. April and May.

1799 Winter Moth *Operophtera brumata* Linnaeus

V.C.H.: "Only too common in most parts of the county". Often a pest on fruit trees.

Post V.C.H.: Abundant throughout.

Flight: October to February, in most habitats.

Larval F/ps: Polyphagous on trees and shrubs. Recorded in Shropshire on hawthorn, blackthorn, alder, maple, birch and apple.

1800 Northern Winter Moth *Operophtera fagata* Scharfenberg

V.C.H.: Less frequent than *O. brumata*. Larvae were recorded on birch around Church Stretton (Newnham, 1901a). Also recorded from Benthall Edge, 1904 (Potts, 1905).

Post V.C.H.: Frequent but not common at the R.I.S. trap at Preston Montford Field Centre (det. Riley); Oswestry, 1928 and Whixall Moss, 1930 (Hignett, 1931); Woore, 1979 to 1982 (Holdsworth); Shirlett, 1980 (Whitney) and Brown Moss, 1988 (Hardwick).

Flight: October to December. Woodlands, heathland, mosses and orchards.

Larval F/ps: Birch* and several fruit trees including apple and plum.

Notes: Although *O. fagata* is doubtless less common than *O. brumata*, its superficial similarity to that species may have led to it being overlooked in Shropshire. Old, unkept orchards are good places to find it.

1802 The Rivulet *Perizoma affinitata* Stephens

V.C.H.: Fairly common at Church Stretton and once at Calverhall (Thornewill).

Post V.C.H.: Frequent throughout in woodlands and hedgebanks.

Flight: May to July.

Larval F/p: Red campion. July to September.

Notes: A specimen of ab. *unicolorae* Gregson was recorded at the R.I.S. trap at Preston Montford Field Centre on 22.vii.1986 (Riley). In this form the white forewing markings are missing, leaving them totally black.
A single male was caught in the R.I.S. trap at Ludlow on 12.ix.1989 (det. Riley) which may represent a partial second emergence for that year.

1803 Small Rivulet *Perizoma alchemillata* Linnaeus

V.C.H.: Generally distributed and fairly common.

Post V.C.H.: Widespread and common in woodlands and on rough ground.

Flight: June and July.

Larval F/p: Hemp-nettle*. August and September.

1804 Barred Rivulet *Perizoma bifaciata* Haworth

V.C.H.: Not noted by Newnham (1908) but recorded by Rea in the Wyre Forest (Coach Road Coppice) in 1902 (Potts, 1903).

Post V.C.H.: Recorded from widely scattered localities but nowhere common: Shrewsbury, 1914 (Pendlebury, 1915); Rodington, 1957 (Briggs); Bucknell, 1970 (Shephard); Stoke-on-Tern, 1976 (R.I.S. trap, det. Nicklen); Bromfield, 1978 (Norton); Hopton Titterhill, 1982 (Hicks); Whixall Moss, 1986 (Cooper); and Ludlow, 28.vii.1990 (R.I.S. trap, det. Riley).

Flight: July and August. Rough meadows, wasteground and the edges of cultivated fields.

Larval F/p: Red bartsia. September and October.

This is an easily overlooked species which bears a superficial resemblence to many other Geometridae. It should be looked for in the southern half of the county where the larval foodplant is most common.

1805 Heath Rivulet *Perizoma minorata ericetata* Stephens

V.C.H.: Unrecorded.

Post V.C.H.: Two unconfirmed records: the racecourse, Oswestry, July 1929 (Hignett, 1931) and Bromfield, 1978 (Norton).

Flight: July and August over limestone hills in bright sunshine.

Larval F/p: Eyebright. September.

Notes: This species has only been recorded in England from Yorkshire and Cumbria. As the specimens are not available for confirmation I must consider these Shropshire records doubtful.

1807 Grass Rivulet *Perizoma albulata* Denis & Schiffermüller

V.C.H.: Very local but common where it occurs. Market Drayton, Prees Road and Twemlows.

Post V.C.H.: Very local but common in damp meadows such as those found in the Ercall Woods (Riley). Also recorded from Llanforda, 1930 (Hignett, 1931); Donnington, 1948 (Christie) and Bromfield, 1947 and 1978 (Norton).

Flight: May to July. One individual was recorded by Woodward (1922b) at the beginning of September, 1922 at Cleobury Mortimer.

Larval F/p: Yellow rattle. July and August.

Notes: A small and easily overlooked species. The foodplant is most common in the hilly parts of the county. *P. albulata*, therefore, should be looked for in upland areas.

1808 Sandy Carpet *Perizoma flavofasciata* Thunberg

V.C.H.: Locally common.

Post V.C.H.: Widespread and fairly common wherever the larval foodplant is found.

Flight: June and July.

Larval F/ps: Red*, white and bladder campion. July and August.

1809 Twin-spot Carpet *Perizoma didymata didymata* Linnaeus

V.C.H.: Common at Calverhall (Thornewill) and frequent around Church Stretton.

Post V.C.H.: Widely distributed, inhabiting many habitat types such as woodlands, rough ground and roadside verges.

Flight: June to August.

Larval F/ps: Polyphagous on many low plants. Very common on bilberry in the Ercall Woods (Riley). April and May.

Notes: The dark form ab. *nigra* Prout is very common in the Ercall Woods (Riley).

Notes on the genera *Eupithecia, Chloroclystis* and *Gymnoscellis*.:

Most of the Pug moths taken in light traps require either examination of the male abdominal plates or microscopic examination of the genitalia if they are to be identified to specific level. Due to the difficulties posed by such techniques, particularly the latter, many species have doubtless been inaccurately and inconclusively recorded. This is not, I hasten to add, only the case in Shropshire as many other county recorders have experienced the same difficulties. However, it is still possible to give a reasonable account of the status of most species. Where this is not the case the records, as presented, are cited with the appropriate comments given under the "Notes" section for each species.

1811 Slender Pug *Eupithecia tenuiata* Hübner

V.C.H.: A very local species. Recorded only from Shavington (Thornewill).

Post V.C.H.: Recorded mainly from the northern half of the county: Llanforda, 1930 (Hignett, 1931); Whixall Moss, 1972 (Rutherford); Dothill, 1978; Ercall Woods and Allscott 1979 (Riley); Preston Montford Field Centre, 23.vii.1987 (R.I.S. trap, det. Riley) and Ludlow, 29.vii.1989 (R.I.S. trap, det. Riley).

Flight: Late June to early August. Damp woodlands and wet places where sallows grow.

Larval F/p: Common sallow*. March and April.

Notes: Although this species appears to be local it is often very common where it occurs. There is every reason to suppose that *E. tenuiata* is widespread throughout the county. The best way to determine its presence in an area is to collect the sallow catkins on which the larvae feed in the spring. These should be kept in an airy breeding cage or muslin covered aquarium and lightly sprayed each day to prevent dessication. If the species is present the adults should appear in due course. Adults taken at light should not be identified from superficial characters alone.

1812 Maple Pug *Eupithecia inturbata* Hübner

V.C.H.: Unrecorded.

Post V.C.H.: Two records only: Pontesbury, 1972 (D. Smith) and Wyre Forest, 18-24.viii.1984 (Plant).

Flight: July and August. Woodland and hedgerows where mature maple grows.

Larval F/p: Field maple*. May to early June.

Notes: Field maple is found throughout the county. *E. tenuiata* is probably widespread in Shropshire but may have been overlooked. The adults come readily to light but great care should be taken over identification as it could easily be mistaken for other species of *Eupithecia*.

1813 Haworth's Pug *Eupithecia haworthiata* Doubleday

V.C.H.: Unrecorded.

Post V.C.H.: Four site records only: Oswestry, 1929 and 1930 (Hignett, 1931); Llany-mynech, 1982 (Anon., B.R.C.); Ironbridge, 1984 and 1987, common (A.M. & D.K. Riley); Wyre Forest, 1987 (Plant); Ludlow, 21.vii.1989 (one) (R.I.S. trap, det. Riley); and Llanymynech, 1982 (Anon., B.R.C.) and 22.vii.1989 (Townsend).

Flight: June and July. Woodland and overgrown hedgerows among the larval foodplant.

Larval F/p: Traveller's-joy*. July and August.

Notes: This easily overlooked species is probably more widely distributed than the present records suggest. The easiest way to detect its presence is to search the flower buds of Traveller's-joy. The young larvae feed internally. Tenanted buds do not open and are dark with a conspicuous black dot-like hole.

1816 Toadflax Pug *Eupithecia linariata* Denis & Schiffermüller

V.C.H.: Not uncommon.

Post V.C.H.: Widespread and frequent on wasteground, disused railway cuttings and roadside verges where the larval foodplant is well established.

Flight: July and August.

Larval F/ps: Toadflax* and possibly cultivated antirrhinums. August and September.

1817 Foxglove Pug *Eupithecia pulchellata pulchellata* Stephens

V.C.H.:   Generally common.

Post V.C.H.:   Widespread and fairly common.

Flight: May and June. Woodland rides, moorland, hedgerows and wasteground.

Larval F/p: Foxglove*. July and August.

1819 Mottled Pug *Eupithecia exiguata exiguata* Hübner

V.C.H.:   Fairly common throughout.

Post V.C.H.:   Widespread. Most frequent in the north-eastern half of the county.

Flight: May and June. Woodland and hedgerows.

Larval F/ps: Hawthorn*, blackthorn* and sycamore. July to October.

Notes: The lack of records from south-west Shropshire is probably due to oversight rather than a genuine absence of the species in this area. *E. exiguata* is common throughout England and Wales.

1821 Valerian Pug *Eupithecia valerianata* Hübner

V.C.H.:   Larvae at Moreton Say and Cloverley (Thornewill).

Post V.C.H.:   A single male was caught at Ludlow on 8.vii.1990 (R.I.S. trap, det. Riley).

Flight: June and July in damp woodland.

Larval F/p: Common valerian. July and August.

Notes: A very easily overlooked species which is best sought in the larval state as the adults are rarely noted at light.

1823 Netted Pug *Eupithecia venosata venosata* Fabricius

V.C.H.:   Scarce and local: Shrewsbury, 1899 (Cortissos, 1900) and Benthall, 1903 (Potts, 1904). Also Market Drayton (Woodforde) and Church Stretton area (Newnham, 1908).

Post V.C.H.:   Widespread and locally frequent.

Flight: May and June in limestone areas.

Larval F/p: Bladder campion*. June and July.

Notes: Due to parasitism the adults are often far less common than the larvae. Searching for larvae in the seed capsules of the foodplant may therefore be more successful than using light to attract the imagines.

1825 Lime-speck Pug *Eupithecia centaureata* Denis & Schiffermüller

V.C.H.:   Generally distributed and common.

Post V.C.H.:   Apparently absent from the south east though widespread and fairly common elsewhere.

Flight: July to early October in two broods. Found in most habitats.

Larval F/ps: Polyphagous. Often common on Ragwort at Dothill, 1976–79 (Riley). July to October.

1827 Freyer's Pug *Eupithecia intricata arceuthata* Freyer

V.C.H.:   Unrecorded.

Post V.C.H.:   Dothill, 1978 and Wellington, 1979 (Riley).

Flight: May and June in gardens.

Larval F/ps: Cypress species. August and September.

Notes: This species is probably widespread throughout the county in gardens where cypresses are grown.

1828 Satyr Pug *Eupithecia satyrata satyrata* Hübner

V.C.H.: Unrecorded.

Post V.C.H.: Ludlow, 1955 and Bromfield, 1954 and 1978 (Norton) and Bucknell, 1973 (Shephard) (all det. Riley).

Flight: May and June in open woodland.

Larval F/ps: Polyphagous, e.g. knapweed and meadowsweet*. July to September.

Notes: Probably more widespread than presently known.

1830 Wormwood Pug *Eupithecia absinthiata* Clerck

V.C.H.: Frequent.

Post V.C.H.: Widespread and fairly common in most habitats.

Flight: June and July.

Larval F/ps: Polyphagous, e.g. mugwort and ragwort*. August to October.

1831 Ling Pug *Eupithecia absinthiata* f. *goossensiata* Mabille

V.C.H.: Not recorded in the V.C.H. but stated by Pendlebury (1950) to have been taken at Shrewsbury in 1898 (Cortissos).

Post V.C.H.: Common on heather-clad moorland and clearings in woods where heather grows.

Flight: June and July.

Larval F/p: Heather. Common on heather on the Wrekin (Riley). August and September.

1832 Currant Pug *Eupithecia assimilata* Doubleday

V.C.H.: Market Drayton, common (Woodforde).

Post V.C.H.: Widespread and frequent though apparently more common in the north-east.

Flight: May and June, and again in August. Gardens, allotments and wasteground.

Larval F/ps: Mainly wild hop, though also redcurrant and blackcurrant*. June, July, September and October.

1833 Bleached Pug *Eupithecia expallidata* Doubleday

V.C.H.: Unrecorded.

Post V.C.H.: One unconfirmed record from Llynclys, 1948 (Hignett, per Pendlebury, 1950).

Flight: July and August in woodland clearings, rides and edges.

Larval F/p: Goldenrod. September and October.

1834 Common Pug *Eupithecia vulgata vulgata* Haworth

V.C.H.: Common throughout.

Post V.C.H.: Common throughout in most habitats.

Flight: May to August in two broods.

Larval F/ps: Polyphagous, e.g. hawthorn, yarrow, ragwort and dandelion.

Notes: The melanic ab. *atropicta* Dietze has not, to my knowledge, been recorded in Shropshire.

1835 White-spotted Pug *Eupithecia tripunctaria* Herrich-Schäffer

V.C.H.: Fairly common around Market Drayton (Woodforde).

Post V.C.H.: Widely distributed but infrequently recorded.

Flight: May and June and August and September in two broods. Hedgerows, damp woodlands and gardens.

Larval F/ps: Larvae have been found in July on elder flowers*, and in August and September on angelica and parsnip.

Notes: This species is locally quite common throughout England and Wales. The same can probably be said for Shropshire. It is easily overlooked as it bears a superficial resemblance to several other Pugs. The melanic ab. *angelicata* Barrett has not, to my knowledge, been recorded in Shropshire.

1836 Campanula Pug *Eupithecia denotata denotata* Hübner

V.C.H.: Not noted by Newnham (1908) but recorded at Benthall, 1904 (Edwards and Potts, per Potts, 1906) as larvae, though the foodplant is not cited. No confirmatory specimens can be found.

Post V.C.H.: Unrecorded.

Flight: July. Woodland clearings and hedgerows.

Larval F/ps: Nettle-leaved bellflower and giant bellflower. The latter is now uncommon in Shropshire (Sinker *et al.*, 1985). August and September.

1837 Grey Pug *Eupithecia subfuscata* Haworth

V.C.H.: Generally distributed and common.

Post V.C.H.: Widespread and generally common.

Flight: May and June, and again in August.

Larval F/ps: Polyphagous on many deciduous plants and trees. Often recorded on hawthorn* and blackthorn* (Riley).

Notes: The melanic form *obscurissima* Prout is frequently recorded.

1838 Tawny-speckled Pug *Eupithecia icterata subfulvata* Haworth

V.C.H.: Recorded only from Market Drayton (Woodforde) and Calverhall (Thornewill).

Post V.C.H.: Widespread and fairly common throughout, mainly on wasteland.

Flight: July and August.

Larval F/p: Yarrow*, September and October.

1839 Bordered Pug *Eupithecia succenturiata* Linnaeus

V.C.H.: Unrecorded.

Post V.C.H.: Widespread throughout the northern half of the county. Fairly common on roadside verges and wasteground.

Flight: July and August.

Larval F/ps: Mugwort* and yarrow*. September and October.

Notes: It appears that *E. succenturiata* was far less common at the turn of the century than it is now. Newman (1869) says of its distribution ". . . occurs in some of our English counties . . ." Shropshire does not seem to have been one of them. At the present time it is widespread throughout Britain, most common in the southern half of England.

1842 Plain Pug *Eupithecia simpliciata* Haworth

V.C.H.:   Unrecorded.

Post V.C.H.:   Very local though often abundant in suitable localities: Oswestry, 1930 (Hignett, 1931); Much Wenlock, 21.vii.1951 (K. G. V. Smith, 1956); Bromfield, 1955 (Norton, det. Riley); Alscott, 1979 (Riley) and Preston Montford Field Centre, 1980 (Anon.).

Flight: Late June to August, mainly on wasteground.

Larval F/ps: Goosefoot and orache. August and September.

Notes: The adults seem to be very sedentary. At Alscott in 1979 an M.V. light would not draw a single individual from hoardes that were feeding only ten feet away on ragwort blossom (Riley). This behaviour may explain the paucity of records for what is probably a fairly widespread species.

1843 Thyme Pug *Eupithecia distinctaria constrictata* Guenée

V.C.H.:   Unrecorded.

Post V.C.H.:   One record only, from Llynclys, 1930 (Hignett, 1931).

Flight: June and July. Should be looked for on limestone hills where wild thyme is abundant.

Larval F/p: Wild thyme. August and September.

1844 Ochreous Pug *Eupithecia indigata* Hübner

V.C.H.:   Very local though abundant at Twemlows (Thornewill).

Post V.C.H.:   One unconfirmed record from Llanymynech, 1931 (Hignett, 1932).

Flight: April and May in pine woods.

Larval F/p: *Pinus sylvestris** and *Picea abies**. July to September.

Notes: Probably widespread and fairly common in pine plantations, but easily overlooked.

1846 Narrow-winged Pug *Eupithecia nanata angusta* Prout

V.C.H.:   Common on the Longmynd among heather.

Post V.C.H.:   Widespread and common on heather-clad moorland. Occasionally recorded from gardens where heather is grown on rockeries etc.

Flight: April to June and again in August and early September.

Larval F/p: Heather*. July to September.

Notes: Ab. *oliveri* Prout is frequent on the Wrekin (Riley).

1849 Ash Pug *Eupithecia fraxinata* Crewe

V.C.H.:   Recorded only from Calverhall (Thornewill).

Post V.C.H.:   Local and uncommon. Recorded from Oswestry, 1930 (Hignett, 1931); Woore, 1980 to 1983 (Holdsworth); the Wrekin, 1979, one larva on ash (Riley) and Preston Montford Field Centre, 9.vi. and 7.ix.1988 (R.I.S. trap, det. Riley).

Flight: May and June with a second generation in August and early September. Woodlands and hedgerows where ash grows.

Larval F/p: Ash*. June, July and September.

Notes: There are two races of this species; one feeding on ash and the other on sea buckthorn. As Shropshire has no coastal habitats where sea buckthorn occurs it is safe to assume that the latter race does not exist in this county. The melanic ab. *unicolor* Prout has not been recorded in Shropshire.

1851 Goldenrod Pug *Eupithecia virgaureata* Doubleday

V.C.H.:   Unrecorded.

Post V.C.H.: Llanymynech, 1932 (Hignett); Ludlow, 1980 (Norton, det. Riley); Woore, 1981 (Holdsworth); Preston Montford Field Centre, 1984 (Reid) and Clee St. Margaret, 1984 (Denman, det. Riley).

Flight: May and June and again in August. Open areas of woods, roadside verges, hedgerows and rough meadows.

Larval F/ps: The first brood foodplant is not known. The second brood lay their eggs on ragwort* and goldenrod. July, September and October.

Notes: *E. virgaureata* is probably more widespread than the records suggest. It is easily mistaken for the more common *E. subfuscata*. The melanic ab. *nigra* Lempke is present in the county.

1852 Brindled Pug *Eupithecia abbreviata* Stephens

V.C.H.:   Recorded from Church Stretton and Calverhall, though rarely at the latter.

Post V.C.H.: Widespread and common in wooded areas.

Flight: April and May.

Larval F/ps: Oak* and hawthorn. June and July.

Notes: The melanic ab. *hirschkii* Bastelberger is common.

1853 Oak-tree Pug *Eupithecia dodoneata* Guenée

V.C.H.:   Unrecorded.

Post V.C.H.: Frequent at Preston Montford Field Centre (R.I.S. trap, det. Riley). Other records: Woore, 1980 to 1983 (Holdsworth) and All Stretton, one at M.V., 29.v.1987 (Langmaid and Pelham-Clinton).

Flight: May and June. Hedgerows, open woodland and woodland edges.

Larval F/ps: Hawthorn* and oak. Late June to August.

1854 Juniper Pug *Eupithecia pusillata pusillata* Denis & Schiffermüller

V.C.H.:   Unrecorded.

Post V.C.H.: Local but widespread and common where it occurs.

Flight: July to September, mainly in gardens.

Larval F/ps: Juniper*, *Thuya* and *Chamaecyparis* species. April to June.

1856 Larch Pug *Eupithecia lariciata* Freyer

V.C.H.:   Cloverley Park and Twemlows but not common (Thornewill).

Post V.C.H.: Widespread and fairly common among larch trees.

Flight: May and June with a possible partial second brood in August and early September (Riley 1986b).

Larval F/p: Larch*. June to August.

Notes: The melanic ab. *nigra* Prout is frequent throughout the county.

1857 Dwarf Pug *Eupithecia tantillaria* Boisduval

V.C.H.:   Unrecorded.

Post V.C.H.: Bromfield, 1954 and 1978 (Norton); Broseley, 1969 (Whitney); Bucknell, 1971 (Shephard, det. Riley); Shirlett, 1978 (Whitney); Hawk Lake, 1985 (Hardwick) and the Wyre Forest, 1987 (Plant).

Flight:	May and June in conifer plantations and large gardens where the larval foodplant is grown.
Larval F/ps:	Norway spruce* and Douglas fir. July and August.

1858 V-Pug *Chloroclystis v-ata* Haworth

V.C.H.:	Unrecorded.
Post V.C.H.:	Widespread and frequently recorded.
Flight:	May to August in two broods. Woodlands, hedgerows and rough meadows.
Larval F/ps:	Polyphagous, e.g. ragwort, mugwort, traveller's-joy* and bramble. June to September.

1859 Sloe Pug *Chloroclystis chloerata* Mabille

V.C.H.:	Unrecorded.
Post V.C.H.:	Two records: Buttonoak, 25.vi.1988 (Blunt) and Preston Montford Field Centre, 30.vi.1988 (R.I.S. trap, det. Riley). The identifications were confirmed by Riley's examination of the genitalia.
Flight:	May and June in the vicinity of the foodplant.
Larval F/p:	Blackthorn in March and April.
Notes:	This species bears a great superficial resemblance to *C. rectangulata* which may have led to it being overlooked in the past. It is unwise to separate these two species by superficial characters alone. *C. chloerata* was only discovered in Britain in 1971 and was not known here in V.C.H. times.

1860 Green Pug *Chloroclystis rectangulata* Linnaeus

V.C.H.:	Fairly common in orchards. Most frequently found as larvae on apple blossom.
Post V.C.H.:	Widespread and fairly common. Sometimes abundant in old orchards.
Flight:	June and July in orchards, gardens and woodland edges.
Larval F/ps:	Apple*, blackthorn*, pear and cherry. April and May.
Notes:	The melanic forms *nigrosericeata* Haworth and *anthrax* Dietze are common. In some places the entire population consists of these forms.

1861 Bilberry Pug *Chloroclystis debiliata* Hübner

V.C.H.:	Recorded at Market Drayton where it was "unusually abundant" in 1900 (Woodforde, 1900e).
Post V.C.H.:	Recorded only from the Wyre Forest where it is quite common (Plant, pers. comm.). Riley has confirmed the identity of a voucher specimen.
Flight:	June and July, in woodlands where bilberry carpets the ground.
Larval F/p:	Bilberry. April and May.

1862 Double-striped Pug *Gymnoscellis rufifasciata* Haworth

V.C.H.:	Unrecorded.
Post V.C.H.:	Frequent throughout in most habitats. Particularly common on heather moorland and the mosses of the north.
Flight:	April to August in two broods. So far as I am aware the autumn generation which sometimes occurs in southern England has not been recorded in Shropshire.
Larval F/ps:	Polyphagous, e.g. gorse, broom, heather*, ragwort* and traveller's-joy*. June to September in two broods.

Notes: An extraordinary aberration, with the median area of the forewings and all but the outer third of the hindwings completely white, was caught in the Wyre Forest (18–24.viii.1984) by Plant. Identification was confirmed by Riley's examination of the genitalia. This specimen appears to be an extreme form of ab. *albescens* Lempke (Lempke, 1951) and has been named ab. *albofasciata* by Plant (Plant, 1989). It was exhibited at the 1988 annual exhibition of the British Entomological and Natural History Society and was photographed for inclusion in that society's journal.

1864 The Streak *Chesias legatella* Denis & Schiffermüller

V.C.H.: Generally distributed.

Post V.C.H.: Widespread and common where the larval foodplant grows.

Flight: September and October on heathland, moorland and in open woodland.

Larval F/p: Broom. May and June.

1865 Broom-tip *Chesias rufata rufata* Fabricius

V.C.H.: Recorded only from Market Drayton (Woodforde).

Post V.C.H.: Widespread. More localised than *C. legatella*, though found in the same habitats.

Flight: April to July.

Larval F/p: Broom. July to September.

1866 Manchester Treble-bar *Carsia sororiata anglica* Prout

V.C.H.: Unrecorded.

Post V.C.H.: Found only on Whixall and Fenn's Mosses where it is well established and often common.

Flight: July and August. Often seen flying in hot sunshine.

Larval F/ps: Bilberry, cranberry and possibly cowberry though the latter is only present on Fenn's Moss. April to June.

1867 Treble-bar *Aplocera plagiata plagiata* Linnaeus

V.C.H.: Frequent at Church Stretton but not recorded elsewhere.

Post V.C.H.: Widespread and frequent in woodlands and moorland.

Flight: May and June and again in August and September.

Larval F/ps: St John's wort species. Fully fed in April and July.

1868 Lesser Treble-bar *Aplocera efformata* Guenée

V.C.H.: Unrecorded. Not regarded as specifically distinct from *A. plagiata*.

Post V.C.H.: Very local. Recorded only from Willey, 1970 (Whitney); Bucknell, 1971 (Shephard); Bromfield, 1978 (Norton) and Preston Montford Field Centre, 1981 (R.I.S. trap, det. Riley).

Flight: May and June and again in August and September, inhabiting openings in woods and wasteground.

Larval F/ps: St. John's wort species. Fully fed in April and July.

1870 Chimney Sweeper *Odezia atrata* Linnaeus

V.C.H.: Quite common around Church Stretton. Also recorded at Wenlock Edge, 1903 (Potts, 1904).

Post V.C.H.: Uncommon and local. Recorded from Church Stretton, 1935 (Pendlebury, 1936) and 1978 (Riley) and Wyre Forest, (Evans; Scott; Plant).

Flight:	June and July on limestone hills and damp meadows and roadside verges. Diurnal.
Larval F/p:	Pignut. April and May.

1872 Blomer's Rivulet *Discoloxia blomeri* Curtis

V.C.H.:	Common on the Wrekin (Woodforde). Also recorded from Benthall, 1905 (Potts, 1906).
Post V.C.H.:	Wrekin, 1913 (over 40 taken) (Pendlebury and Pendlebury, 1914) and 1980 (Riley); the Ercall, 1978 and 1980 (Minshall and Riley); Shirlett, 1986 (Whitney) and Easthope Wood, 1987 and 1989 (Coleshaw).
Flight:	May to early July in woodlands containing wych elm.
Larval F/p:	Wych elm*. August and September.
Notes:	Wych elm has been severely reduced by Dutch elm disease though Sinker *et. al.* (1985) states that it continues to recover through vigorous suckering. *D. blomeri* seems to be maintaining its population well in the woodlands around the Wrekin and Ercall hills.

1873 Welsh Wave *Venusia cambrica* Curtis

V.C.H.:	Recorded only from Market Drayton where it was fairly common (Woodforde, 1900e).
Post V.C.H.:	Two records only, from Shirlett, 1969 and 1976 (Whitney).
Flight:	Late June to mid-August. Skinner (1984) states woodlands and mountain moorland.
Larval F/p:	Rowan. August and September.

1874 Dingy Shell *Euchoeca nebulata* Scopoli

V.C.H.:	Woodforde (1900f and 1901c) found several near Market Drayton in 1900 and 1901.
Post V.C.H.:	Common on Whixall Moss and frequent at Preston Montford Field Centre (R.I.S. trap, det. Riley). Also recorded from Cleobury Mortimer, July 1922 (one) (Woodward, 1922b); Church Stretton, 1935 (Pendlebury); Ludlow, 1939 (Bretherton); Donnington, 1948 (Christie); Wyre Forest (Blunt; Evans; Plant) and Woore, 1984 (Holdsworth).
Flight:	June and July in damp localities.
Larval F/p:	Alder. July and August.

1875 Small White Wave *Asthena albulata* Hufnagel

V.C.H.:	Recorded only from Church Stretton and Shavington.
Post V.C.H.:	Apparently absent from the Clun Forest Upland and the Welsh borders but widespread, though not common, elsewhere.
Flight:	Mid-May to mid-July with a partial second generation in August (Preston Montford Field Centre, 1979, det. Riley). Usually found in woodlands.
Larval F/ps:	Many trees including hazel* and birch. July and August.

1876 Small Yellow Wave *Hydrelia flammeolaria* Hufnagel

V.C.H.:	Frequent at Church Stretton.
Post V.C.H.:	Frequently recorded from Whixall Moss, otherwise local and uncommon: Cleobury Mortimer, July 1922 (one) (Woodward, 1922b); Rodington, 1958 (Briggs); Pontesbury, 1974 (D. Smith); Shirlett, 1979 and 1985 (Whitney); Woore, 1984 (Holdsworth); Wyre Forest, 1984–88 (Blunt; Plant) and Preston Montford Field Centre, 1987 (R.I.S. trap, det. Riley).

Flight: June and July in woodlands and hedgerows.

Larval F/ps: Probably maple, though in the north of England it feeds on alder. August and September.

1877 Waved Carpet *Hydrelia sylvata* Denis & Schiffermüller

V.C.H.:   Not rare in woods planted with alders around Church Stretton (Newnham, 1901a and 1908). Woodforde (1901c) states that he found over 100 individuals in one day (22.vi.1901) near Market Drayton.

Post V.C.H.: Unrecorded.

Flight: June and July in woodland.

Larval F/ps: Alder*, birch, sallow and sweet chestnut. July and August.

Notes: This is a local and generally uncommon species in Britain. It is easily mistaken for *V. cambrica* and initially one might suspect that the V.C.H. identifications are erroneous. However, the author's observations associating the specimens with alder would suggest that they are genuine. (The larval foodplant of *V. cambrica* is Rowan.)

1878 Drab Looper *Minoa murinata* Scopoli

V.C.H.:   Unrecorded in the V.C.H. but noted from the Wyre Forest by Blatch (1886).

Post V.C.H.: Fairly common in the Wyre Forest (Blunt; Evans; Plant) but very local and infrequent elsewhere. Recorded from Shrewsbury, 1913 (Pendlebury) and Munslow, 1970 (Whitney).

Flight: May and June in woodland rides and clearings.

Larval F/p: Wood spurge. July and August.

1879 Seraphim *Lobophora halterata* Hufnagel

V.C.H.:   Unrecorded.

Post V.C.H.: On the whole local and uncommon. Recorded from Rednall, 1948 (Hignett); Pontesbury, 1971 (D. Smith); Ercall Woods, 1976 (Riley); Preston Montford Field Centre, 1967 (Heath) and 1978 (R.I.S. trap, det. Riley); Woore, 1980 to 1984 (Holdsworth) and Monkhopton, 1985 (Jacques).

Flight: May and June on rough ground and open woodland.

Larval F/ps: Aspen and poplars. June and July.

1880 Barred Tooth-striped *Trichopheryx polycommata* Denis & Schiffermüller

V.C.H.:   Unrecorded.

Post V.C.H.: One record only: Pontesbury, 1978 (D. Smith).

Flight: March and April, mainly in open woodland and scrubland.

Larval F/ps: Wild privet and ash. May and June.

1881 Early Tooth-striped *Trichopteryx carpinata* Borkhausen

V.C.H.:   Abundant at Market Drayton in 1893 (Woodforde, 1894) and Benthall, 1905 (Potts, 1906).

Post V.C.H.: Widespread and fairly common in woodlands.

Flight: April and May.

Larval F/ps: Honeysuckle, birch*, sallow and alder. June and July.

1882 Small Seraphim *Pterapherapteryx sexalata* Retzius

V.C.H.: Recorded only from Church Stretton, where it was not uncommon.

Post V.C.H.: A local species. Easily overlooked and infrequently recorded, though regularly caught at the R.I.S. trap at Preston Montford Field Centre. The only other records are from the Ercall Woods, 1978 (Riley); Whixall Moss, 1985 (Hardwick) and Pontesbury, 1983 (D. Smith).

Flight: June and July (in Shropshire) in damp woodland. It is not certain whether our records, which range from 4th June to 24th July, represent one brood or the two which occur in southern Britain (May and June and July and August). Further investigations are required to determine this.

Larval F/ps: Sallow* and willow spp. July to September.

1883 Yellow-barred Brindle *Acasis viretata* Hübner

V.C.H.: Wyre Forest, 1902 (Rea, per Pendlebury, 1950) though not recorded in the V.C.H.

Post V.C.H.: Recorded only a few times from the northern half of the county: Candy, 22.v.1932 (Hignett, 1933); Broseley, 1969 (Whitney); Pontesbury, 1978 (D. Smith); Preston Montford Field Centre, Aug. 1979 (R.I.S. trap, det. Riley) and Shirlett, 1979 (Whitney).

Flight: May to early September in two broods. The second of these broods, which occurs only in southern Britain, is represented by the record from Preston Montford Field Centre. *A. viretata* inhabits woodland, hedgerows and rough ground.

Larval F/ps: Holly, ivy, dogwood, privet and guelder-rose. June, July, September and October.

1884 The Magpie *Abraxas grossulariata* Linnaeus

V.C.H.: Abundant everywhere.

Post V.C.H.: Common throughout in most habitats including moorland, woodland and gardens.

Flight: July and August.

Larval F/ps: Polyphagous, including gooseberry*, currant, hawthorn, blackthorn and hazel.

1885 Clouded Magpie *Abraxas sylvata* Scopoli

V.C.H.: Fairly common around Church Stretton and the Wrekin. Often abundant in the woods near Staley's Cottage (Newnham, 1901a). Also recorded from Bridgnorth, 1898 (Cortissos, 1899); Farley Dingle, 1902 (Potts) (per Pendlebury, 1950) and Market Drayton, 1901 (Woodforde).

Post V.C.H.: Well recorded from the southern half of the county with the exception of the Clun Forest Uplands.

Flight: May to July in woodlands containing elm.

Larval F/ps: Wych elm* and English elm. August to October.

Notes: This species appears to have declined in recent years as a result of Dutch elm disease on the larval foodplant. In the mid to late 1970s it was abundant in the Ercall Woods. Hundreds could be seen at dusk along the paths through the trees and Riley recorded dozens floating on the surface of the old reservoir there. Larvae were also very common on wych elm. Ingrams (1917) also states that it swarmed in hundreds on 20.vi.1915 at Broseley. Over the last few years it seems to have become far less common, though the larvae are still present on suckering wych elms throughout the woodlands surrounding the Wrekin. Continued observations should be made to monitor the populations of this species though at present there seems to be no immediate danger of extinction. Sinker, *et al.* (1985) states that wych elm is recovering well throughout the county.

1887 Clouded Border *Lomaspilis marginata* Linnaeus

V.C.H.: Recorded only from Church Stretton where it was common.

Post V.C.H.: Common throughout in woodlands, hedgerows and damp meadows.

Flight: June and July.

Larval F/ps: Mainly sallow* and hazel*. Also possibly aspen and poplar. August and September.

1888 Scorched Carpet *Ligdia adustata* Denis & Schiffermüller

V.C.H.: Not noted by Newnham (1908) but recorded from Shrewsbury, 1897 (Cortissos, 1898) and Benthall, 1905 (Potts, 1906).

Post V.C.H.: Widely distributed throughout the county but not common.

Flight: May to August in two broods, inhabiting woodlands, hedgerows and rough ground.

Larval F/p: Spindle tree. June, July, late August and September.

1889 Peacock *Semiothisa notata* Linnaeus

V.C.H.: Recorded regularly at Market Drayton during the early 1900's (Woodforde, 1900e and 1902b).

Post V.C.H.: Unrecorded.

Flight: May and June in woodlands. A second generation occurs in southern England during August.

Larval F/p: Birch. July and possibly September if the species is bivoltine in Shropshire.

Notes: This species is figured on Plate 11.

1893 Tawny-barred Angle *Semiothisa liturata* Clerck

V.C.H.: Not uncommon at Twemlows (Thornewill); frequent around Church Stretton and recorded once from Shirlett, 1907 (Potts, 1908).

Post V.C.H.: Widely distributed and often common in and around pine or spruce plantations.

Flight: June and July.

Larval F/ps: Scots pine* and spruce. July to early October.

Notes: Newnham does not mention the melanic form *nigrofulvata* Collins. At present it is common in Shropshire, sometimes dominant over the type.

1894 Latticed Heath *Semiothisa clathrata clathrata* Linnaeus

V.C.H.: Common at Church Stretton but not recorded elsewhere.

Post V.C.H.: Recorded from Woore, 1974 (Holdsworth), otherwise only from the southern half of the county where it is widespread and fairly common in open woodlands, hedgerows, rough fields and meadows.

Flight: May to September in two broods.

Larval F/ps: Clovers, trefoils and lucerne. June to October.

1897 V-Moth *Semiothisa wauaria* Linnaeus

V.C.H.: Generally distributed.

Post V.C.H.: Widespread throughout the county and frequently recorded from gardens and allotments where its foodplant is grown.

Flight: July and August.

Larval F/ps: Gooseberry*, red currant* and black currant. April to June.

1901 Little Thorn *Cepphis advenaria* Hübner

V.C.H.: Wyre Forest (Rea).

Post V.C.H.: Stated by Skinner (1984, p. 54) to be local in Shropshire. This was based on the strength of comments made by South (1939, p. 275). However no specific localities were given by South and none are known to Skinner (Skinner, pers. comm.). The only known record is of a single specimen caught in the Limekiln Woods, near Wellington, in 1969 (Parker, 1969).

Flight: May and June in open woodland.

Larval F/p: Bilberry. July and August.

1902 Brown Silver-lines *Petrophora chlorosata* Scopoli

V.C.H.: Hawkstone, Twemlows and Shavington, abundant (Thornewill); Wyre Forest.

Post V.C.H.: Common wherever bracken grows, often abundant.

Flight: May and June.

Larval F/p: Bracken*. July to September.

1903 Barred Umber *Plagodis pulveraria* Linnaeus

V.C.H.: Once at Calverhall and once at Prees (Thornewill); not infrequent around Church Stretton.

Post V.C.H.: Widely distributed in woodlands throughout the county but never common.

Flight: May and June.

Larval F/ps: Sallow (*S. caprea** and *S. cinerea**) and birch. K. G. V. Smith (1954) recorded the larvae on hazel at Blakeway Coppice. Feeds during July and August.

1904 Scorched Wing *Plagodis dolabraria* Linnaeus

V.C.H.: Wyre Forest, Blatch (1886) and 1879 and 1899 (Rea).

Post V.C.H.: Widespread and not uncommon in or near woodlands and mature gardens.

Flight: May and June.

Larval F/ps: Oak, birch and sallow. July to September.

1906 Brimstone *Opisthograptis luteolata* Linnaeus

V.C.H.: Abundant everywhere.

Post V.C.H.: Common throughout in most habitats.

Flight: April to October in three broods.

Larval F/ps: Deciduous trees from April to September. Most commonly noted on hawthorn* and blackthorn*.

1907 Bordered Beauty *Epione repandaria* Hufnagel

V.C.H.: Common everywhere.

Post V.C.H.: Widespread and frequent in damp localities.

Flight: July to September.
Larval F/p: Sallow*. May to July.

1909 Speckled Yellow *Pseudopanthera macularia* Linnaeus

V.C.H.:   Ellesmere (Thompson) and Church Stretton, abundant.
Post V.C.H.: Widespread, with the exception of the north-western quarter of the county. Flies in bright sunshine in and near woods.
Flight: May and June.
Larval F/p: Wood sage*. July to August.

1910 Lilac Beauty *Apeira syringaria* Linnaeus

V.C.H.:   Generally distributed.
Post V.C.H.: Well recorded from throughout the county.
Flight: June and July in woods, thickets and mature gardens.
Larval F/ps: Wild cherry* (Newnham, 1901a), honeysuckle, wild privet and ash. September to May.

1911 Large Thorn *Ennomos autumnaria* Werneberg

V.C.H.:   Unrecorded.
Post V.C.H.: Two individuals were caught by Norton in 1955 at Bromfield.
Flight: September and October, usually in or near woodlands.
Larval F/ps: Deciduous trees. May to September.
Notes: This species is only usually recorded regularly in the south-eastern counties of England. Resident populations are, it is believed, supplemented by immigration and this probably explains the two records cited.

1912 August Thorn *Ennomos quercinaria* Hufnagel

V.C.H.:   Calverhall, occasional (Thornewill); Church Stretton, not uncommon.
Post V.C.H.: Recorded frequently from woodlands throughout the county, though never common.
Flight: August and September.
Larval F/ps: Deciduous trees such as birch*, oak and hawthorn*. May to July.

1913 Canary-shouldered Thorn *Ennomos alniaria* Linnaeus

V.C.H.:   Frequent around Church Stretton. No other localities cited.
Post V.C.H.: Widespread and fairly common. Woods, gardens, heathland, mosses etc.
Flight: August to October.
Larval F/ps: Deciduous trees such as alder*, birch and sallow. May to July.

1914 Dusky Thorn *Ennomos fuscantiaria* Haworth

V.C.H.:   Occurs sparingly around Stretton. No other recorded localities.
Post V.C.H.: Widespread and fairly common though apparently absent from the north-west of the county.
Flight: August to October in woods and gardens where the larval foodplant grows.
Larval F/p: Ash. May to July.

1915 September Thorn *Ennomos erosaria* Denis & Schiffermüller
V.C.H.:   Recorded once from Church Stretton in 1899; scarce at Market Drayton (Woodforde) and Oswestry, 1907 (Pendlebury, per Potts, 1908).

Post V.C.H.: Frequent, though not common, in woods, parkland and gardens.

Flight: July to October.

Larval F/ps: Oak, lime and birch. May to July.

1917 Early Thorn *Selenia dentaria* Fabricius
V.C.H.:   Frequent thoughout.

Post V.C.H.: Widespread and common in most habitats.

Flight: April and May and again in August and September.

Larval F/s: Polyphagous on deciduous trees and bushes. Recorded in Shropshire on hawthorn, blackthorn and birch. May, June, August and September.

Notes: The melanic forms have not been recorded in the county.

1918 Lunar Thorn *Selenia lunularia* Hübner
V.C.H.:   Recorded only from Church Stretton, where it was less common than *S. dentaria*, and Benthall Edge (Allen, per Potts, 1908).

Post V.C.H.: Frequently recorded from the R.I.S. trap at Preston Montford Field Centre (det. Riley). There are other records from Shrewsbury, 1913 (three) (Pendlebury & Pendlebury, 1914) and 1922 (Henstock, per Ingrams, 1923); Oswestry, 9.vi.1929 (Hignett, 1931); Minsterley, 1960 and Pontesbury, 1970 (D. Smith); Shirlett, 1980 (Whitney) and Monkhopton, 1985 (Jacques).

Flight: May and June, in and near woods.

Larval F/ps: Deciduous trees, mainly oak and birch. July to September.

Notes: Although melanic forms are known from the Midlands, none have been recorded in Shropshire.

1919 Purple Thorn *Selenia tetralunaria* Hufnagel
V.C.H.:   Unrecorded.

Post V.C.H.: Widespread but local and never common.

Flight: April and May and again in July and August, mainly in woods and mature gardens.

Larval F/ps: Deciduous trees, mainly birch*, oak, sallow and alder. June to September in two broods.

1920 Scalloped Hazel *Odontopera bidentata* Clerck
V.C.H.:   Very common throughout.

Post V.C.H.: Widespread, generally distributed and common.

Flight: May and June.

Larval F/ps: Many trees including some conifers. Recorded in Shropshire on birch and oak (Riley). July to September.

Notes: Newnham (1908) did not mention the presence of the melanic form *nigra* Prout in Shropshire. (It was not officially described until 1912). South (1939) states that it was only found on the mosses of Lancashire and in Yorkshire. This form is now known to occur frequently in the more industrialised areas of Britain and occasionally elsewhere. It is recorded regularly throughout Shropshire.

1921 Scalloped Oak *Crocallis elinguaria* Linnaeus

V.C.H.: Common, with the apparent exception of the Market Drayton area.

Post V.C.H.: Recorded regularly from throughout the county in most habitats.

Flight: Late June to August.

Larval F/ps: Polyphagous on deciduous trees and bushes. Recorded in Shropshire on oak (Riley). April to July.

1922 Swallow-tailed Moth *Ourapteryx sambucaria* Linnaeus

V.C.H.: Common throughout.

Post V.C.H.: Fairly common throughout. Generally distributed and often found in mature gardens.

Flight: June and July.

Larval F/ps: Ivy and many trees and shrubs. Newnham (1901a) states that larvae were often found on ivy, oak, elder and bramble. August to June.

1923 Feathered Thorn *Colotois pennaria* Linnaeus

V.C.H.: Well distributed and common.

Post V.C.H.: Widely distributed and common, particularly in wooded areas.

Flight: September to November

Larval F/ps: Many deciduous trees and shrubs including birch*, oak*, apple* and ash*. April to June.

1924 Orange Moth *Angerona prunaria* Linnaeus

V.C.H.: Recorded only from the Wyre Forest (Rea; Blatch, 1886).

Post V.C.H.: Frequent in the Wyre Forest (Evans). Elsewhere recorded only from Bucknell, 1971 (Shephard).

Flight: June and July. Woodland and heathland.

Larval F/ps: Many plants and trees including hawthorn, blackthorn, plum, birch, lilac, privet, heather and traveller's-joy. August to May.

Notes: It is pleasing to see that the Wyre Forest is still a stronghold for *A. prunaria* as Shropshire is on the northern limit of this species' range in Britain. The banded form *corylaria* Thunberg was first recorded in the Wyre Forest in 1906 (Rea). Plant (pers. comm.) states that this form is still present there.

1925 Small Brindled Beauty *Apocheima hispidaria* Denis & Schiffermüller

V.C.H.: Rare at Cloverley Park (Thornewill) and uncommon at Church Stretton where the larvae were occasionally found on oak (Newnham, 1901a).

Post V.C.H.: Scarce and local: Shrewsbury, 27.ii.1913 (Pendlebury, 1915); Oswestry, 1947 (Hignett, per Pendlebury, 1950); Woore, 1980 (Holdsworth) and Preston Montford Field Centre, 1981 and 1986 (R.I.S. trap, det. Riley).

Flight: February and March, usually in or near woods.

Larval F/ps: Usually oak*, though it has been found on hazel, elm and sweet chestnut (Skinner, 1984). April to June.

1926 Pale Brindled Beauty *Apocheima pilosaria* Denis & Schiffermüller

V.C.H.: Frequent.

Post V.C.H.: Widespread and common, particularly in woodlands. The adults sometimes feed at sallow catkins in large numbers.

Flight: January to March.

Larval F/ps: Polyphagous on deciduous trees and shrubs including birch*, hawthorn* and oak*. April to June.

Notes: The melanic form *monochraria* Staudinger is common throughout the county. It was not recorded by Newnham (1908).

1927 Brindled Beauty *Lycia hirtaria* Clerck

V.C.H.: Occasionally recorded at Helmeth and Ragleth Woods.

Post V.C.H.: Widely distributed throughout the county, with the exception of the south-east quarter, though never common.

Flight: March and April, usually in or near woods or mature hedgerows.

Larval F/ps: Many deciduous trees including birch*, alder and hawthorn. May to July.

1930 Oak Beauty *Biston strataria* Hufnagel

V.C.H.: Found sparingly throughout.

Post V.C.H.: Recorded regularly, in low numbers, from woodlands throughout the county.

Flight: March and April.

Larval F/ps: Many deciduous trees including elm*, oak*, hazel and alder. May to July.

1931 Peppered Moth *Biston betularia* Linnaeus

V.C.H.: Frequent throughout.

Post V.C.H.: Widespread and fairly common throughout in most habitat types.

Flight: May to August.

Larval F/ps: Polyphagous. Recorded in the Ercall Woods on birch, elm and oak (Riley). July to September.

Notes: The melanic form *carbonaria* Jordan and the superficially intermediate form *insularia* Thierry-Mieg are common throughout though the former does not appear to have been recorded so frequently in recent years. *Carbonaria* was well-known to Newnham, having been recorded at many localities in the county.

1932 Spring Usher *Agriopis leucophaeria* Denis & Schiffermüller

V.C.H.: Frequent over a greater part of the county. Sometimes abundant on oak around Church Stretton (Newnham, 1901a) and Market Drayton (Woodforde, 1902a).

Post V.C.H.: Frequently recorded from wooded areas throughout the county. Often very common in some of the larger woods such as the Ercall (Minshall and Riley) and the Wyre Forest (Evans).

Flight: February and March.

Larval F/p: Oak*. April and May.

1933 Scarce Umber *Agriopis aurantiaria* Hübner

V.C.H.: Very common in and near woods around Church Stretton.

Post V.C.H.: Widespread and common in wooded areas throughout the county.

Flight: October and November.

Larval F/ps: Polyphagous on deciduous trees. Larvae are often common in the Ercall Woods, feeding on many trees including oak, hazel, birch, ash, elm and alder (Riley). April to June.

1934 Dotted Border *Agriopis marginaria* **Fabricius**

V.C.H.: Generally distributed and common.

Post V.C.H.: Widespread and common.

Flight: February to April though a single male was caught at Preston Montford on 26.xii.1987 (Riley, 1989a). Woodlands, hedgerows and gardens.

Larval F/ps: Many plants and most deciduous trees. Larvae are often abundant in the Ercall Woods, feeding on deciduous trees including birch, oak, elm and hazel (Riley). April to June.

Notes: The melanic form *fuscata* Mosley is frequently recorded from throughout the county.

1935 Mottled Umber *Erannis defoliaria* **Clerck**

V.C.H.: Common throughout.

Post V.C.H.: Common throughout and often abundant in the larger woods, the larvae sometimes severely defoliating deciduous trees.

Flight: October to December. Woodlands, hedgerows and gardens.

Larval F/ps: Polyphagous on deciduous trees and shrubs. Larvae are abundant most years on all deciduous tree species. April to June.

Notes: Although variation is very common, to the author's knowledge the melanic form *nigra* Bandermann has not been recorded in Shropshire.

1936 Waved Umber *Menophra abruptaria* **Thunberg**

V.C.H.: Common at Calverhall and Church Stretton; scarce at Market Drayton.

Post V.C.H.: Widespread and frequently recorded from woodlands and gardens, though never common.

Flight: April to June.

Larval F/ps: Privet and lilac. June to September.

Notes: The melanic form *fuscata* Tutt has been recorded once from Dothill, 1979 (Riley).

1937 Willow Beauty *Peribatodes rhomboidaria* **Denis & Schiffermüller**

V.C.H.: Common in most larger gardens.

Post V.C.H.: Widespread and fairly common throughout, especially in woods and gardens. Sometimes abundant.

Flight: June to August.

Larval F/ps: Ivy, traveller's-joy, privet* and many trees including birch* and willow*. September to May.

1938 Bordered Grey *Selidosema brunnearia scandinavaria* **Staudinger**

V.C.H.: Unrecorded.

Post V.C.H.: Apart from a strong colony at Whixall Moss this species has only been recorded from Bucknell, 1971 (Shephard).

Flight: July and August on heathland and mosses.

Larval F/p: Heather*. September to June.

1940 Satin Beauty *Deileptenia ribeata* **Clerck**

V.C.H.: Unrecorded.

Post V.C.H.: A single specimen was caught at light on 22.vii.1989 at Llanymynech by M. Townsend (pers. comm.). This is the only record for Shropshire though the species may have been overlooked due to its superficial resemblance to *A. repandata* and *P. rhomboidaria*.

Flight: Late June to mid-August, usually in or near woodlands.

Larval F/ps: Several species of coniferous and deciduous trees. August to May.

1941 Mottled Beauty *Alcis repandata repandata* Linnaeus

V.C.H.:   Very common over the greater part of the county.

Post V.C.H.:   Common throughout, often abundant in woodlands.

Flight: June and July. Woods, gardens and wasteground.

Larval F/ps: Polyphagous. Often found in the Ercall Woods on deciduous trees and bushes such as birch, oak and hawthorn (Riley). August to May.

1943 Great Oak Beauty *Boarmia roboraria* Denis & Schiffermüller

V.C.H.:   Wyre Forest, (Blatch, 1886), 1899 (Rea; Woodforde, 1902c) and Helmeth and Ragleth Woods, Church Stretton, 1901 (Newnham).

Post V.C.H.:   This species now only occurs in the Wyre Forest where it is fairly common.

Flight: June and July. Associated strictly with oak woodland.

Larval F/p: Oak*. August to May.

1944 Pale Oak Beauty *Serraca punctinalis* Scopoli

V.C.H.:   Unrecorded in the V.C.H. but noted from the Wyre Forest by Blatch (1886).

Post V.C.H.:   One record from the Wyre Forest, 1987 (Plant) though the specimen was not retained.

Flight: End of May to mid-July in woodlands.

Larval F/ps: Mainly oak and birch in July and August. Also recorded on sallow and sycamore (Skinner, 1984).

1945 Brussel's Lace *Cleorodes lichenaria* Hufnagel

V.C.H.:   Not scarce. Often found at rest on lichen-covered trees.

Post V.C.H.:   Recorded only from Earl's Hill, Pontesbury, 1968 (Heath).

Flight: June to August in wooded areas.

Larval F/p: Lichens growing on old oaks, blackthorns and fences. September to May (Skinner, 1984). Newnham (1901) noted larvae feeding on lichens on trees but did not state which species.

Notes: Newnham's comments on the frequency of this species are misleading. They are probably based solely on his own research in the Church Stretton area and not the observations of his other correspondents throughout the county. As no precise localities are cited we should assume that no other entomologists sent him records of this species. This implies that *C. lichenaria* was, as it is now, very local.

1947 The Engrailed *Ectropis bistortata* Goeze

V.C.H.:   Calverhall and Twemlows (Thornewill).

Post V.C.H.:   Widely distributed and common in woodlands and gardens.

Flight: March and April and again in June and July.

Larval F/ps: Many trees and shrubs including birch* and oak*. May, June and August.

Notes: Great care should be taken in separating this and the next species as the adults are usually indistinguishable. Efforts should be made to study their biology and phenology before identifications are made. The date of capture can sometimes be useful.

1948 Small Engrailed *Ectropis crepuscularia* Denis & Schiffermüller

V.C.H.:	Fairly plentiful in the woods around Church Stretton.
Post V.C.H.:	Fewer records than for *E. bistortata* though it is fairly common in woodlands throughout the county.
Flight:	May to mid-June.
Larval F/ps:	Many trees and shrubs, mainly birch* and sallow. July and August.

1950 Brindled White-spot *Paradarisa extersaria* Hubner

V.C.H.:	Unrecorded.
Post V.C.H.:	Apart from the Wyre Forest, where it is common (Evans), this species has only been recorded from Pontesbury, 1976 (D. Smith).
Flight:	April to June in woodlands.
Larval F/ps:	Birch and oak. July to September.
Notes:	Where the two *Ectropis* species are common at light it is easy to overlook *E. extersaria* due to its similar superficial appearance. It is wise to look carefully at any such individuals that are attracted to the sheet or trap.

1951 Grey Birch *Aethalura punctulata* Denis & Schiffermüller

V.C.H.:	Occasional in the woods around Church Stretton.
Post V.C.H.:	Widespread. Found commonly in most woods.
Flight:	May and June
Larval F/ps:	Birch and alder. July and August.

1952 Common Heath *Ematurga atomaria atomaria* Linnaeus

V.C.H.:	Common on unbroken wasteground throughout the county.
Post V.C.H.:	Common on heathland, moorland, mosses and in open woodland.
Flight:	May and June and again in August.
Larval F/ps:	Heather*, heaths, clovers and trefoils. July to September.

1954 Bordered White *Bupalus piniaria* Linnaeus

V.C.H.:	Generally distributed. Found in fir woods.
Post V.C.H.:	Often very common in pine plantations. Also found in mixed woodland where Scots pine grows.
Flight:	May and June.
Larval F/ps:	Scots pine*. July to September.

1955 Common White Wave *Cabera pusaria* Linnaeus

V.C.H.:	Common throughout.
Post V.C.H.:	Common throughout. Woods, gardens, hedgerows and scrubland.
Flight:	May and early June and again in late July and August.
Larval F/ps:	Many trees and shrubs including birch*, oak*, sallow and alder.
Notes:	Newnham (1908) records a species called *Cabera rotundaria* Haworth as being rare about Market Drayton (Woodforde). "The Round-winged White Wave" (*C. rotundaria*) is described in Newman (1869, p. 85) as a distinct species. It is now known to be merely a form of *C. pusaria* L. which can be induced by underfeeding the larvae (Skinner, pers. comm.).

1956 Common Wave *Cabera exanthemata* Scopoli

V.C.H.: Frequent throughout.

Post V.C.H.: Less widespread than *C. pusaria* due to the specificity of the larval foodplant but even so it is still common in most woodlands and damp localities throughout the county.

Flight: May to August in two broods, the former (May to July), being the larger.

Larval F/ps: Mainly sallow but also aspen.

1957 White-pinion Spotted *Lomographa bimaculata* Fabricius

V.C.H.: Unrecorded.

Post V.C.H.: Three site records only: Bromfield, 1955 (Norton); Blakeway Coppice, 1987 and 1989 (three individuals) (Coleshaw) and the Wyre Forest, 1984–88 (Blunt; Plant).

Flight: May and June in woodlands and along hedgerows.

Larval F/ps: Hawthorn and blackthorn. June to August.

Notes: This species is understood to be very local in the Midlands.

1958 Clouded Silver *Lomographa temerata* Denis & Schiffermüller

V.C.H.: Common in the Helmeth and Ragleth Woods. No other localities cited.

Post V.C.H.: Widespread and frequently recorded from woodland, rough ground, hedgerows and gardens.

Flight: May and June.

Larval F/ps: Hawthorn*, apple*, blackthorn, cherry, plum and aspen. July and August (Skinner, 1984).

1960 Early Moth *Theria primaria* Haworth

V.C.H.: Common throughout.

Post V.C.H.: Common. Woodland rides and edges, hedgerows, gardens and rough ground throughout the county.

Flight: January and February.

Larval F/ps: Hawthorn* and blackthorn. April and May.

1961 Light Emerald *Campaea margaritata* Linnaeus

V.C.H.: Calverhall, occasional (Thornewill); common at Church Stretton.

Post V.C.H.: Widespread and common in woodlands throughout the county.

Flight: July and August. A partial second brood has been recorded in September.

Larval F/ps: Polyphagous on deciduous trees including birch*, oak* and hawthorn*. September to May.

1962 Barred Red *Hylaea fasciaria* Linnaeus

V.C.H.: Recorded infrequently from the Twemlows and Church Stretton.

Post V.C.H.: Widespread, and fairly common in coniferous woodland throughout the county.

Flight: June to August.

Larval F/ps: Several coniferous trees including Scots pine* (Newnham, 1901a) and Norway spruce. September to April, pupating amongst the roots of its foodplant in the spring.

Notes: The green ab. *prasinaria* Denis & Schiffermüller was recorded at Middleton Hill, 17.vi.1928 (one) and June 1929 (two) (Hughes, per Ingrams, 1929 and 1930).

1964 The Annulet *Gnophos obscurata* Denis & Schiffermüller

V.C.H.: Recorded from the Wyre Forest (Blatch, 1886) and a locality known as Lover's Walk in the vicinity of Church Stretton. This latter site had already been developed by the time the V.C.H. was published, thus destroying one of only two known localities in the county at that time.

Post V.C.H.: Very local and usually scarce. Recorded as common at Llanymynech in 1930 (Hignett, 1931) and once at the same locality on 22.vii.1989 by Townsend. Other records from: Earl's Hill, 1968 (Heath); Ironbridge, 1974 (Derry) and the Wrekin, 1974 (Riley).

Flight: July and August, usually associated with heathland and moorland.

Larval F/ps: Skinner (1984) lists the following: heather, bird's-foot-trefoil, common rock rose, salad burnet and shining cranesbill. It is also stated to feed on chickweed, groundsel and strawberry in captivity (South, 1939). September to May.

1969 Grey Scalloped Bar *Dyscia fagaria* Thunberg

V.C.H.: Recorded only from Whixall Moss (Thornewill) and the Longmynd where the larvae were found on heather (Newnham, 1901a and 1908).

Post V.C.H.: This species may no longer be present in Shropshire as it has not been seen since 23.vi.1929 when Hignett (1931) recorded one specimen from Llynclys Hill. A great deal of collecting is carried out at Whixall Moss but no recent records have been forthcoming. The Longmynd and Llanymynech have not been worked extensively in recent years and therefore more research is needed before an accurate assessment of *D. fagaria*'s status can be made. It is still known to occur in the West Midlands.

Flight: May to July on heathland, moorland and mosses.

Larval F/ps: Heather* and heaths. September to April.

1970 Grass Wave *Perconia strigillaria* Hübner

V.C.H.: Recorded only from the Wyre Forest, Blatch (1886) and 7.vi.1895 and 19.vi.1899 (Rea).

Post V.C.H.: This species is still fairly common in the Wyre Forest (Evans). It is also frequently recorded from Whixall and Wem Mosses. There is one record from Prees Heath, 1936 (Henstock).

Flight: June and July. Moorland, heathland, mosses and woodland clearings.

Larval F/ps: Heather, heaths, broom and gorse. August to May.

FAMILY: SPHINGIDAE

1972 Convolvulus Hawk-moth *Agrius convolvuli* Linnaeus

V.C.H.: Bridgnorth, 1900 (Pitt, per Potts, 1910); Coalport, 1902 (Garrett); Ellesmere (Peake, 1897) and 4.x.1903 and 16.ix.1906 (Thompson, per Potts, 1904 and 1907); Baschurch, 1904 (Sankey, per Potts, 1905) and Church Stretton, sparingly (Newnham).

Post V.C.H.: A rare migrant which has been recorded only infrequently. Singletons have been noted in the following years: 1921, '22, '29, '30, '33, '50, '64, '67, '70, '76, '77 and '82. The largest immigration was recorded by Pendlebury (1935) when three were noted at Broseley, Pontesbury and Shrewsbury.

| Flight: | The Shropshire records have all been during August and September though, depending on the weather, adults could arrive any time during the summer and early autumn. They could occur in any habitat though the adults are attracted to the flowers of tobacco where this is grown in gardens. |
| Larval F/ps: | Bindweeds, especially field bindweed. The larvae are only rarely recorded in Britain. |

1973 Death's-head Hawk-moth *Acherontia atropos* Linnaeus

V.C.H.:	Occurs in favourable years all over the county, on rare occasions in large numbers. Woodforde recorded the numbers he took near Market Drayton and they make fascinating reading. ". . . eleven specimens in 1895, four in 1897, two in 1899, and in 1900 over 200, principally pupae . . ." (Newnham, 1908).
Post V.C.H.:	Recorded in the following years from widely scattered localities throughout the county. Apart from 1952 when two were recorded, they are of single individuals: 1913, '14, '20, '29, '34, '38, '45, '72, '83 and '88.
Flight:	May to September. As a migrant the adult could turn up in any habitat type.
Larval F/ps:	Potato and, in captivity, is easily reared on privet. August to October.
Notes:	The huge numbers of larvae and pupae which were recorded in the V.C.H. occurred at a time before spraying of crops was common practice. We are unlikely to see such large numbers reported again. It is important to bear in mind, however, that *A. atropos* cannot survive British winters. Therefore restraint on crop spraying will do nothing to encourage an indigenous population.

1976 Privet Hawk-moth *Sphinx ligustri* Linnaeus

V.C.H.:	Apparently quite rare: Coalport, 1902 (Garrett); Church Stretton (two larvae), 4.ix.1899 (Newnham 1901a & 1908) and Wyre Forest (Blatch, 1886).
Post V.C.H.:	Very rarely recorded though probably resident: Shrewsbury, 1941 (Wood-Taylor, 1941); Quatford, 1960 (D'Arcy); Bucknell, 1971 (Shephard); Wellington, 1972 (Broome) and Westhope, 1985 (Dyer).
Flight:	June and July in woodlands and gardens.
Larval F/ps:	Usually privet* and lilac. Also recorded on holly and ash (Skinner, 1984). July and August.

1979 Lime Hawk-moth *Mimas tilae* Linnaeus

V.C.H.:	"Appears to be rare in this county". One record only, Broseley, 2.vii.1902 (Potts).
Post V.C.H.:	Not uncommon, mainly in parks and gardens where limes are grown.
Flight:	May and June.
Larval F/ps:	Mainly lime* but also English elm, alder and birch (Skinner, 1984).
Notes:	This species is extremely variable and one ab. *transversa* Jordan, in which the forewing median spots are joined to form a broad median band, was caught in Wellingtron, 1978, (Riley).

1980 Eyed Hawk-moth *Smerinthus ocellata* Linnaeus

V.C.H.:	Fairly common.
Post V.C.H.:	Widely distributed and fairly common throughout the county.
Flight:	May to July in gardens, orchards and damp woodlands.
Larval F/ps:	Usually willow* and apple*, though also sallow* and aspen*.

Notes: In 1973 several larvae were found on willow in a garden in Shrewsbury. One of these resulted in ab. *monochromica* Cockayne on which the pink colour of the hindwing is replaced by dull olive buff (Riley). The presence of larvae in urban areas can sometimes be detected easily by looking for frass below willow trees where they are planted in front gardens and overhang the pavement.

1981 Poplar Hawk-moth *Laothoe populi* Linnaeus

V.C.H.:   Common throughout the county.

Post V.C.H.:   Generally distributed and common.

Flight: May to July with a partial second brood in August in some years.

Larval F/ps: Mainly willow*, sallow*, aspen* and poplar. Newnham (1908) says "I have repeatedly found larvae of *S. populi* on laurel."

Notes: Ab. *pallida* (Newnham), a pale whitish form which Newnham bred from larvae feeding on aspen, and ab. *violacea* Newnham which has a violet flush over the wings, have been recorded at Church Stretton (Newnham, 1901).

1982 Narrow-bordered Bee Hawk-moth *Hemaris tityus* Linnaeus

V.C.H.:   Scarce at Market Drayton (Woodforde) and in the Wyre Forest.

Post V.C.H.:   This species was found in clearings along the railway which ran through the Wyre Forest and at Dowles Brook in the same locality. These habitats have changed considerably over the last fifty years and *H. tityus* has not been recorded there since 1937. Evans recorded the species from another part of the forest in 1960. It has also been noted at Astley Abbots, where it was plentiful in 1918 (Pitt, per Ingrams, 1919); Cleobury Mortimer, 1922, when it was stated to be not as common as usual (Woodward, 1922b) and Llanymynech, 1946 (Owen).

Flight: May and June. Diurnal in woodlands and damp heathland and moorland, flying in bright sunshine.

Larval F/p: Devil's-bit scabious. July and August.

Notes: This species is figured on Plate 11.

1983 Broad-bordered Bee Hawk-moth *Hemaris fuciformis* Linnaeus

V.C.H.:   Wyre Forest, 1902 (Rea, per Pendlebury, 1950). Not noted in the V.C.H. itself.

Post V.C.H.:   Two records only: Rhodes Farm, Astley Abbots, 1918, plentiful (Pitt, per Ingrams, 1919) and from the Shropshire/Montgomeryshire border (10 km square SJ21) in 1940 (G. Smith, per BRC, Monkswood). No further details of the latter record are available.

Flight: May and June in woodland rides and clearings. Diurnal, flying in bright sunshine.

Larval F/p: Honeysuckle. July and August.

Notes: This species is figured on Plate 11.

1984 Humming-bird Hawk-moth *Macroglossum stellatarum* Linnaeus

V.C.H.:   Found throughout but of uncertain appearance. The larvae were common at Church Stretton in 1893 (Newnham, 1894b).

Post V.C.H.:   A frequently recorded migrant species which has occurred throughout the county, though never in large numbers. One or two are recorded most years when the adults visit flowers in gardens, hanging baskets, etc.

Flight:	The majority of Shropshire records are from June to August. *M. stellatarum* is diurnal, preferring bright sunshine, though it has been taken occasionally at light.
Larval F/ps:	Lady's bedstraw*, hedge-bedstraw and wild madder. July and August.

1990 Striped Hawk-moth *Hyles lineata livornica* Esper

V.C.H.:	Unrecorded.
Post V.C.H.:	This rare migrant has only been recorded twice in Shropshire: Cleobury Mortimer, August 1943 (Crump) and Donnington, September 1949 (Christie) (see Dannreuther, 1950).
Flight:	Could occur between April and October.
Larval F/ps:	Hedge bedstraw, snapdragon, dock, fuchsia and grape vines. June and July.
Notes:	The larvae are only rarely recorded in Britain, usually in years of large early immigration such as those of 1943 and 1949. The early stages have never been recorded in Shropshire.

1991 Elephant Hawk-moth *Deilephila elpenor* Linnaeus

V.C.H.:	Fairly common throughout.
Post V.C.H.:	Widespread and fairly common. Generally distributed.
Flight:	May to July. The partial second brood which occasionally occurs in southern England has not, so far as I am aware, been recorded in Shropshire.
Larval F/ps:	Mainly willowherb* and garden fuchsias*. July to September. Pendlebury (1950) noted larvae feeding on apple at Broseley in 1912 and on a species of nightshade at Shrewsbury in 1940 and 1941.
Notes:	During late August and September one often sees articles in the local newspapers of startled citizens finding "monster caterpillars with four eyes and a hugh sting". Often they are accompanied by a photograph of a fully grown *D. elpenor* larva which has been feeding on their garden fuchsias. Newham (1901a) bred a specimen of ab. *cinerescens* Newnham from a larva found at Church Stretton in June 1891. This form has the "Forewings clouded with grey, so as to absorb, in part, the other colours." The green form of the normally brown larva was recorded once in Wellington, 1977 (Riley) feeding on fuchsia.

1992 Small Elephant Hawk-moth *Deilephila porcellus* Linnaeus

V.C.H.:	Ellesmere (Peake, 1897; Thompson); Calverhall (Thornewill, per Potts, 1909); Whixall Moss (Peake); Whattall Moss (Thompson); Market Drayton, scarce (Woodforde) and Church Stretton, common most years, hovering over honeysuckle and rhododendron with *D. elpenor*.
Post V.C.H.:	Apparently absent from the south west of the county. Otherwise widespread and frequently recorded from woodland, heathland, moorland and the northern mosses.
Flight:	May to July.
Larval F/ps:	Bedstraw species including lady's bedstraw*. July to September and occasionally into October (Newnham, 1908). Whitney (pers. comm.) reports a strong colony of this species on willowherb at Shirlett.

1993 Silver-striped Hawk-moth *Hippotion celerio* Linnaeus

V.C.H.:	One female was taken at light in a garden in Broseley by Potts, 18.x.1897 (Newnham, 1897b and 1901a).
Post V.C.H.:	This very rare migrant has not been recorded since publication of the V.C.H.

| Flight: | Could occur any time between May and November, though usually it is noted in the late summer and autumn. |
| Larval F/ps: | Grape vines, bedstraws, fuchsia, willowherb and Virginia creeper. June and again from August to October (Heath, 1979). |

FAMILY: NOTODONTIDAE

1994 Buff-tip *Phalera bucephala* Linnaeus

V.C.H.:	Abundant throughout, sometimes defoliating woodland trees around Church Stretton (Newnham, 1901a).
Post V.C.H.:	Common throughout. Generally distributed, though most common in woods.
Flight:	June and July.
Larval F/ps:	Many deciduous trees including sallow*, lime*, elm* and oak.

1995 Puss Moth *Cerura vinula* Linnaeus

V.C.H.:	Common everywhere.
Post V.C.H.:	Widespread and common wherever the larval foodplants grow. The larvae are often found in gardens on willow.
Flight:	May to July.
Larval F/ps:	Willow*, poplar, sallow and aspen.

1996 Alder Kitten *Furcula bicuspis* Borkhausen

V.C.H.:	". . . one of our greatest entomological prizes." Scarce about Market Drayton (Woodforde). At Church Stretton Newnham (1901a) occasionally found the pupa on alder and birch. The larva had only been found three times (Barnett; Bradburne; Newnham).
Post V.C.H.:	Well distributed in central and northern districts but only infrequently recorded: Whixall Moss (Burrows, per Fielding, 1974a); Llynclys, 1948 (Hignett, per Pendlebury, 1950); Minsterley, 1960 (D. Smith); Broseley, 1968 and 1971 (Whitney); Pontesbury, 1971 (D. Smith); Ironbridge, 1974 (Derry); Shirlett, 1977 (Whitney); Ercall Woods, 1978 and 1979 (Riley); Hawk Lake, 1985 (Hardwick) and the Wyre Forest, 1987 (Plant).
Flight:	May to July in woodland.
Larval F/ps:	Alder* and birch*. July to September.

1997 Sallow Kitten *Furcula furcula* Clerck

V.C.H.:	Although Newnham speculated that this species probably occurred throughout the county the only specific records cited are from Church Stretton where the larvae could be found on sallow or, rarely, on poplar (Newnham, 1901a).
Post V.C.H.:	Apparently absent from the south-west though widespread over the rest of the county. Frequent, though never common, in damp localities.
Flight:	May and June and again in August.
Larval F/ps:	Principally sallow* but also black poplar* and aspen. June to September in two broods.

1998 Poplar Kitten *Furcula bifida* Brahm

V.C.H.: Market Drayton, occasional (Woodforde); Broseley, 1898 (Potts, per Cortissos, 1899); Lyth Hall, 1908 (Ingrams, per Potts, 1909) and Church Stretton.

Post V.C.H.: This seems to be the rarest of the *Furcula* species in Shropshire. Records are very sparse: Whixall Moss (Burrows, per Fielding, 1974a); Oswestry, "an old record" and 1929 (Hignett, 1931); Minsterley, 1960 and Pontesbury, 1971 (D. Smith); Shirlett, 1977 (Whitney); Woore, 1984 (Holdsworth) and Button Oak, 1984–88 (Blunt).

Flight: May to July in the vicinity of poplars.

Larval F/ps: Aspen* (Newnham, 1901) and black poplar*. July to September.

Notes: Although variation in the wing markings of this species is neither common or extensive, Newnham records ab. *urocera* Boisduval and ab. *aurea* Newnham at Church Stretton. The latter, which he reared from ova found on poplar in 1893, is described as being particularly striking with strong orange suffusion in the median band of the forewings (Newnham, 1895a and 1901a).

1999 Lobster Moth *Stauropus fagi* Linnaeus

V.C.H.: Wyre Forest, June 1899 and June 1900 (presumably Rea) and 1902 and 1904 (Rea, per Potts, 1903 and 1905).

Post V.C.H.: Fairly common in the Wyre Forest. There are no other known localities in Shropshire.

Flight: May to July in mature woodland.

Larval F/ps: Oak, hazel, birch and beech. July to September.

Notes: It appears that *S. fagi* has become more common in the Wyre Forest since V.C.H. times. Newnham (1908) refers to it as "This scarce insect . . .". Shropshire is on the northern fringe of its range in England.

2000 Iron Prominent *Notodonta dromedarius* Linnaeus

V.C.H.: Generally distributed. Larvae not uncommon on alder and birch (Newnham, 1901a).

Post V.C.H.: Widely distributed and fairly common throughout the county with the exception of the Clee Hills Platform and the Clun Forest Upland.

Flight: May and June and again in August.

Larval F/ps: Birch*, alder*, hazel and oak. July to September in two broods.

2003 Pebble Prominent *Eligmodonta ziczac* Linnaeus

V.C.H.: Fairly common at Calverhall (Thornewill), Market Drayton (Woodforde) and Church Stretton.

Post V.C.H.: Widely distributed and fairly common in the vicinity of its foodplants.

Flight: May and June and again in August.

Larval F/ps: Poplar*, willow*, sallow* and aspen.

2005 Great Prominent *Peridea anceps* Goeze

V.C.H.: Infrequently found around Church Stretton. A single female was also caught at sugar at Market Drayton on 25.vi.1902 (Woodforde, 1902c). Also recorded from Shrewsbury by Stainton (1857, Vol. 1: 126).

Post V.C.H.: Apart from the Wyre Forest, where it is fairly common, it has only been recorded from the following localities: Shrewsbury, 29.v.1913 (Pendlebury & Pendlebury, 1914); Oswestry, 1934 (Hignett, per Pendlebury, 1950); Pontesbury, 1978 (D. Smith) and Shirlett, 1979 and 1980 (Whitney).

Flight: April to June in mature woods containing oak.

Larval F/p: Oak*. June to August. Newnham (1901a) cites ova laid on oak and hawthorn.

2006 Lesser Swallow Prominent *Pheosia gnoma* Frabricius

V.C.H.: Market Drayton, frequent (Woodforde); Broseley (Potts) and Church Stretton, frequent.

Post V.C.H.: Recorded frequently throughout the county. Generally distributed.

Flight: May and June and again in August.

Larval F/p: Birch. June to September in two broods.

2007 Swallow Prominent *Pheosia tremula* Clerck

V.C.H.: Fairly common among poplars in most parts of the county.

Post V.C.H.: Widely distributed and fairly common though not as frequently recorded as *P. gnoma*.

Flight: May and June and again in August, in the vicinity of its foodplants.

Larval F/ps: Poplar*, aspen, sallow and willow. June to September in two broods.

2008 Coxcomb Prominent *Ptilodon capucina* Linnaeus

V.C.H.: Generally distributed and common.

Post V.C.H.: Fairly common throughout the county. Generally distributed.

Flight: May and June and again in August and September.

Larval F/ps: Polyphagous on deciduous trees including oak* and birch*. June to September in two broods.

2011 Pale Prominent *Pterostoma palpina* Clerck

V.C.H.: Twemlows and Calverhall (Thornewill); Broseley, common (Potts and Bradburne) and Church Stretton.

Post V.C.H.: Generally common throughout the county.

Flight: May and June and again in August.

Larval F/ps: Willow*, aspen* and sallow*.

2014 Marbled Brown *Drymonia dodonea* Denis & Schiffermüller

V.C.H.: Church Stretton (occasional) and Wyre Forest.

Post V.C.H.: Apart from the Wyre Forest, where it is common (Evans) this species was also recorded from Pontesbury as occasional singletons between 1971 and 1977 (D. Smith).

Flight: May and June in oak woods.

Larval F/ps: Oak* and birch*. July to September.

2015 Lunar Marbled Brown *Drymonia ruficornis* Hufnagel

V.C.H.: Larvae found sparingly at Church Stretton on oak (Newnham, 1901a and 1908).

Post V.C.H.: Widely distributed and not uncommon in woods containing oak.

Flight: April and May.

Larval F/p: Oak*. July and August.

2017 Small Chocolate-tip *Clostera pigra* Hufnagel

V.C.H.: Not rare some years both on poplars and sallows around Church Stretton (Newnham, 1901).

Post V.C.H.: Cleobury Mortimer, 21.viii.1922 (one) (Woodward, 1922b).

Flight: May and again in August, usually in damp localities.

Larval F/ps: Poplar*, sallow*, creeping willow and aspen.

Notes: Nationally *C. pigra* is most common in south-east England with a very sporadic distribution elsewhere. It is a very localised species and may have been overlooked in Shropshire. Further investigation is required to ascertain its true status in the county. It is figured on Plate 11.

2019 Chocolate-tip *Clostera curtula* Linnaeus

V.C.H.: Church Stretton, occasionally as larvae on sallow.

Post V.C.H.: Apart from Preston Montford Field Centre, where it is fairly common at the R.I.S. trap (det. Riley), this species appears to be uncommon. It has been recorded at Bucknell, 1971 (Shephard); Shirlett, 1974 and 1977 (Whitney) and the Wyre Forest, occasional to 1986 (Evans).

Flight: April and May and again in July and August, mainly in damp localities.

Larval F/ps: Sallow*, poplar*, aspen and willow. May and June and August and September.

2020 Figure of Eight *Diloba caeruleocephala* Linnaeus

V.C.H.: Abundant and universal.

Post V.C.H.: Widespread, generally distributed and very common.

Flight: October and the first half of November.

Larval F/ps: Many deciduous trees, mainly blackthorn*, hawthorn*, apple*, crab apple* and pear*. May and June.

FAMILY: LYMANTRIIDAE

2025 Scarce Vapourer *Orgyia recens* Hübner

V.C.H.: Recorded only from the Wyre Forest as a larva, 23.vii.1897 (Rea).

Post V.C.H.: The Wyre Forest colony persisted until at least 1929 but the area where it was found has since been planted with conifers. It appears that the species is now extinct in Shropshire.

Flight: Mainly June and July with a partial second generation between August and October, mainly in damp localities.

Larval F/ps: Sallow, hawthorn, oak and many other deciduous trees and shrubs. July to May.

Notes: The re-afforestation of the section of the Wyre Forest where this species occurred may have been the direct cause of its extinction in Shropshire. On the other hand *O. recens* has declined dramatically throughout the country over the last century. Whereas it was formally widespread in the southern half of Britain it is now restricted to Yorkshire, Lincolnshire and the Norfolk Broads. The reference to this species occurring in the Bewdley Forest (South, 1939, Vol. 1: p. 115) cannot be substantiated (Skinner, pers. comm.). Plate 11.

2026 The Vapourer *Orgyia antiqua* Linnaeus

V.C.H.: Common but, not abundant, throughout the county.

Post V.C.H.: Widespread and fairly common. Often found in gardens.

Flight: July to October in two broods. The second brood is only partial.

Larval F/ps: Polyphagous on deciduous trees and shrubs including birch* and rose*.

2028 Pale Tussock *Calliteara pudibunda* Linnaeus

V.C.H.: Shavington, one larva (Thornewill); Market Drayton, common (Woodforde) and Church Stretton, common.

Post V.C.H.: Widespread and common, mainly in rural areas.

Flight: May and June.

Larval F/ps: Polyphagous on deciduous trees, including hawthorn*, poplar* and elm*. July to September.

2029 Brown-tail *Euproctis chrysorrhoea* Linnaeus

V.C.H.: Broseley, 1898 (Potts, per Cortissos, 1899); Ellesmere (Thompson) and common at Caynton, near Newport (Paddock).

Post V.C.H.: Rodington, 12.viii.1957 (two) and 27.vii.1958 (Briggs).

Flight: July and August.

Larval F/ps: Many deciduous trees and shrubs including hawthorn, blackthorn and various fruit trees. September to May.

Notes: This species is usually regarded as being coastal though it is often abundant in the London area where it sometimes reaches pest proportions. Its apparent presence in Shropshire, particularly as it was reported as being common at Caynton, is something of a mystery. If the records were not mis-identifications (which seems unlikely for such a distinctive species) we may assume that transient colonies existed for a short time resulting from chance immigration.

2030 Yellow-tail *Euproctis similis* Fuessly

V.C.H.: Fairly common throughout.

Post V.C.H.: Generally distributed and common throughout the county.

Flight: July and August. A single male was caught at Preston Montford on 29.x.1989 (R.I.S. trap, det. Riley), suggesting a partial second emergence that year.

Larval F/ps: Polyphagous on deciduous trees. Often common on hawthorn* and blackthorn* hedges. Also recorded on poplar* and birch*. September to May.

2031 White Satin *Leucoma salicis* Linnaeus

V.C.H.: Not uncommon. Larvae are found on poplar (Newnham, 1901a and 1908).

Post V.C.H.: Recorded mainly in the northern half of the county. Of erratic appearance and never common, though it seems to have become more widespread in recent years. Apart from one report on 16.vii.1932 from Oswestry (Hignett, 1933), all the other records have been during the 1970's and '80's.

Flight: July and August, mainly in damp localities.

Larval F/ps: Poplar*, willow and sallow. August to June.

Notes: The fact that this species is a known migrant, as well as a resident, may help to explain the fluctuation in the numbers reported each year in Shropshire.

2033 Black Arches *Lymantria monacha* Linnaeus

V.C.H.: Unrecorded.

Post V.C.H.: One record from the Knowles Coppice Reserve in the Wyre Forest, 1984 (Plant).

Flight: July and August in woodland.

Larval F/p: Oak. April to June.

FAMILY: ARCTIIDAE

2035 Round-winged Muslin *Thumatha senex* Hübner

V.C.H.: Stainton (1857. Vol. 1: 141–142) gives Shrewsbury as a locality for this species. The only other reference is to rough unbroken ground near Market Drayton (Woodforde).

Post V.C.H.: Fairly common at Preston Montford Field Centre (R.I.S. trap, det. Riley), the Ercall Woods (Riley) and Whixall Moss (many recorders). Apart from these sites it has been recorded only from Loynton Moss, 1971 (Warren); Alscott, 1978 (several) and Wellington, 1979 (two) (Riley); Woore, 1984 (Holdsworth) and the Wyre Forest, 1987 (Plant).

Flight: July and August in wet localities.

Larval F/ps: Various lichens and mosses. September to May.

Notes: This species is very easily overlooked. Further investigation would probably reveal it to be far more widespread and common than the present records suggest.

2036 Dew Moth *Setina irrorella* Linnaeus

V.C.H.: Unrecorded.

Post V.C.H.: Two specimens were caught at Bromfield in 1950 (Norton). These are now in the Ludlow Museum collection and their identity was confirmed in 1985 (Riley).

Flight: June and July. In Shropshire it should be sought on limestone hills.

Larval F/ps: Various lichens growing on rocks. (In Shropshire probably strictly associated with limestone outcrops). August to May.

Notes: This species is usually regarded as being coastal although it does occur at a few inland sites in southern England and south Wales. Its presence in Shropshire is unusual as it is by far the most inland site known in Britain.

2037 Rosy Footman *Miltochrista miniata* Forster

V.C.H.: Unrecorded.

Post V.C.H.: One record from Goldstone Common, near Cheswardine, 1986 (Cooper).

Flight: June to August in wooded areas.

Larval F/ps: Lichens growing on trees. September to May.

Notes: This species is not uncommon in southern Britain. It may have been overlooked in Shropshire though its distinctive appearance should make it easy enough to identify where it does occur.

2038 Muslin Footman *Nudaria mundana* Linnaeus

V.C.H.: Church Stretton, not uncommon at light and on lichen-covered walls (Newnham, 1901a and 1908) and Shrewsbury, (Stainton, 1857. Vol.1: 141–142).

Post V.C.H.: Fairly common at the R.I.S. trap at Preston Montford Field Centre (det. Riley). Other records come from Candy, 1930, common (Hignett, 1931); Ludlow, 1939 (Bretherton); Bromfield, 1940 and 1978 (Norton); Bucknell, 1970 (Shephard); Hopton Titterhill, 1982 (Hicks); Llanymynech, 1982 (Anon., B.R.C.) and Pontesbury (scarce) (D. Smith).

Flight: June to August on rough ground, scrubland and woodland edges, etc.

Larval F/ps: Lichens growing on walls, fences, etc. September to May.

Notes: An easily overlooked species which is probably more widespread than the present records suggest.

2039 Red-necked Footman *Atolmis rubricollis* Linnaeus

V.C.H.: Not common. Found occasionally clinging to grass in old pastures etc (Newnham, 1901a and 1908).

Post V.C.H.: Unrecorded.

Flight: June and July, usually in woodland.

Larval F/ps: Lichens growing on the trunks of oak, beech and larch. August to October. Skinner (1984) also cites those growing on some species of coniferous trees.

Notes: This is a very local species in Britain. It may still occur in Shropshire though it is more likely to be found in woodlands rather than, as Newnham (1908) found, in pastures.
Plate 11.

2040 Four-dotted Footman *Cybosia mesomella* Linnaeus

V.C.H.: Recorded only from the Wyre Forest (Rea; Blatch, 1886).

Post V.C.H.: Fairly common on the mosses of the north and in the Wyre Forest in the south. Other occasional records have come from Bomere, 14.vii.1926 (Pendlebury, per Ingrams, 1927) and Preston Montford Field Centre (R.I.S. trap, det. Riley).

Flight: June to August on heathland and open woodland.

Larval F/ps: Many species of lichen and algae. August to May.

2044 Dingy Footman *Eilema griseola* Hübner

V.C.H.: Wyre Forest (Rea).

Post V.C.H.: This species still occurs infrequently in the Wyre Forest. Other records from: Roden, 31.vii.1953 (K. G. V. Smith, 1954); Rodington, 1955 & 1960 (Briggs); Shirlett and Whixall Moss, 1930 (Hignett), 1947 (Platts, per Pendlebury, 1950) and 1982 (both f. *stramineola* Doubleday) (Whitney).

Flight: July and August in damp woodland.

Larval F/ps: Various species of lichen. September to June.

Notes: Care should be taken in the field not to mistake this species for *E. lurideola* or *E. complana*, to which it bears a superficial resemblance.

2047 Scarce Footman *Eilema complana* Linnaeus

V.C.H.: More local and less common than *E. lurideola*: Church Stretton district (Ashes Valley), Caradoc and Staley's Cottage. Also Benthall, 1905 (Potts, 1906) and Shrewsbury (Stainton, 1857. Vol. 1: 138).

Post V.C.H.: Local and uncommon: Wyre Forest, one record, date unknown (Evans) and Plant, 1987; Preston Montford Field Centre, 1967 (R.I.S. trap, det. Nicklen); Whixall Moss, 1972 (Rutherford) and 1975 (Hull); Pontesbury, 1975 (D. Smith); Shirlett, 1980 (Whitney) and Llanymynech, 1982 (Anon., B.R.C.) and 22.vii.1989 (Townsend).

Flight:	July and August on heathland and in woodlands.
Larval F/ps:	Various species of lichen. September to June.
Notes:	This species is easily mistaken for the much commoner *E. lurideola*. The reader is referred to Riley (1987) for details of their separation.

2048 Northern Footman *Eilema sericea* Gregson

V.C.H.:	Unrecorded. At the time of publication this species was only known from Lancashire and Cheshire.
Post V.C.H.:	Recorded frequently from Whixall Moss which is now the best known locality in Britain. There is one record from Wem Moss, 1968 (D. Smith) and one from Shirlett, 1980. These specimens are indistinguishable from those of Whixall (Whitney and Smith).
Flight:	July.
Larval F/ps:	Various species of lichen, usually those growing on heather. September to June.
Notes:	It is uncertain whether this is a species in its own right or merely a form of *E. complana*. Structurally there is no difference between the two. It is interesting to note that *E. sericea* is unknown outside Britain. This, of course, attaches particular and obvious importance to preservation of the Whixall colony.

2050 Common Footman *Eilema lurideola* Zincken

V.C.H.:	Generally distributed and common.
Post V.C.H.:	Widespread and common throughout.
Flight:	July and August in many habitats.
Larval F/ps:	Various species of lichen growing on trees, fences, walls etc. September to June.
Notes:	Newnham (1901a) states that this species comes freely to sugar.

2053 Speckled Footman *Coscinia cribraria* Linnaeus

V.C.H.:	"This rare species has been taken in the Wyre Forest according to Dr. C. Hastings." (Newnham, 1908).
Post V.C.H.:	Unrecorded.
Flight:	July and August.
Larval F/ps:	Dandelion and other herbaceous plants (Skinner, 1984). September to June.
Notes:	Two subspecies of *C. cribraria* occur in Britain. The first, ssp. *bivittata* South, is resident and is found in Hampshire, westwards to Dorset. The second, ssp. *arenaria* Lempke, is a rare immigrant occasionally recorded in southern England. The Wyre Forest specimen is no longer traceable but was probably of the latter race.

2056 Wood Tiger *Parasemia plantaginis plantaginis* Linnaeus

V.C.H.:	Found on all the moorlands of the county. Abundant on the Longmynd.
Post V.C.H.:	*P. plantaginis* is still found on most moorland sites but nowhere is it abundant.
Flight:	May to July. Males can often be seen flying during the day in bright sunshine.
Larval F/ps:	Polyphagous on herbaceous plants. August to April.
Notes:	Newnham (1893, 1896, 1897a and 1901a) records ab. *hospita* Dennis & Schiffermüller, in which the hindwings and the sides of the abdomen are

white; ab. *matronalis* Freyer, in which they are almost entirely black and ab. *rufa* Tutt, in which they are rosy red, at Church Stretton. Newnham (1901a) states that only male ab. *hospita* are found and that they appear to be more common following a severe winter. He also notes that most of the Longmynd females have red abdomens. Newnham (1897a) mentions the occurrence of an autumnal brood during the September and October of 1896.

2057 Garden Tiger *Arctia caja* Linnaeus

V.C.H.:   Fairly common.

Post V.C.H.: Widespread and common throughout. Generally distributed.

Flight: July and August.

Larval F/ps: Polyphagous on herbaceous plants including dandelion* and dock*. September to June.

Notes: Newnham (1901a) cites records of ab. *flavescens* Newnham, in which the red colouring is replaced by yellow; ab. *rosacea* Newnham, in which the forewings are flushed with a rosy shade, and ab. *albescens* Newnham, in which the white markings on the forewings are greatly increased, at Church Stretton.

2058 Cream-spot Tiger *Arctia villica britannica* Oberthür

V.C.H.:   Unrecorded.

Post V.C.H.: Entered only on the strength of one unconfirmed record from Whitchurch (date unknown, B.R.C., Ludlow). This should not be regarded as proof of *A. villica's* presence in Shropshire.

Flight: May and June. Woodland and downland.

Larval F/ps: Polyphagous on herbaceous plants. August to April.

2059 Clouded Buff *Diacrisia sannio* Linnaeus

V.C.H.:   Regular at Whixall Moss, Wyre Forest and Ragleth Wood near Church Stretton.

Post V.C.H.: Two records only: Church Stretton, 1959 (Knill-Jones) and Hodnet Heath, 1970 (D. Smith).

Flight: June and July on heathland and in open woodland. The males fly in bright sunshine.

Larval F/ps: Polyphagous on low-growing, moorland associated plants such as heather. August to May.

Notes: It would appear that Shropshire is in danger of losing this species, if it has not become extinct already. This is rather strange as it is known to be locally common over most of the British Isles. Further investigation is urgently needed to confirm the status of *D. sannio* in Shropshire.

2060 White Ermine *Spilosoma lubricipeda* Linnaeus

V.C.H.:   Common throughout.

Post V.C.H.: Common throughout. Generally distributed.

Flight: May to July.

Larval F/ps: Polyphagous, mainly on herbaceous plants including dock* and bilberry*. August and September.

Notes: A single specimen of the form commonly found in Scotland, which has brownish forewings, was caught in the Rothamsted Insect Survey light trap at Preston Montford Field Centre in 1984 (Riley).

2061 Buff Ermine *Spilosoma luteum* Hufnagel

V.C.H.: Common throughout.

Post V.C.H.: Common throughout. Generally distributed.

Flight: May to July.

Larval F/ps: Polyphagous on herbaceous plants including forget-me-not*. August and September.

Notes: Newnham (1908) records ab. *walkeri* Curt., in which the black spots are elongated into interrupted lines, as pretty frequent around Church Stretton.

2062 Water Ermine *Spilosoma urticae* Esper

V.C.H.: Near "World's End" (two, ". . . many years ago.") and one in 1900 (W. Jones, no locality).

Post V.C.H.: One at Dothill, 1976 (Riley). Determined by examination of the genitalia.

Flight: June and July in damp localities.

Larval F/ps: Polyphagous on marsh associated plants, e.g. yellow loosestrife, water dock, lousewort, yellow iris, and mint.

2063 Muslin Moth *Diaphora mendica* Clerck

V.C.H.: Recorded as common around Shrewsbury (Stainton, 1857. Vol. 1: 148) and sparingly from Church Stretton and the Wyre Forest.

Post V.C.H.: Widely distributed but only infrequently recorded, apart from the Wyre Forest where it is not uncommon.

Flight: May and June. Gardens, rough ground and open woodland.

Larval F/ps: Polyphagous on herbaceous plants. July to September.

2064 Ruby Tiger *Phragmatobia fuliginosa fuliginosa* Linnaeus

V.C.H.: Market Drayton, occasional (Woodforde); Ercall Heath, near Newport (Paddock) and the Longmynd, frequent.

Post V.C.H.: Frequently recorded from throughout the county.

Flight: May and June with occasional specimens recorded in August. Open woodland, heathland, gardens and scrubland.

Larval F/ps: Polyphagous on herbaceous plants including heather*. July to April.

Notes: Newnham (1901a) recorded ab. *borealis* Staudinger as more common than the type on the Longmynd. This form has the hindwings almost completely black and darker forewings than the type. It appears to conform to ssp. *borealis* Staudinger which is found in Scotland.

2067 Jersey Tiger *Euplagia quadripunctaria* Poda

V.C.H.: Unrecorded.

Post V.C.H.: One specimen was caught in Ludlow by a local hairdresser (Steer) in 1943. This was taken to Ludlow Museum where its identity was confirmed.

Flight: July to September in gardens and wasteground.

Larval F/ps: Many low plants. September to May.

Notes: Outside south Devon this species has only been recorded very rarely as a vagrant.

2069 Cinnabar Moth *Tyria jacobaeae* Linnaeus

V.C.H.: Fairly common though apparently fluctuating in numbers in some localities.

Post V.C.H.: Very common throughout. The distinctive larvae are often abundant on ragwort.

Flight: May to July in most habitats.

Larval F/ps: *Senecio* species including ragwort* and groundsel*. July and August.

Notes: Ab. *flavescens* Thierry-Mieg, which has all the red replaced by yellow, has been recorded from Church Stretton, 1902 and 1905 (Newnham and Harding, per Potts, 1906) and Stoke-on-Tern, 1976 to 1979 (Littlewood). At the latter locality, this form appears to predominate in one small pasture where the larvae feed on ragwort. Potts (1906) notes that in 1905 this species was very variable at Church Stretton. Newnham and Harding recorded forms ". . . from chrome yellow through orange and pale pink to the type."

FAMILY: NOLIDAE

2077 Short-cloaked Moth *Nola cucullatella* Linnaeus

V.C.H.: Calverhall, regular (Thornewill); Market Drayton district, frequent (Woodforde) and Church Stretton (larvae on blackthorn and hawthorn) (Newnham, 1901a).

Post V.C.H.: Widespread and fairly common in woodlands and along hedgerows.

Flight: June and July.

Larval F/ps: Blackthorn*, hawthorn*, apple and plumb. August to May.

2078 Least Black Arches *Celama confusalis* Herrich-Schäffer

V.C.H.: Two records only: 1899 and 1900. No localities cited. Not mentioned in the V.C.H. are Woodforde's record (Woodforde, 1900b and 1902b) of *C. confusalis* at Market Drayton where it was said to be numerous.

Post V.C.H.: Widespread but local and easily overlooked.

Flight: May and June. Woodlands, hedgerows and orchards.

Larval F/ps: Lichens growing on tree trunks. July and August.

FAMILY: NOCTUIDAE

2080 Square-spot Dart *Euxoa obelisca grisea* Tutt

V.C.H.: Church Stretton, in some numbers at light, flowers and sugar in 1896 (Newnham, 1897a).

Post V.C.H.: Unrecorded.

Flight: August and September, usually in coastal localities.

Larval F/ps: Unknown.

Notes: This coastal moth is so similar to *E. tritici* that Newnham's records from Church Stretton are probably attributable to that species. It is unlikely that *E. obelisca* should be found in such a locality. However, Newnham was surprised to find it at Church Stretton (Newnham, 1897a) as he realised that it is usually a coastal insect. This would suggest that he checked his identifications carefully. As the specimens can no longer be traced the mystery must remain unsolved.

2081 White-line Dart *Euxoa tritici* Linnaeus

V.C.H.: Market Drayton, scarce (Woodforde) and Wellington (Paddock).

Post V.C.H.: Recorded infrequently from heathlands throughout the county.

Flight: July and August.

Larval F/ps: Polyphagous on herbaceous plants. March to June.

2082 Garden Dart *Euxoa nigricans* Linnaeus

V.C.H.: Infrequent at Shrewsbury (Stainton, 1857. Vol. 1: 225–226), Broseley, Church Stretton and the Wyre Forest.

Post V.C.H.: Widespread but not common.

Flight: July and August. Wasteground, gardens, allotments etc.

Larval F/ps: Polyphagous. March to June.

2084 Light-feathered Rustic *Agrotis cinerea* Denis & Schiffermüller

V.C.H.: Occasional in the Wyre Forest.

Post V.C.H.: One unconfirmed record from Ironbridge, 1974 (Derry).

Flight: May and June. Limestone hillsides, quarries etc.

Larval F/p: Wild thyme. July to September.

2085 Archer's Dart *Agrotis vestigialis* Hufnagel

V.C.H.: Unrecorded.

Post V.C.H.: Two unconfirmed records from Rodington, 1956 (Briggs) and one from Quatford, 1960 (D'Arcy).

Flight: July to September. Usually regarded as a coastal species.

Larval F/ps: Polyphagous on grasses and low plants. September to May.

2087 Turnip Moth *Agrotis segetum* Denis & Schiffermüller

V.C.H.: Common throughout.

Post V.C.H.: Widespread, generally distributed and common.

Flight: May and June and August and September.

Larval F/ps: Polyphagous on most wild and cultivated herbaceous plants. October to April and July and August.

Notes: This species is occasionally regarded as an agricultural pest, commonly called a "Cutworm" because of the larva's habit of eating through the stem of the host plant at ground level and, in effect, felling it. The parasitoid *Ctenichneumon panzeri* Wesm. (Hymenoptera) was associated with this species by K.G.V. Smith (1952).

2088 Heart and Club *Agrotis clavis* Hufnagel

V.C.H.: Infrequent but generally distributed.

Post V.C.H.: Noted from Whixall Moss (Burrows, per Fielding, 1974a) and one unconfirmed record from Stoke-on-Tern, 1976 (Littlewood).

Flight: June and July on wasteground.

Larval F/ps: Polyphagous on herbaceous plants. August to November.

Notes: Reference to the species distribution map given by Heath (1983, p. 140) reveals many recent records from around Shropshire. Further investigation will probably show *A. clavis* to be more common in the county than currently known.

2089 Heart and Dart *Agrotis exclamationis* Linnaeus

V.C.H.: Abundant everywhere.

Post V.C.H.: Generally distributed and very common throughout.

Flight: May to July.

Larval F/ps: Polyphagous on many wild and cultivated herbaceous plants. July to October.

2091 Dark Sword-grass *Agrotis ipsilon* Hufnagel

V.C.H.: Scarce or uncommon throughout.

Post V.C.H.: Widespread and generally distributed though never common. Regularly found at ivy blossom in the autumn and sallow catkins in the spring.

Flight: As a migrant it can be found any time between March and November.

Larval F/ps: Polyphagous. Throughout the summer. Abroad it is occasionally a pest of wheat and cotton.

Notes: It is uncertain at the present time whether this species is actually resident in Shropshire. It is possible that all the available records are attributable to immigrant specimens.

2092 Shuttle-shaped Dart *Agrotis puta puta* Hübner

V.C.H.: Unrecorded.

Post V.C.H.: Found frequently throughout the county in gardens and wasteground etc.

Flight: April to October in two or three broods.

Larval F/ps: Polyphagous on wild and cultivated herbaceous plants. Possibly throughout the year.

Notes: Its absence from the V.C.H. list may, at first, seem surprising. However, Newman (1896) regarded it as quite a local species, restricted to southern England. It has since become more widespread in Britain, occurring as far north as Lancashire and Yorkshire.

2093 Sand Dart *Agrotis ripae* Hübner

Blatch (1886) records this species from the Wyre Forest but this was probably an erroneous identification as *A. ripae* is a coastal species.

2098 The Flame *Axylia putris* Linnaeus

V.C.H.: Shrewsbury (Stainton, 1857. Vol. 1: 198); Market Drayton, scarce (Woodforde) and Wyre Forest (Edwards).

Post V.C.H.: Widespread and fairly common throughout.

Flight: June and July with a partial second emergence in September in some years.

Larval F/ps: Polyphagous on low plants. Sometimes found on herbaceous plants in gardens. July to September.

Notes: Its apparent scarcity in Shropshire during the last century is surprising as it was fairly common at that time throughout England and Wales. (Newman, 1869).

2099 Portland Moth *Ochropleura praecox* Linnaeus

V.C.H.: Recorded by M. J. Harding at, or near, Shrewsbury (Stainton, 1857. Vol. 1: 227).

Post V.C.H.: One unconfirmed record from the pre-1974 Flintshire/Shropshire border, 1940 (G. Smith, per B.R.C., Monkswood).

Flight:	August and September. In inland localities it is found along fine shingle river banks.
Larval F/ps:	Sandhill-associated plants such as creeping willow and tree lupin. September to June.
Notes:	This species is mainly coastal in England with a few inland sites in Lincolnshire and Nottinghamshire. The Shropshire records were probably vagrants though it is interesting to note that there is a thriving naturalised colony of tree lupin (*Lupinus arboreus*) at a sand and gravel pit near Dorrington, approximately four miles south of Shrewsbury. Obviously this site should be thoroughly investigated. Creeping willow is now an endangered species in Shropshire and is restricted to three localities in the north of the county (Sinker *et al.*, 1985). *O. praecox* comes readily to light.

2102 Flame Shoulder *Ochropleura plecta* Linnaeus

V.C.H.:	Common everywhere.
Post V.C.H.:	Widespread, generally distributed and common.
Flight:	April to September in two protracted and overlapping broods.
Larval F/ps:	Polyphagous on herbaceous plants. Often found in gardens. June to October.

2103 Plain Clay *Eugnorisma depuncta* Linnaeus

V.C.H.:	Infrequently recorded at Church Stretton (Newnham, 1897a, 1901a and 1908).
Post V.C.H.:	One record from the pre-1974 Montgomery/Shropshire border, 1940 (G. Smith, per B.R.C., Monkswood).
Flight:	July to September on the edges of deciduous woodland.
Larval F/ps:	Polyphagous on herbaceous plants. September to May.
Notes:	Further investigations are required to ascertain the current status of this species in Shropshire. It is figured on Plate 11.

2104 Northern Rustic *Standfussiana lucernea* Linnaeus

V.C.H.:	Church Stretton, at the foot of the Devil's Chair, flying commonly over scree in the hot sunshine (Newnham, 1896).
Post V.C.H.:	One record from the Worcestershire/Shropshire border in 1940 (per B.R.C., Monkswood).
Flight:	June to September over mountain scree. Skinner (1984) states that the female may aestivate for part of the summer, shortly after mating.
Larval F/ps:	Polyphagous on grasses and herbaceous plants.
Notes:	In 1987 Riley made an unsuccessful search for this species at the site given in the V.C.H.. However the weather was unsuitable, being dull and very windy. The locality seems suitable and further investigations there are required. A specimen (not from Shropshire) is figured on Plate 11.

2105 Dotted Rustic *Rhyacia simulans* Hufnagel

V.C.H.:	Unrecorded.
Post V.C.H.:	Two records: Woore, 22.vii.1981 (Holdsworth) and Wenlock Edge, 1987 (Coleshaw).
Flight:	June and July and again from August to October with a period of aestivation in between. Often more common in urban areas where the adult can be found "roosting" during the day beneath piles of timber and bricks or in outhouses etc.

Larval F/ps: Unknown. September to Spring.

Notes: This species has been something of a rarity in the Midlands, being found mainly south of a line from the Severn estuary to the Wash. However, in recent years it has become more widespread and is now quite common in some of the northern counties of England.

2107 Large Yellow Underwing *Noctua pronuba* Linnaeus

V.C.H.:   Common everywhere.

Post V.C.H.:   Very common throughout. Generally distributed.

Flight: July to September.

Larval F/ps: Polyphagous. Often found in gardens on cultivated plants. September to April.

2108 Lunar Yellow Underwing *Noctua orbona* Hufnagel

V.C.H.:   A few on the Longmynd among heather.

Post V.C.H.:   Local and generally uncommon: Shrewsbury, 1913 (Pendlebury & Pendlebury, 1914); Oswestry, 1930 (Hignett, 1931); Quatford, 1960 (D'Arcy); Bromfield, 1952 & 1978 (Norton) and Church Stretton 1979 (Riley).

Flight: June, and again in August and September after aestivation. Mainly in sandstone areas.

Larval F/ps: Grasses and small herbaceous plants. September to April.

Notes: This species has declined in Britain over recent years. It is important, therefore, to establish its exact status in Shropshire. It can be easily confused with *N. comes* from which it differs in having a distinct black subapical dash similar to that in *N. pronuba*. The record for Shrewsbury, 1913 (Pendlebury & Pendlebury, 1914) may be erroneous as *N. comes*, which is the commoner species, does not appear on this list.

2109 Lesser Yellow Underwing *Noctua comes* Hübner

V.C.H.:   Common everywhere.

Post V.C.H.:   Widespread, generally distributed and very common.

Flight: July to September.

Larval F/ps: Polyphagous. Recorded in Shropshire on hawthorn and snowberry. September to April.

2110 Broad-bordered Yellow Underwing *Noctua fimbriata* Schreber

V.C.H.:   Calverhall, once; Market Drayton, common (Woodforde, 1900f); Church Stretton, infrequent, and the Wyre Forest.

Post V.C.H.:   Widespread and frequently recorded, mainly from wooded localities.

Flight: July to September, part of which is spent in aestivation.

Larval F/ps: Polyphagous. September to April.

2111 Lesser Broad-bordered Yellow Underwing *Noctua janthina* Denis & Schiffermüller

V.C.H.:   Calverhall, common (Thornewill); Market Drayton, scarce (Woodforde) and Church Stretton, infrequent.

Post V.C.H.:   Widespread, generally distributed and fairly common.

Flight: July to September.

Larval F/ps: Polyphagous. September to April.

2112 Least Yellow Underwing *Noctua interjecta caliginosa* Schawerda

V.C.H.: Scarce at Market Drayton, Church Stretton and Broseley. Also recorded from Shrewsbury (Stainton, 1857. Vol. 1: 230) and Wyre Forest (Blatch, 1886).

Post V.C.H.: Recorded mainly as singletons from Rodington, 1955 & 1962 (Briggs); the Wyre Forest, 1959 (Evans); Minsterley, 1960 and Pontesbury, 1972 (D. Smith); Wellington, 1974 and Dothill, 1976 (Riley); Dawley, 1975 (Jacques); Woore, 1981 (Holdsworth) and Preston Montford Field Centre, 1982 (R.I.S. trap, det. Riley) and Shirlett, 1982 (fairly common) (Whitney).

Flight: July and August on rough ground and wasteland.

Larval F/ps: Polyphagous on grasses and herbaceous plants. September to May.

2113 Stout Dart *Spaelotis ravida* Denis & Schiffermüller

V.C.H.: Occurs sparingly throughout the county.

Post V.C.H.: Rodington, 1954 & 1955 (Briggs) and Wilderhope, 1974 (White).

Flight: July to September, aestivating for part of this period.

Larval F/ps: Unknown. September to May. Will feed on dandelion and dock in captivity.

Notes: Sugaring may prove this species to be more widespread than the present records suggest as it is rarely common at light.

2114 Double Dart *Graphiphora augur* Fabricius

V.C.H.: Generally distributed. Fluctuates in numbers.

Post V.C.H.: Widespread in woodlands and on wasteground and scrubland. Fairly common.

Flight: June and July.

Larval F/ps: Hawthorn*, blackthorn*, birch, elm, dock and raspberry.

2117 Autumnal Rustic *Paradiarsia glareosa glareosa* Esper

V.C.H.: Recorded only from Market Drayton (Woodforde, 1894) and Church Stretton.

Post V.C.H.: Fairly common on moorland, heathland and woodland edges.

Flight: August and September.

Larval F/ps: Polyphagous. Newnham (1901a) cites oak. October to May.

Notes: Newnham (1901a) notes that some individuals from Church Stretton are suffused with pink.

2118 True-lover's Knot *Lycophotia porphyrea* Denis & Schiffermüller

V.C.H.: Common at Church Stretton, Market Drayton and Whixall Moss. Also recorded at Shrewsbury (Stainton, 1857. Vol. 1: 227).

Post V.C.H.: Common on heathland and moorland amongst heather.

Flight: June to August.

Larval F/ps: Heather*. August to May.

2119 Pearly Underwing *Peridroma saucia* Hübner

V.C.H.: Generally distributed but scarce. Often found near clover fields (Newnham, 1901a).

Post V.C.H.: A migrant species recorded most years, often at ivy blossom, though never common.

Flight: Usually found in the autumn but could occur during any month of the year.

Larval F/ps: Polyphagous on herbaceous plants. Smith (1952) noted larvae on heather at Church Stretton between 1948 and 1952. Most likely to be found during the summer. It cannot survive our winters.

2120 Ingrailed Clay *Diarsia mendica mendica* Fabricius

V.C.H.:   Common.

Post V.C.H.:   Very common throughout. Generally distributed.

Flight: June to August.

Larval F/ps: Polyphagous. September to April.

Notes: Newnham (1897a and 1901a) mentions a small brightly marked race associated with heather on the Longmynd. This was regarded at the time as *Noctua conflua* Newman (Lesser Ingrailed) (Newman, 1869). Newnham (1901a) states that f. *subrufa* Haw., in which the space between the stigmatica is the same colour as the rest of the forewing, was as common as the type at Church Stretton.

2121 Barred Chestnut *Diarsia dahlii* Hübner

V.C.H.:   Common at Market Drayton, 1900 (Woodforde, 1900f) and 1907 (Pendlebury, per Potts, 1908); Wyre Forest (Peed) and infrequent at Church Stretton (Newnham, 1897a).

Post V.C.H.:   Uncommon. Shrewsbury, 1913 (Pendlebury & Pendlebury, 1914) and 1922 (Pendlebury, per Ingrams, 1923); Market Drayton, 1940 (Anon.); Whixall Moss, 1972 (Rutherford); Wellington, 1978 (Riley); Shirlett, 1980 (Whitney) and the Wyre Forest, 1987 (Plant).

Flight: August and September on moorland and in deciduous woodland.

Larval F/ps: Many trees and plants including birch and bilberry. September to April.

2122 Purple Clay *Diarsia brunnea* Denis & Schiffermüller

V.C.H.:   Common at Broseley (Potts, per Cortissos, 1898), and Church Stretton and Market Drayton (Woodforde, 1900f).

Post V.C.H.:   Widespread and fairly common in deciduous woods.

Flight: June to August.

Larval F/ps: Polyphagous on deciduous trees and herbaceous plants. September to April.

2123 Small Square-spot *Diarsia rubi* Vieweg

V.C.H.:   Common.

Post V.C.H.:   Widespread, generally distributed and common.

Flight: May and June and again in August and September.

Larval F/ps: Polyphagous on herbaceous plants. September to July in two broods.

2126 Setaceous Hebrew Character *Xestia c-nigrum* Linnaeus

V.C.H.:   Common at Market Drayton, occasional at Calverhall and frequent at Church Stretton and Broseley.

Post V.C.H.:   Widespread, generally distributed and common.

Flight: May to early July and again from late August to October.

Larval F/ps: Polyphagous on herbaceous plants. September to April and June and July.

2127 Triple-spotted Clay *Xestia ditrapezium* Denis & Schiffermüller

V.C.H.: Unrecorded.

Post V.C.H.: Widespread but infrequently recorded. Regular from Preston Montford Field Centre (R.I.S. trap, det. Riley) and Whixall Moss and occasional in the Wyre Forest (Evans). Other records, mainly singletons, come from Minsterley, 1960 (D. Smith); Quatford, 1960 (D'Arcy); Pontesbury, 1979 (D. Smith); Woore, 1982 (Holdsworth) and Hopton Titterhill, 1982 (Hicks).

Flight: June to August in wooded localities.

Larval F/ps: Polyphagous. September to April.

2128 Double Square-spot *Xestia triangulum* Hufnagel

V.C.H.: Calverhall, infrequent (Thornewill); Market Drayton, frequent (Woodforde) and Church Stretton, at sugar, 1899 (Newnham).

Post V.C.H.: Widespread and fairly common in deciduous woodlands.

Flight: June and July.

Larval F/ps: Polyphagous. September to April.

2130 Dotted Clay *Xestia baja* Denis & Schiffermüller

V.C.H.: Generally common.

Post V.C.H.: Fairly common in woodlands and on heathlands throughout the county.

Flight: July and August.

Larval F/ps: Polyphagous. September to May.

2131 Square-spotted Clay *Xestia rhomboidea* Esper

V.C.H.: Frequent at thistle flowers in the Church Stretton area (Newnham, 1897a and 1901a).

Post V.C.H.: Local and uncommon. Recorded only from Llanforda, 8.vii.1931 (Hignett, 1932); Hopton Titterhill, 1982 (Hicks) and Pontesbury, 1982 (D. Smith).

Flight: August in deciduous woodlands.

Larval F/ps: Polyphagous on trees and herbaceous plants. September to May.

Notes: This species is regarded as very local nationally, occurring mainly in the south-eastern counties.

2132 Neglected Rustic *Xestia castanea* Esper

V.C.H.: The typical form is not uncommon at Market Drayton (Woodforde, 1900f) and on the Longmynd (Newnham, 1908). The greyish form *neglecta* Hübner predominating over the rest of the county.

Post V.C.H.: The only two known localities for this species at present are the Wyre Forest, where it is fairly common (Evans) and Rodington, 1958 (Briggs). It has not been looked for at Church Stretton since the publication of the V.C.H.

Flight: August and September on moorland and heathland. It is attracted to heather flowers.

Larval F/ps: Heather* and various species of heath. October to May.

Notes: Skinner (1984) mentions the occurrence of a rare yellowish form, ab. *xanthe* Woodforde, in Shropshire (see also Woodforde, 1900f and 1901a). Although the specimens, which are presently in the national collection at the British Museum (Natural History), are labelled "Market Drayton" they were actually caught in Staffordshire (Newnham, 1908) and not in Shropshire.

2133 Six-striped Rustic *Xestia sexstrigata* Haworth

V.C.H.: Common. Often found at thistle blossoms (Newnham, 1901a).

Post V.C.H.: Widespread and common. Often found at ragwort flowers in rough fields.

Flight: July and August.

Larval F/ps: Polyphagous on herbaceous plants. September to April.

2134 Square-spot Rustic *Xestia xanthographa* Denis & Schiffermüller

V.C.H.: Common throughout.

Post V.C.H.: Generally distributed and very common throughout.

Flight: July to September.

Larval F/ps: Polyphagous on grasses and herbaceous plants. September to April.

Notes: The uniformally grey form *cohaesa* H.-S. is found occasionally throughout the county. Larvae feeding on a lawn at Much Wenlock in February and March 1950 and 1951 are recorded as being heavily parasitized by *Apanteles fulvipes* Haliday (Hymenoptera) and *Wagneria lentis* Meigen (Diptera) (K. G. V. Smith, 1952). The latter was noted as being a new parasite-host record.

2135 Heath Rustic *Xestia agathina agathina* Duponchel

V.C.H.: Unrecorded.

Post V.C.H.: A very local species. Recorded only from Quatford, 1960 (D'Arcy) and Whixall Moss, 1977 where it was stated to be not uncommon (Hull).

Flight: September on heathland and moorland.

Larval F/p: Heather. October to May.

Notes: This species may have been overlooked on some of the large tracts of moorland around Church Stretton.

2136 The Gothic *Naenia typica* Linnaeus

V.C.H.: Frequent at Market Drayton (Woodforde) and Church Stretton. Apparently absent elsewhere.

Post V.C.H.: Widespread and fairly common. Often found in gardens.

Flight: June and July.

Larval F/ps: Polyphagous. August to March.

2137 Great Brocade *Eurois occulta* Linnaeus

V.C.H.: One at sugar, 6.vii.1899, Church Stretton.

Post V.C.H.: One at Pontesbury, 1977 (D. Smith). A rare immigrant.

Flight: Usually recorded during July and August.

Larval F/p: Bog myrtle. September to May. This species is only established as a British resident in the Scottish Highlands.

2138 Green Arches *Anaplectoides prasina* Denis & Schiffermüller

V.C.H.: Occasional at Church Stretton and the Wyre Forest.

Post V.C.H.: Restricted to deciduous woodland but not uncommon where it occurs.

Flight: June and July.

Larval F/ps: Honeysuckle, bilberry, sallow and various other plants. August to April.

Notes: A melanic form, ab. *demuthi* Richardson, occurs at Cannock Chase in neighbouring Staffordshire but this has not, to my knowledge, been recorded in Shropshire.

2139 Red Chestnut *Cerastis rubricosa* Denis & Schiffermüller

V.C.H.: Frequent or common throughout.

Post V.C.H.: Apparently absent from the south-west but otherwise widespread and often common, especially in woodlands.

Flight: March and April. Found commonly at Sallow catkins.

Larval F/ps: Polyphagous on herbaceous plants. May and June.

2140 White-marked *Cerastis leucographa* Denis & Schiffermüller

V.C.H.: Wyre Forest, 1902 (Rea, per Potts, 1903; Newnham, 1908) and once at sallow bloom at Church Stretton (Newnham, 1901a and 1908).

Post V.C.H.: Broseley, 1969 (Whitney); Bucknell, 1971 (Shephard, det. Riley); Shirlett, 1977, not uncommon (Whitney); Pontesbury, 1987, common (D. Smith) and Ludlow, 1.v.1989 (one) (R.I.S. trap, det. Riley).

Flight: March and April in open woodland.

Larval F/ps: Unknown in the wild but it feeds readily on many herbaceous plants in captivity (Skinner, 1984). May and June.

Notes: This species may be more widespread than presently known as it is easily mistaken for *C. rubricosa* (the Bucknell specimen was placed under *C. rubricosa* in the Shephard collection and it was not until later examination that it was discovered to be *C. leucographa*). Like *C. rubricosa* it is fond of sallow catkins. Great care should be taken when recording.

2142 Beautiful Yellow Underwing *Anarta myrtilli* Linnaeus

V.C.H.: Found wherever there are large tracts of heather. Very common on the Longmynd. Larvae often found feeding openly on heather (Newnham, 1901a).

Post V.C.H.: Still common on most heather-clad moorlands, heathlands and mosses.

Flight: Diurnal, flying in the hot sunshine in two overlapping broods. April to August.

Larval F/ps: Heather*. July to October.

2145 The Nutmeg *Dicestra trifolii* Hufnagel

V.C.H.: Recorded only once from Church Stretton.

Post V.C.H.: Locally common. Gardens, allotments, wasteground etc.

Flight: June and July.

Larval F/ps: Mainly goosefoot* and orache. July and August.

2147 The Shears *Hada nana* Hufnagel

V.C.H.: Generally distributed and common.

Post V.C.H.: Widely distributed but not common.

Flight: May to July on rough ground, wasteland etc.

Larval F/ps: Hawk's-beard, hawkweed, dandelion, knotgrass and chickweed. July and August.

2148 Pale Shining Brown *Polia bombycina* Hufnagel

V.C.H.: Wyre Forest (Edwards).

Post V.C.H.: Longmynd, 1952 (Bretherton).

Flight: June and July on downland and moorland. Probably restricted to limestone areas.

Larval F/ps: Unknown in the wild but takes dock, dandelion and sliced carrot in captivity (Skinner, 1984). August and September (Newman & Leeds, 1913).

2149 Silvery Arches *Polia trimaculosa* Esper

V.C.H.:   Recorded only from the Wyre Forest by Blatch (1886) and in 1898, 1899 and 1902 (Rea) and Woodforde (1902c). Woodforde (1900e) noted that this species was the most numerous at sugar at Market Drayton on 20.vi.1900. Another specimen was taken in Market Drayton in 1901 by J.C. Lavin, which is now in the Keighley Museum collection.

Post V.C.H.:   Fairly common in the Wyre Forest (Evans). The only other recorded specimens are from Rednall, 1933 (Hignett, per Pendlebury, 1950); the pre-1974 Shropshire/Flintshire border, 1949 (G. Smith, per B.R.C., Monkswood); Wem Moss, 7.vii.1963 (Warren); Whixall Moss, 1970 (Hull) and 1972 (Rutherford) and Pontesbury (one) 1987 (D. Smith).

Flight: June and July. Woodland and heathland.

Larval F/ps: Mainly birch but also bog myrtle, sallow and hawthorn. September to May.

2150 Grey Arches *Polia nebulosa* Hufnagel

V.C.H.:   Generally distributed and frequent.

Post V.C.H.:   Locally quite common, particularly in woodlands.

Flight: June and July.

Larval F/ps: Polyphagous. August to May.

2152 White Colon *Sideridis albicolon* Hübner

V.C.H.:   One specimen taken by Newnham at the foot of Ragleth Hill, Church Stretton, around 1898 (Newnham, 1908).

Post V.C.H.:   Unrecorded.

Flight: May and June, its inland habitat being heathland.

Larval F/ps: Polyphagous. July.

Notes: This is an interesting record as *S. albicolon* is most often found on coastal sandhills. Further investigation is required to establish its status in Shropshire. It is possible that Newnham mistook his identification as this species is superficially very similar to *Mamestra brassicae*, *Apamea remissa*, *A. furva* and *Dicestra trifolii*.

2153 Bordered Gothic *Heliophobus reticulata marginosa* Haworth

V.C.H.:   One specimen at Church Stretton (Newnham, 1901a and 1908) and a few at sugar in the Wyre Forest, 1902 (Woodforde, 1902c).

Post V.C.H.:   Three unconfirmed records: Shrewsbury, 1913 (Pendlebury & Pendlebury, 1914); Wood-Taylor (1941) and Rodington, 1956 (Briggs).

Flight: June and July on rough ground and downland.

Larval F/ps: Unknown. In captivity it accepts knotgrass and soapwort (Skinner, 1984). July to September.

Notes: This is a very localised and scarce species in the midlands. It is interesting to note that a specimen was recorded at Burnt Wood in 1940 by Warren. This is near Market Drayton but just over the county boundary into Staffordshire.

2154 Cabbage Moth *Mamestra brassicae* Linnaeus

V.C.H.:   Common throughout.

Post V.C.H.:   Widespread, generally distributed and common.

Flight: May to October in three broods.

Larval F/ps: Polyphagous. Found in gardens on many species of herbaceous plant throughout the summer. K. G. V. Smith (1952) stated that this species was often a pest on cabbage.

2155 Dot Moth *Melanchra persicariae* Linnaeus

V.C.H.: Calverhall, two larvae, 1899 (Thornewill); Market Drayton, scarce (Woodforde) and Church Stretton, very scarce.

Post V.C.H.: Widespread, generally distributed and fairly common.

Flight: July and August.

Larval F/ps: Polyphagous. August to October.

2156 Beautiful Brocade *Lacanobia contigua* Denis & Schiffermüller

V.C.H.: Wyre Forest (Rea; Woodforde, 1902c) and Church Stretton where it was uncommon. Woodforde (1900f) cites finding over 70 larvae in two days at Market Drayton though no precise date or foodplant is given.

Post V.C.H.: This species is still found frequently in the Wyre Forest. There are other records from Shrewsbury, 5.vi.1914 (Pendlebury, 1915); Oswestry, 1948 (Hignett, per Pendlebury, 1950); Rodington, 1954 (Briggs) and Pontesbury, 1980 (D. Smith).

Flight: June and July. Woodland, heathland and moorland.

Larval F/ps: Polyphagous. August and September.

Notes: This local species may have been overlooked as it bears a superficial resemblance to *L. thalassina* and *Apamea remissa*.

2157 Light Brocade *Lacanobia w-latinum* Hufnagel

V.C.H.: Common at sugar at Church Stretton. Also recorded from Broseley, 1899 (Potts, per Cortissos, 1900) and the Wyre Forest, 1902 (Rea, per Pendlebury, 1950; Woodforde, 1902c).

Post V.C.H.: A very local and uncommon species. Recorded from Shrewsbury, 1913 (Pendlebury & Pendlebury, 1914); Oswestry, "an old record" (Hignett, 1931); Rodington, 1954 (Briggs); Quatford, 1960 (D'Arcy); Ironbridge, 1961 (Derry & Whitney); Pontesbury, 1970 (D. Smith); Bucknell, 1972 (Shephard); Shirlett, 1980 (Whitney) and Button Oak, Wyre, 1986 (Blunt).

Flight: May to July, mainly in calcareous areas.

Larval F/ps: Polyphagous. July and August.

Notes: This species is known to be very local and generally uncommon in the West Midlands and Wales (Skinner, 1984). Newnham (1901) explains that a good method of finding the adult is to part the grass at the bases of posts, etc, where the moth often hides during the day. He notes that on 13.vi.1898 he found six within an hour and a half using this technique whereas previously he had considered this species to be something of a rarity.

2158 Pale-shouldered Brocade *Lacanobia thalassina* Hufnagel

V.C.H.: Apparently frequent throughout.

Post V.C.H.: Widespread and common, particularly in wooded districts.

Flight: May to July. The partial second generation said to occur occasionally in southern England has not been recorded in Shropshire.

Larval F/ps: Polyphagous. July to September.

2159 Dog's Tooth *Lacanobia suasa* Denis & Schiffermüller

V.C.H.:	Shrewsbury (Stainton, 1857. Vol. 1: 276); Wyre Forest (Edwards) and Calverhall, 1895, at rhododendron flowers, but rare since.
Post V.C.H.:	Two records only: the pre-1974 Shropshire/Flintshire border in 1940 (G. Smith, per B.R.C., Monkswood) and Oswestry, 1948 (Hignett, per Pendlebury, 1950).
Flight:	Northern England, June and July; southern England May to early July and late July to early September (Skinner, 1984). The precise flight period in Shropshire is not known. It inhabits wasteground and moorland.
Larval F/ps:	Polyphagous on herbaceous plants. June to September or early October.

2160 Bright-line Brown-eye *Lacanobia oleracea* Linnaeus

V.C.H.:	Generally distributed and common.
Post V.C.H.:	Common throughout in most habitats.
Flight:	May to July.
Larval F/ps:	Polyphagous. Recorded on snowberry in Wellington, 1978 (Riley). June to September.

2162 Glaucous Shears *Papestra biren* Goeze

V.C.H.:	Shrewsbury (Stainton, 1857. Vol. 1: 275) and Church Stretton, where the larvae were occasionally found on heather (Newnham, 1901a).
Post V.C.H.:	Abundant at Ashes Hollow and Polebank, Longmynd, in May 1990 (Riley). Also recorded from Shirlett, 1977 (Whitney).
Flight:	May and June on moorland.
Larval F/ps:	Polyphagous, including heather*. July and August.
Notes:	This species is locally common in Wales and the Midlands. It has probably been overlooked in Shropshire.

2163 Broom Moth *Ceramica pisi* Linnaeus

V.C.H.:	Generally distributed and common. Larvae are particularly common on bracken around Church Stretton (Newnham, 1901).
Post V.C.H.:	Widespread and fairly common throughout.
Flight:	May to July.
Larval F/ps:	Polyphagous including bracken* and thistle* (Riley). July to September.
Notes:	Ab. *splendens* Staudinger has been recorded once from Dothill in 1976 (Riley).

2164 Broad-barred White *Hecatera bicolorata* Hufnagel

V.C.H.:	Shrewsbury (Stainton, 1857. Vol. 1: 263-264); Wyre Forest (Blatch, 1886), and Church Stretton, common.
Post V.C.H.:	Locally common on wasteground and, occasionally, heathland.
Flight:	June to August.
Larval F/ps:	Possibly many herbaceous plants but mainly hawkweed and hawk's-beard. August and September.

2166 Campion *Hadena rivularis* Fabricius

V.C.H.:	Frequent at Church Stretton flying over *Lychnis* species, pinks etc. (Newnham, 1901a). Also Broseley, 1899 (Potts).

Post V.C.H.: Widely distributed but local and rather uncommon. Recorded from Shrewsbury, 1913 (Pendlebury & Pendlebury, 1914); Oswestry, 1948 (Hignett, per Pendlebury, 1950); Rodington, 1954 (Briggs); Wyre, 1960 (Scott); Quatford, 1960 (D'Arcy); Pennerley, 1970 (Poynton); Willey, 1970 (Whitney); Ironbridge, 1974 (Derry); Pontesbury, 1975 and Minsterley, 1982 (D. Smith).

Flight: May and June in damp localities.

Larval F/ps: Various species of campion and catchfly. Ragged robin is said to be the favoured inland foodplant (Heath, 1979) and Hignett recorded *H. rivularis* on this plant at Oswestry, 1948 (per Pendlebury, 1950). July to September.

2167 Tawny Shears *Hadena perplexa perplexa* Denis & Schiffermüller

V.C.H.: Occasional at Church Stretton flying over blossoms of honeysuckle and rhododendron (Newnham, 1901a).

Post V.C.H.: Local and uncommon. Recorded only from Kingsland, July 1922 (Ingrams, 1923); Oswestry, 1930 (Hignett, 1931) and Quatford, 1960 (D'Arcy).

Flight: May and June and again in August. Usually associated with calcareous soils.

Larval F/ps: Various species of campion and catchfly. July and August.

2171 Marbled Coronet *Hadena confusa* Hufnagel

V.C.H.: Recorded by Woodforde as scarce at Market Drayton.

Post V.C.H.: Unrecorded.

Flight: May to early July. Usually associated with calcareous soils.

Larval F/ps: Various species of campion. July and August.

2173 Lychnis *Hadena bicruris* Hufnagel

V.C.H.: Generally distributed and frequent.

Post V.C.H.: Widespread and fairly common wherever the foodplants occur.

Flight: May to September in two broods.

Larval F/ps: Various species of campion and catchfly with an apparent preference for red campion and sweet William (Heath, 1979).

2176 Antler Moth *Cerapteryx graminis* Linnaeus

V.C.H.: Common at Calverhall (Thornewill) and Church Stretton.

Post V.C.H.: Common on moorland, heathland and mosses.

Flight: July to September.

Larval F/ps: Various grasses. March to June.

2177 Hedge Rustic *Tholera cespitis* Denis & Schiffermüller

V.C.H.: Generally distributed but uncommon, though frequent at Church Stretton (Newnham, 1897a and 1901a) and Market Drayton (Woodforde, 1900c).

Post V.C.H.: Widespread and frequent on rough grassland.

Flight: August and September.

Larval F/ps: Various grasses, particularly annual meadow grass (Newnham, 1897a).

2178 Feathered Gothic *Tholera decimalis* Poda

V.C.H.: Shrewsbury (Stainton, 1857. Vol. 1: 203-204); Calverhall, common (Thornewill); Market Drayton, common (Woodforde) and Church Stretton, frequent.

Post V.C.H.: Fairly common throughout the county in rough grassy places.

Flight: August and September.

Larval F/ps: Polyphagous on grasses. March to July.

2179 Pine Beauty *Panolis flammea* Denis & Schiffermüller

V.C.H.: Twemlows (Thornewill) and Church Stretton, in all fir plantations.

Post V.C.H.: Usually common in pine plantations throughout the county.

Flight: March to May.

Larval F/p: Scots pine*. June and July.

2182 Small Quaker *Orthosia cruda* Denis & Schiffermüller

V.C.H.: Common throughout.

Post V.C.H.: Very common throughout. Often abundant at sallow catkins in the Spring.

Flight: March and April, usually in woodlands.

Larval F/ps: Many trees including sallow*. May and June.

2183 Blossom Underwing *Orthosia miniosa* Denis & Schiffermüller

V.C.H.: One at Church Stretton in 1897. Also recorded from the Wyre Forest (Edwards).

Post V.C.H.: Apart from the Wyre Forest, where it is fairly common (Evans), this local species has only been recorded from Quatford, 1960 (D'Arcy) and Preston Montford Field Centre, 1984 (R.I.S. trap, det. Riley).

Flight: March and April in oak woods.

Larval F/p: Oak. May and June.

2184 Northern Drab *Orthosia opima* Hübner

V.C.H.: Wyre Forest (Abbott) and Church Stretton, a few at sallows.

Post V.C.H.: Only presently known from the Wyre Forest, where it is frequent (Evans).

Flight: April and May in many habitats, including heathland and wasteground.

Larval F/ps: Polyphagous. May and June.

2185 Lead-coloured Drab *Orthosia populeti* Fabricius

V.C.H.: Shrewsbury (Stainton, 1857. Vol. 1: 243) and Church Stretton, a few at sallows.

Post V.C.H.: Apart from Preston Montford Field Centre, where it is regularly recorded at the R.I.S. trap (det. Riley), this species appears to be uncommon. Other records are from Shrewsbury, 1913 (Pendlebury & Pendlebury, 1914); Wyre Forest, 1970 (Scott); Broseley, 1971 (Whitney); Stoke-on-Tern, 1978 (R.I.S. trap, det. Riley); Woore, 1979 (Holdsworth) and Shirlett, 1982 (Whitney).

Flight: March and April in the vicinity of aspens.

Larval F/p: Aspen. May and June.

2186 Powdered Quaker *Orthosia gracilis* Denis & Schiffermüller

V.C.H.: Calverhall, occasional (Thornewill); Market Drayton, frequent (Woodforde) and Wyre Forest.

Post V.C.H.: Generally distributed and recorded frequently from throughout the county.

Flight: April and May.

Larval F/ps: Polyphagous, including sallow* and birch*. June and July.

2187 Common Quaker *Orthosia cerasi* Fabricius

V.C.H.: Common throughout.

Post V.C.H.: Widespread, generally distributed and very common.

Flight: March and April. Often abundant at sallow catkins.

Larval F/ps: Polyphagous on trees such as birch*, oak* and hazel*. May and June.

2188 Clouded Drab *Orthosia incerta* Hufnagel

V.C.H.: Common throughout.

Post V.C.H.: Widespread, generally distributed and common.

Flight: March to May. Often common at sallow catkins.

Larval F/ps: Polyphagous on trees including birch*. May and June.

2189 Twin-spotted Quaker *Orthosia munda* Denis & Schiffermüller

V.C.H.: Fairly common throughout.

Post V.C.H.: Common in woodlands throughout the county.

Flight: March and April. Often common at sallow catkins.

Larval F/ps: Polyphagous on trees. Recorded in Shropshire on birch. May and June.

Notes: Newnham (1901a) reared a specimen of ab. *immaculata* Staudinger, in 1893, in which the black spots of the forewings were absent.

2190 Hebrew Character *Orthosia gothica* Linnaeus

V.C.H.: Common throughout.

Post V.C.H.: Very common throughout the county. Generally distributed.

Flight: March and April. Often abundant at sallow catkins.

Larval F/ps: Polyphagous, including hawthorn* and blackthorn*. May and June.

2191 Double-line *Mythimna turca* Linnaeus

V.C.H.: Unrecorded.

Post V.C.H.: Recorded only from Bucknell, 1971 (Shephard). Specimens in Ludlow Museum collection.

Flight: June and July in woodland.

Larval F/ps: Various grasses. August to May.

2192 Brown-line Bright-eye *Mythimna conigera* Denis & Schiffermüller

V.C.H.: Common at Church Stretton. Apparently absent elsewhere.

Post V.C.H.: Widespread, generally distributed and common.

Flight: June to August. Often attracted to lime blossoms (Newnham, 1901a).

Larval F/ps: Grasses. September to April.

2193 Clay Wainscot *Mythimna ferrago* Fabricius

V.C.H.: Common.

Post V.C.H.: Common throughout in most habitats.

Flight: July and August.

Larval F/ps: Polyphagous, mainly on grasses. September to May.

2195 Delicate Wainscot *Mythimna vitellina* Hübner

V.C.H.: Unrecorded.

Post V.C.H.: This immigrant species has only been recorded once, at Pontesbury in 1977 (D. Smith).

Flight: Can occur at any time between May and November with the peak in September.

Larval F/ps: Continuously brooded on grasses. Unrecorded as a larva in Shropshire.

2196 Striped Wainscot *Mythimna pudorina* Denis & Schiffermüller

V.C.H.: Unrecorded.

Post V.C.H.: A very local and generally uncommon species. Recorded only from Rodington, 1954 and 1955 (Briggs); Bucknell, 1971 (Shephard, three specimens in Ludlow Museum Collection, det. Riley) and Rowton, 1977 (R.I.S. trap, det. Littlewood).

Flight: June and July in marshes and damp areas of heathland.

Larval F/ps: Common reed and various grasses. August to May.

2197 Southern Wainscot *Mythimna straminea* Treitschke

V.C.H.: Unrecorded.

Post V.C.H.: A rare species in Shropshire which has only been recorded once from Wem Moss in 1968 (Heath).

Flight: July and August in wet localities such as marshes and roadside ditches.

Larval F/ps: Common reed and canary-grass. September to May.

2198 Smoky Wainscot *Mythimna impura impura* Hübner

V.C.H.: Common flying in damp meadows.

Post V.C.H.: Very common throughout in most habitats.

Flight: June to October in two broods.

Larval F/ps: Polyphagous on grasses. September to May.

2199 Common Wainscot *Mythimna pallens* Linnaeus

V.C.H.: Generally abundant, flying in damp meadows.

Post V.C.H.: Very common throughout. Generally distributed.

Flight: From the data collected at R.I.S. traps it appears that *M. pallens* is bivoltine in Shropshire. Adults fly in two overlapping broods between mid-June and early October.

Larval F/ps: Polyphagous on grasses. September to May.

Notes: Newnham (1901a) states that ab. *ectypa* Boisduval, which has reddish ochreous forewings, was found occasionally at Church Stretton.

2205 Shoulder-striped Wainscot *Mythimna comma* Linnaeus

V.C.H.: Common.

Post V.C.H.: Fairly common throughout in gardens.

Flight: June and July. Sometimes attracted to rhododendron blossoms (Newnham, 1901a).

Larval F/ps: Various grasses. August and September.

2211 Wormwood Shark *Cucullia absinthii* Linnaeus
V.C.H.:   Unrecorded.
Post V.C.H.: Recorded only once at Donnington in 1949 (Christie, 1952).
Flight: July on wasteground, spoil heaps and quarries.
Larval F/ps: Wormwood and mugwort. August and September.

2214 Chamomile Shark *Cucullia chamomillae* Denis & Schiffermüller
V.C.H.:   Common at Market Drayton (Woodforde, 1900).
Post V.C.H.: Widespread in the north-eastern half of the county though never common.
Flight: April to June on wasteground, roadsides, waysides and field margins.
Larval F/ps: Mayweeds* and chamomile. June and early July.

2216 The Shark *Cucullia umbratica* Linnaeus
V.C.H.:   Generally common. Larvae often found around Church Stretton on sow thistles and cultivated lettuce (Newnham, 1901a).
Post V.C.H.: Widespread but never common.
Flight: June and July, mainly on wasteground and in gardens.
Larval F/ps: Smooth sow-thistle*, perennial sow-thistle* and lettuce*. July to September.

2221 The Mullein *Cucullia verbasci* Linnaeus
V.C.H.:   Recorded from the Wyre Forest (Blatch, 1886). Larvae common at Church Stretton on mullein, feeding openly during the day (Newnham, 1901a). Larvae also found at Benthall, 1904 (Potts, 1905).
Post V.C.H.: Widespread and locally common in gardens and wasteground.
Flight: April and May.
Larval F/ps: Mullein*, figworts* and occasionally *Buddleia* species*. June and July.

2225 Minor Shoulder-knot *Brachylomia viminalis* Fabricius
V.C.H.:   Generally distributed. Larvae often found on sallow and poplar around Church Stretton (Newnham, 1901a).
Post V.C.H.: Fairly frequently recorded from woodlands and damp localities in the north and east of the county.
Flight: July and August.
Larval F/ps: Poplar*, sallow* and willow. April to June.
Notes: The darker forms approaching ab. *obscura* Staudinger are prevalent in Shropshire. Newnham (1901a) recorded this form occasionally.

2227 The Sprawler *Brachionycha sphinx* Hufnagel
V.C.H.:   Shrewsbury (Stainton, 1857. Vol. 1: 125–126) and Botyville (larvae on elm), 23.vi.1902 (Newnham).
Post V.C.H.: Widespread and fairly common in woodlands throughout the county.
Flight: November and early December.
Larval F/ps: Polyphagous on various trees including elm*. May and June.

2231 Deep-brown Dart *Aporophyla lutulenta* Denis & Schiffermüller
V.C.H.:   Recorded only from the Wyre Forest by Dobré-Fox in 1898.
Post V.C.H.: Very local and uncommon: Donnington, one at sugar, 1948 (Christie); Wyre Forest, three in 1961 (Evans); Ironbridge, 1974 (Derry) and the Ercall Woods, one at light in 1978 (Riley).

| Flight: | September and October. Wasteland, rough ground and woodland edges and clearings. |
| Larval F/ps: | Polyphagous, mainly on grasses but also hawthorn* and blackthorn. October to June. |

2232 Black Rustic *Aporophyla nigra* Haworth

V.C.H.:	Unrecorded.
Post V.C.H.:	Very local and uncommon. Recorded from Wyre Forest, one in 1961 (Evans); Pontesbury, 1973 (D. Smith) and Preston Montford Field Centre, 1984 (one), 1987 (one) and 1988 (one) (R.I.S. trap, det. Riley).
Flight:	September and October. Heathland, wasteland and rough ground.
Larval F/ps:	Polyphagous on low-growing plants including grasses. October to May.

2233 Goldenrod Brindle *Lithomoia solidaginis* Hübner

V.C.H.:	Occasional at Church Stretton (Newnham 1896, 1897a and 1901a).
Post V.C.H.:	A scarce species in Shropshire. Recorded from Ardmillan, "an old record" (Hignett, 1931); Church Stretton, 2.ix.1951 (K. G. V. Smith, 1952); Minsterley, 1960 (D. Smith); Quatford, 1960 (D'Arcy) and Pontesbury, 1971 and 1973 (D. Smith).
Flight:	August and September on moorland and open woodland.
Larval F/ps:	Polyphagous on moorland plants. April to July. Newnham (1901a) stated that he found larvae on bilberry on the Longmynd and hawthorn in the valleys around Church Stretton.

2235 Tawny Pinion *Lithophane semibrunnea* Haworth

V.C.H.:	Unrecorded.
Post V.C.H.:	Local and uncommon: Shrewsbury, 1948 (Tanner); Llynclys, 1948 (Hignett, per Pendlebury, 1950); Shirlett, 1977 (Whitney); Ercall Woods; 1978 (Riley); Woore, 1979 (Holdsworth); Preston Montford Field Centre, 1980 and 1983 (R.I.S. trap, det. Riley) and Pontesbury, 1987 (D. Smith).
Flight:	October, November and, after hibernation, from March to May, inhabiting open woodland. Sometimes attracted to sallow catkins.
Larval F/p:	Ash. May to July.

2236 Pale Pinion *Lithophane hepatica* Clerck

V.C.H.:	Recorded only from the Wyre Forest (Peed).
Post V.C.H.:	Very scarce in Shropshire. Recorded only from the Wyre Forest, four specimens at sugar in 1959 (Evans) and Quatford, 1960 (D'Arcy).
Flight:	October, November and, after hibernation, from March to May, in woodlands. Sometimes attracted to sallow catkins.
Larval F/ps:	Various trees and shrubs including sallow. May to July.

2237 Grey Shoulder-knot *Lithophane ornitopus lactipennis* Dadd

| V.C.H.: | Frequent at Church Stretton and also recorded from Shrewsbury (Stainton, 1857. Vol. 1: 283; Potts, 1908). |
| Post V.C.H.: | Not uncommon in the Wyre Forest (Evans) and the Ercall Woods (Riley). There are other records from Aston, 12.v.1931 (Hignett, 1932); Pontesbury, 1973 (D. Smith); Shirlett, 1977 (common) (Whitney) and Bromfield, 1940 and 1978 (Norton). |

Flight:	September, October and, after hibernation, from February to April. Principally a woodland species which is often found at the flowers of ivy and sallow.
Larval F/p:	Oak*. April to June.

2240 Blair's Shoulder-knot *Lithophane leautieri hesperica* Boursin

V.C.H.:	Unrecorded.
Post V.C.H.:	One male at Ludlow, 27.x.1990 (R.I.S. trap, det. Riley).
Flight:	October and November in the vicinity of the foodplant. Often found in gardens.
Larval F/ps:	Monterey cypress and possibly other cypress cultivars.

2241 Red Sword-grass *Xylena vetusta* Hübner

V.C.H.:	Not rare in damp marshy localties around Church Stretton. Also recorded at Shrewsbury (Stainton, 1857. Vol. 1: 282) and Benthall, 1902 (Potts, 1903).
Post V.C.H.:	Local and uncommon. Recorded from Meole Brace, 1929 (Henstock); Sweeney, 22.x.1929 at ivy (Hignett, 1931); Culmington, 1967 (Coates) and Ironbridge, 1979 (Whitney).
Flight:	September, October and, after hibernation, in March and April. It inhabits high moorland and damp localties. It is attracted to the flowers of ivy and sallow.
Larval F/ps:	Polyphagous on low plants and various deciduous trees and shrubs including dock* and various *Scabiosa** (Newnham, 1908). May to July.

2242 Sword-grass *Xylena exsoleta* Linnaeus

V.C.H.:	Shrewsbury (Stainton, 1857. Vol. 1: 282); Church Stretton, fairly common at sugar; Broseley, 1898 (Potts, per Cortissos, 1899); Calverhall, one at sugar, 1900 and one at sallow blossom 10.iv.1908 (Thornewill, per Potts, 1909); Market Drayton (Woodforde, 1900f) and Caynton.
Post V.C.H.:	A very uncommon species which has been recorded only sporadically prior to 1978 and not at all since: Wellington, at plum blossom 7.iv.1914 (Pendlebury, 1915); Sweeney, 17.x.1929 and 1930, at ivy (Hignett, 1931); Chetwynd, 1949 (Christie); Bucknell, 1970 (Shephard); Craven Arms, 1973 (Feeste) and Bromfield, 1978 (Norton).
Flight:	September, October and, after hibernation, in March and April. Regularly visits ivy and sallow blossoms on moorland and in open woodland.
Larval F/ps:	Polyphagous on low plants. May to July.
Notes:	*X. exsoleta* has dramatically declined in England and Wales since the turn of the century. This is reflected in the paucity of recent Shropshire records. A specimen (not from Shropshire) is figured on Plate 11.

2243 Early Grey *Xylocampa areola* Esper

V.C.H.:	Shrewsbury (Stainton, 1857. Vol. 1: 280); frequent at Church Stretton around honeysuckle on which the larvae were often found (Newnham, 1901a); common at Market Drayton and once at Cloverley Park, Calverhall.
Post V.C.H.:	Widespread and often common in woodlands, gardens and on rough ground throughout the county.
Flight:	March to May.
Larval F/p:	Honeysuckle*. April to early June.

2245 Green Brindled Crescent *Allophyes oxyacanthae* Linnaeus
V.C.H.: Both the type and the melanic ab. *capaucina* Milliere were common throughout.

Post V.C.H.: Both forms are common throughout the county. Woodlands, hedgerows and scrubland.

Flight: September to November. Often common at ivy blossom.

Larval F/ps: Hawthorn* and blackthorn*. April to June.

2247 Merveille du Jour *Dichonia aprilina* Linnaeus
V.C.H.: Common throughout.

Post V.C.H.: Widespread and often common in woodlands containing oak.

Flight: September and October.

Larval F/p: Oak*. April to June. Newnham (1908) records finding a larva on elm a long way from any oak. Easily found by searching crevices in oak bark during May and early June.

2248 Brindled Green *Dryobotodes eremita* Fabricius
V.C.H.: Generally distributed and common.

Post V.C.H.: Widespread and fairly common in woodlands containing oak.

Flight: August and September.

Larval F/ps: Oak* and hawthorn. April to June.

2250 Dark Brocade *Blepharita adusta* Esper
V.C.H.: Market Drayton, abundant in 1893 (Woodforde, 1894); Calverhall, at Rhododendron flowers and sugar and Church Stretton at light and sugar.

Post V.C.H.: Widespread but local. Recorded from Shrewsbury, 1914 (Pendlebury, 1915); Llynclys, 1949 (Asterley, per Pendlebury, 1950); Longmynd, 1952 (Bretherton); Broseley, 1969 (Whitney); Pennerley, 1970 (Poynton); Shirlett, 1977 (Whitney); Pontesbury, 1978 (D. Smith); Woore, 1979 (Holdsworth) and Wellington, 1979 (Riley).

Flight: June and July, mainly on heathland and moorland.

Larval F/ps: Polyphagous on grasses and low plants. July to September.

2252 Large Ranuculus *Polymixis flavicincta* Denis & Schiffermüller
V.C.H.: Unrecorded.

Post V.C.H.: There are only two old records for this species: Meole Brace, 3.ix.1921 (Henstock); and Chetwynd, 1949 (Christie).

Flight: September and October, inhabiting gardens, wasteground etc.

Larval F/ps: Polyphagous on herbaceous plants. April to July.

Notes: *P. flavicincta* becomes very local north of a line from the Severn estuary to The Wash. Further investigation is needed to determine the true status of this species in Shropshire.

2254 Grey Chi *Antitype chi* Hufnagel
V.C.H.: Universal and frequent.

Post V.C.H.: Widespread but local and not common. Mainly associated with upland grassland such as that found in the Oswestry Uplands and the Welsh Border Vales.

Flight: August and September.

Larval F/ps: Polyphagous, mainly on low plants. April to June.

2255 Feathered Ranunculus *Eumictis lichenea lichenea* Hübner

V.C.H.: Unrecorded.

Post V.C.H.: The only record of this usually coastal species is a larva found on hound's tongue fern at Llanymynech in 1930. The adult emerged on 12.ix.1930 (Hignett, 1931).

Flight: August to October.

Larval F/ps: Polyphagous. October to May.

2256 The Satellite *Eupsilia transversa* Hufnagel

V.C.H.: Common throughout.

Post V.C.H.: Widespread and common in woodlands and mature gardens throughout the county.

Flight: September to April, flying in mild weather throughout the winter.

Larval F/ps: Polyphagous on deciduous trees, including birch*. May and June.

2257 Orange Upperwing *Jodia croceago* Denis & Schiffermüller

V.C.H.: Recorded only from the Wyre Forest (Edwards; Rea, per Potts, 1903).

Post V.C.H.: Apart from Meole Brace where this species was recorded by Pendlebury in 1922 (per Ingrams, 1923), *J. croceago* has recently been noted from only one locality in Shropshire. At the request of the recorder, and bearing in mind the severe decline of the species nationally, I have been asked not to publish the name of the site.

Flight: October, November and, after hibernation, from March to May. A woodland species, often found at sallow and ivy blossom.

Larval F/p: Oak, possibly preferring young growth on stools. May to July.

Notes: Further studies are required to find the ecological requirements of this species so that the necessary steps can be taken to safeguard its future, not only in Shropshire, but also the rest of Britain. It is figured on Plate 11.

2258 The Chestnut *Conistra vaccinii* Linnaeus

V.C.H.: Common throughout.

Post V.C.H.: Widespread, generally distributed and common.

Flight: September to May, particularly in woodlands. Often abundant at ivy blossom.

Larval F/ps: Polyphagous, mainly on trees, including hazel*. May and June.

2259 Dark Chestnut *Conistra ligula* Esper

V.C.H.: Frequent throughout.

Post V.C.H.: Widespread and generally distributed but not as common as *C. vaccinii*.

Flight: October to January or February. Frequently found at ivy blossom.

Larval F/ps: Hawthorn, sallow and oak. April to June.

Notes: The concave apex to the forewings will separate this species from *C. vaccinii* to which it bears a strong superficial resemblance.

2262 The Brick *Agrochola circellaris* Hufnagel

V.C.H.: Generally distributed and common.

Post V.C.H.: Widespread and fairly common, particularly in woodlands.

Flight: August to October. Often found at ivy blossom.

Larval F/ps: Mainly wych elm* but also poplar and ash. Newnham (1901a) states that larvae were commonly beaten from beech around Church Stretton. April to June.

Notes: It is interesting to note that numbers of this species do not appear to have been drastically effected by Dutch elm disease.

2263 Red-line Quaker *Agrochola lota* Clerck

V.C.H.:   General but not common.

Post V.C.H.:   Fairly common in woodlands, heathlands and damp places throughout the county.

Flight: September and October. Often found at ivy blossom.

Larval F/ps: Sallow and willow. April to June.

2264 Yellow-line Quaker *Agrochola macilenta* Hübner

V.C.H.:   Broseley (Potts); scarce at Market Drayton; very common at Church Stretton.

Post V.C.H.:   Widespread and common, particularly in woodlands.

Flight: September to November. Sometimes very common at ivy blossom.

Larval F/ps: Hawthorn*, beech, poplar, willow and oak. Later instars feed on herbaceous plants in the vicinity of these trees. April to June.

Notes: Ab. *obsoleta* Tutt, which lacks the black dot in the reniform stigma, is frequent.

2265 Flounced Chestnut *Agrochola helvola* Linnaeus

V.C.H.:   Calverhall, occasional at sugar and ivy blossom; Church Stretton; Market Drayton and Wyre Forest.

Post V.C.H.:   Widespread and frequent, mainly on moorlands but also in some of the larger woodlands.

Flight: September and October.

Larval F/ps: Polyphagous. April to June.

2266 Brown-spot Pinion *Agrochola litura* Linnaeus

V.C.H.:   General and common.

Post V.C.H.:   Generally distributed, widespread and fairly common, particularly in woodlands.

Flight: September and October. Frequently found at ivy blossom.

Larval F/ps: Polyphagous. April and May.

2267 Beaded Chestnut *Agrochola lychnidis* Denis & Schiffermüller

V.C.H.:   Common throughout.

Post V.C.H.:   Widespread, generally distributed and very common.

Flight: September and October. Sometimes abundant at ivy blossom.

Larval F/ps: Polyphagous on grasses and low plants. March to June.

2269 Centre-barred Sallow *Atethmia centrago* Haworth

V.C.H.:   Calverhall, once; Shrewsbury, 1893, at light and occasional at Church Stretton near ash (Newnham, 1896 and 1901a).

Post V.C.H.:   Widespread and not uncommon in the vicinity of ash.

Flight: August and September.

Larval F/p: Ash. April to June.

2270 Lunar Underwing *Omphaloscelis lunosa* Haworth

V.C.H.: Recorded as very common at Shrewsbury (Stainton, 1857. Vol. 1: 248) and frequent at Church Stretton.

Post V.C.H.: Widespread and common on rough ground throughout the county.

Flight: August to October. Common at ivy blossom.

Larval F/ps: Polyphagous on grasses. October to May.

2271 Orange Sallow *Xanthia citrago* Linnaeus

V.C.H.: Fairly common in the north-east. Abundant at Church Stretton.

Post V.C.H.: More widespread in the northern half of the county but generally uncommon and restricted to areas where lime is established. Recorded from Shrewsbury, 1913 and 1979 (Pendlebury, 1914; D. Smith) Selattyn, 1.ix.1929 (Hignett, 1931); Oswestry, 1953 (K.G.V. Smith, 1954); Preston Montford Field Centre, 1967, 1969 and 1970 (R.I.S. trap, det. Nicklen) and Woore, 1979 (Holdsworth) and Preston Montford Field Centre, 9.ix.1988 (R.I.S. trap, det. Riley).

Flight: August and September.

Larval F/p: Lime*. March to June.

2272 Barred Sallow *Xanthia aurago* Denis & Schiffermüller

V.C.H.: Recorded only from Church Stretton, 7.x.1896 (Newnham, 1901a).

Post V.C.H.: Widespread but local and never common. Recorded as occasional in the Wyre Forest (Evans) and fairly frequent from the R.I.S. trap at Preston Montford Field Centre. Other records have been received from Shrewsbury, 1913 (Pendlebury, 1914); Bucknell, 1970 (Shephard); Broseley, 1970 (Whitney); Pontesbury, 1970, 1973 & 1977 (D. Smith); Wellington, 1978 (Riley); Quatford, 1978 (Holdsworth) and Shirlett, 1980 (Whitney).

Flight: September and October, inhabiting woodland and hedgerows.

Larval F/ps: Beech* and maple. April to July.

2273 Pink-barred Sallow *Xanthia togata* Esper

V.C.H.: Common at Market Drayton (Woodforde, 1894); occasional at Whitchurch and Church Stretton. Also recorded from Shrewsbury (Stainton, 1857. Vol. 1: 252-253).

Post V.C.H.: Widespread and fairly common in damp localities where sallows occur.

Flight: September and October.

Larval F/ps: Sallow* and, in later instars, on various low plants. March to June.

2274 The Sallow *Xanthia icteritia* Hufnagel

V.C.H.: Shavington, uncommon (Thornewill); Market Drayton, common (Woodforde, 1894) and Church Stretton, frequent.

Post V.C.H.: Widespread and usually common wherever sallows occur.

Flight: September and October.

Larval F/ps: Sallow* and, in later instars, on various low plants. March to June.

Notes: Individuals referable to ab. *flavescens* Esper, in which the forewing markings are greatly reduced, are found frequently throughout the county.

2275 Dusky Lemon Sallow *Xanthia gilvago* Denis & Schiffermüller

V.C.H.: Generally distributed: Shrewsbury (Stainton, 1857. Vol. 1: 253); Calverhall, frequent (Thornewill, 1895); Market Drayton, rare (Woodforde) and Church Stretton, larvae often beaten from elm (Newnham, 1901a).

PLATE ONE: One of the quarries on Llanymynech Rocks (Oswestry Uplands) where the brown argus butterfly is found. *Photo: D. J. Smith*

PLATE TWO: Whixall Moss (Morraines, Mosses and Meres). A raised peat bog where many of Shropshire's most interesting species occur, including the northern footman moth and the large heath butterfly. *Photo: D. J. Smith*

PLATE THREE: Prees Heath (North-eastern Plain). A heathland habitat on the site of an old airfield. Attempts are being made to protect this area as it is home to several important species. It is constantly under threat from surrounding agriculturalisation as indicated here by the presence of the large barn on the left of the photograph. *Photo: A. M. Riley*

PLATE FOUR: Middletown Hill (Welsh Border Vales) looking over the Shropshire plains. *Photo: D. J. Smith*

PLATE FIVE: Hinkshay showing an old industrial landscape with wild areas typical of the Wrekin Spur. *Photo: D. J. Smith*

PLATE SIX: The Clun Valley from Clun Forest showing typically intensive upland grazing. Only fragments of old woodland remain in the Clun Forest Uplands. *Photo: B. Brazier*

PLATE SEVEN: Ashes Hollow (West Central Hills). A typical valley on the Longmynd much frequented by F.B. Newnham at the turn of the century. This area was once home to the small lappet moth — a species now possibly extinct in Britain. As seen here the vegetation is dominated by bracken, heather and bilberry. These upland areas are sheep-grazed all year round. *Photo: A. M. Riley*

PLATE EIGHT: A small meadow on the Wenlock limestone (Ludlow-Wenlock Escarpment). A very rich area both entomologically and botanically. *Photo: D. J. Smith*

PLATE NINE: Brown Clee (Clee Hills Platform) from near Stoke St. Milborough showing arable farming dominant in the lower areas, giving way to upland grazing on the hilltops. *Photo: B. Brazier*

PLATE TEN: A ride in the Wyre Forest (Lower Severn Valley). *Photo: A. M. Riley*

Red-necked footman	Kentish glory	The mocha
A. rubicollis L.	*E. versicolora* L.	*C. annulata* Schulze

Sharp-angled carpet	Broad-bordered	Narrow-bordered	The peacock
E. unangulata Haw.	bee hawk	bee hawk	*S. notata* L.
	H. fuciformis L.	*H. tityus* L.	

Small chocolate-tip	Small lappet	Scarce vapourer
C. pigra Hufn.	*P. ilicifolia* L.	*O. recens* Hb.

Plain clay	Union rustic	Northern rustic
E. depuncta L.	*A. pabulatricula* Brahm.	*S. lucernea* L.

Reddish light arches	Sword-grass	Coronet
A. sublustris	*X. exsoleta* L.	*C. ligustri* D. & S.

Marbled Green	Orange upperwing
C. muralis Forst.	*J. croceago* D. & S.

PLATE ELEVEN: None of the above moth species has been recorded in Shropshire in recent years. They may now be extinct in the county but further investigation in suitable localities may reveal their continued presence. *Photo: G. Higgins*

Emperor moth
P. pavonia L.
typical female

Emperor moth
P. pavonia L.
typical male

Emperor moth
P. pavonia L.
ab. *rosacea* Newnh.

Emperor moth
P. pavonia L.
ab. *infumata* Newnh.

Green-veined white
P. napi L.
Dark Longmynd
specimen

Silver-studded
blue
P. argus L.
Shropshire
male

Silver-studded
blue
P. argus L.
Hampshire
male

Gatekeeper
P. tithonus L.
ab *crassiexcessa* Leeds

Silver-studded
blue
P. argus L.
Shropshire
female

Silver-studded
blue
P. argus L.
Hampshire
female

PLATE TWELVE: Some of the unusual forms referred to in the text. *Photo: G. Higgins*

PLATE THIRTEEN: Small skipper butterfly (*T. sylvestris* Poda). *Photo: D. Porter*

PLATE FOURTEEN: Dingy skipper butterfly (*E. tages* Linn.). *Photo: D. Porter*

PLATE FIFTEEN: Wood white butterfly (*L. sinapis* Linn.). *Photo: H. D. Loxdale*

PLATE SIXTEEN: Green hairstreak butterfly (*C. rubi* Linn.). *Photo: P. Graham*

PLATE SEVENTEEN: Purple hairstreak butterfly (*Q. quercus* Linn.). *Photo: D. Porter*

PLATE EIGHTEEN: White-letter hairstreak butterfly (*S. w-album* Knoch). *Photo: M. Davies*

PLATE NINETEEN: Small blue butterfly (*C. minimum* Fuess.). *Photo: C. Marsay*

PLATE TWENTY: Silver-studded blue butterfly (*P. argus* Linn.). *Photo: R. Hatton*

PLATE TWENTY-ONE: Larva of white admiral butterfly (*L. camilla* Linn.). *Photo: D. Porter*

PLATE TWENTY-TWO: Adult of white admiral butterfly. *Photo: C. Marsay*

PLATE TWENTY-THREE: Small tortoiseshell butterfly (*A. urticae* Linn.). *Photo: M. Williams*

PLATE TWENTY-FOUR: Comma butterfly (*P. c-album* Linn.). *Photo: W. Raymond*

PLATE TWENTY-FIVE: Small pearl-bordered fritillary butterfly (*B. selene* D. & S.).
Photo: C. Marsay

PLATE TWENTY-SIX: Pearl-bordered fritillary butterfly (*B. euphrosyne* Linn.).
Photo: C. Marsay

PLATE TWENTY-SEVEN: High brown fritillary butterfly (*A. adippe* D. & S.).
Photo: D. Porter

PLATE TWENTY-EIGHT: Dark green fritillary butterfly (*A. aglaja* Linn.). *Photo: D. Porter*

PLATE TWENTY-NINE: Grayling butterfly (*H. semele* Linn.). *Photo: P. Salmon*

PLATE THIRTY: Gatekeeper butterfly (*P. tithonus* Linn.). *Photo: D. Porter*

PLATE THIRTY-ONE: Large heath butterfly (*C. tullia* Müll.). *Photo: D. Porter*

PLATE THIRTY-TWO: Ringlet butterfly (*A. hyperantus* Linn.). *Photo: C. Marsay*

Post V.C.H.:   Widely distributed but not common and restricted to woodlands etc. where mature wych elms occur, as the larvae require seeds on which to feed.

Flight: August to October.

Larval F/p: Wych elm*. April to June.

Notes: This species is never recorded in great numbers at light, sugar or flowers so it is difficult to assess the effect of Dutch elm disease on its status in Shropshire. However, I have received no records since 1980 and further investigations are urgently required.

2278 Poplar Grey *Acronicta megacephala* Denis & Schiffermüller

V.C.H.:   Fairly common at Market Drayton and frequent at Church Stretton, where the larvae are found on poplars (Newnham, 1901a).

Post V.C.H.:   Widespread and frequent in woodlands throughout the county.

Flight: May to August.

Larval F/ps: Poplars* (usually black poplar), including aspen, and occasionally sallow. July to September. The present author found a pupa of this species at the base of a willow tree at Preston-on-the-Weald in 1977.

Notes: So far as I am aware the melanic ab. *nigra* Shaw has not been recorded in Shropshire. Newnham (1901a and 1908) mentions a specimen of ab. *rosea* Engr., in which the forewings are suffused with a rosy tinge, from Church Stretton.

2280 The Miller *Acronicta leporina* Linnaeus

V.C.H.:   Newnham (1908) states that it was restricted to northern Shropshire. However, Rea recorded it from the Wyre Forest on 10.vi.1899 and Newnham himself caught it at Church Stretton on 23.vi.1905.

Post V.C.H.:   Widespread and frequently recorded from woodlands, heathlands and mosses.

Flight: June to August.

Larval F/ps: Mainly birch and alder though occasionally poplar and sallow. July to October.

Notes: To my knowledge all records refer to f. *grisea* Cochrane.

2281 Alder Moth *Acronicta alni* Linnaeus

V.C.H.:   Generally rare. More frequent in the south-west and south-east.

Post V.C.H.:   Locally common in woodlands throughout the county.

Flight: May and June.

Larval F/ps: Polyphagous on deciduous trees including alder*, black poplar*, ash*, rose*, damson* and sycamore*. July and August.

Notes: The melanic form *suffusa* Tutt occurs occasionally at Preston Montford Field Centre (R.I.S. trap, det. Riley).

Notes on *Acronicta tridens* Denis & Schiffermüller and *A. psi* Linnaeus

The adults of these species cannot be separated by superficial characters alone; examination of the genitalia is essential. Therefore it must be stated that the records for *A. tridens* and *A. psi* must be regarded with due care as not all of them will have been determined by such methods. However, from the genitalia examination carried out by several recorders, it appears that *A. psi* is more common and widespread than *A. tridens*. The larvae are very easily distinguished and records of these support this view. † Denotes records which have been confirmed by examination of the genitalia.

2283 Dark Dagger *Acronicta tridens* Denis & Schiffermüller

V.C.H.: Shrewsbury (Stainton, 1857. Vol. 1: 180); Calverhall, larvae, 1900 (Thornewill) and Church Stretton, several larvae.

Post V.C.H.: Quatford, 1960 (D'Arcy); Wem Moss, 1968† (Heath); Broseley, 1968† (Whitney); Pontesbury, 1973† (D. Smith); Shirlett, 1977† (Whitney); Woore, 1979 (Holdsworth); Alscott, 1978† and Wellington, 1979† (Riley) and Preston Montford, 1980† (Heath).

Flight: June and July in woodlands, gardens, orchards and allotments.

Larval F/ps: Polyphagous on deciduous trees and shrubs. August to October.

2284 Grey Dagger *Acronicta psi* Linnaeus

V.C.H.: Generally distributed.

Post V.C.H.: Widely distributed and fairly common. Woodlands, heathlands and gardens.

Flight: June to August.

Larval F/ps: Polyphagous on deciduous trees. August to October.

Notes: Newnham (1908) recorded ab. *suffusa* Tutt, in which the forewings are suffused with black, on 20.vi.1900. Unfortunately no locality is given.

2286 Light Knot Grass *Acronicta menyanthidis menyanthidis* Esper

V.C.H.: Shrewsbury (Stainton, 1857. Vol. 1: 183) and on boggy parts of the Longmynd. Not common.

Post V.C.H.: Local and generally uncommon: Longmynd (K.G.V. Smith, 1952); Wem Moss, 7.vii.1963 (Warren); Ironbridge, 1974 (Derry); Monkhopton, 1977 (Whitney); Fenn's Moss, 1972 (Rutherford) and 1980 (Watson) and Whixall Moss, 1930 (Hignett), 1935 (Warren), 1960 (Scott); 1985 (Hardwick) and 1988 (Riley).

Flight: May to July on heathland, moorland and the mosses, usually in damp places.

Larval F/ps: Polyphagous on moorland and heathland plants including bilberry* and deciduous trees. August and September.

2289 Knot Grass *Acronicta rumicis* Linnaeus

V.C.H.: Frequent, especially in central Shropshire.

Post V.C.H.: Widespread and fairly common, with the exception of the south west. Generally distributed.

Flight: May to July.

Larval F/ps: Polyphagous on herbaceous plants and deciduous trees.

Notes: The melanic ab. *salicis* Curtis is frequently found throughout the county.

2291 The Coronet *Craniophora ligustri* Denis & Schiffermüller

V.C.H.: Uncommon at Church Stretton, at rest on ash trunks and once in the Wyre Forest, 1902 (Rea).

Post V.C.H.: Unrecorded.

Flight: June and July, inhabiting woodland, downland and commons (Skinner, 1984).

Larval F/ps: Ash* and wild privet. August and September.

Newnham (1897a) stated that a form tinged with violet was dominant at Church Stretton whereas elsewhere the green-tinged form prevailed. Evans has not recorded this species from the Shropshire part of the Wyre Forest in recent years (pers. comm.). It is possible that it is now extinct in this locality. Insufficient recording has been carried out in the Church Stretton area to make any assumptions about its status there. The species is figured on Plate 11.

2293 Marbled Beauty *Cryphia domestica* Hufnagel

V.C.H.: Common in most parts of the county. The larvae are often found on lichen-covered walls around Church Stretton (Newnham, 1901a).

Post V.C.H.: Widely distributed and frequently recorded from throughout the county. Often found in gardens.

Flight: July and August.

Larval F/ps: Various species of lichen growing on roofs and walls, etc. September to May.

2295 Marbled Green *Cryphia muralis* Forster (presumably ssp. *muralis* Forst.)

V.C.H.: Woodforde (1901e) cites a specimen of *Bryophila* (= *Cryphia*) *muralis* caught in 1901. No locality is given and one can only assume that it was caught at or near Market Drayton — the address stated on the correspondence. The article discusses exceptional sizes of various Lepidoptera captured by the author (the present species is entered by virtue of an adult with a wingspan of 0.77 inches). No other lists for Shropshire written by this author include *C. muralis* and no mention is made of its status at the locality of capture.

Post V.C.H.: One record only: Cleobury Mortimer, 20.vi.1922 (one) (Woodward, 1922b).

Flight: July and August in similar habitats to *C. domestica* Hufn.

Larval F/ps: Lichens growing on walls etc. October to May.

Notes: Further investigation is required to ascertain this species' status in Shropshire. It is figured on Plate 11.

Notes on *Amphipyra pyramidea* Linnaeus and *A. berbera svenssoni* Fletcher

The adults of these two species, which have only recently been given separate specific status, are sometimes difficult to distinguish by superficial characters, though reference to Skinner (1984, p. 123) shows how this can be done. However, the older records, submitted before they were separated, cannot now be attributed to one species or the other as the specimens no longer exist. I have included here only those records which have been checked. Combined records and comments are given to show the general status of the pair (or possibly one of the species) at, and since, the publication of the V.C.H.:

Combined records for *A. pyramidea* and *A. berbera*

V.C.H.: Recorded only from Church Stretton, where it was frequent at sugar.

Post V.C.H.: Fairly frequent in woodlands and hedgerows throughout the county.

Notes: More common at sugar than at light.

2297 Copper Underwing *Amphipyra pyramidea* Linnaeus

Post V.C.H.: Broseley, 1967 & 1968 (Whitney); Earl's Hill, 1968 (Heath); Dothill, 1975 (Riley); Shirlett, 1977 (Whitney); Preston Montford Field Centre (occasional at R.I.S. trap, det. Riley); Whixall, 1985 (Hardwick) and the Wyre Forest, 1987 (Plant).

Flight: August to October. Woodland and hedgerows.

Larval F/ps: Polyphagous on deciduous trees and shrubs. April and May.

2298 Svensson's Copper Underwing *Amphipyra berbera svenssoni* Fletcher

Post V.C.H.: Broseley, 1968 (Whitney); Preston Montford and Earl's Hill, 1968 (Heath); Shirlett, 1977 (Whitney); Wellington 1977, 1978 & 1979; Dothill, 1978 & 1979 (Riley) and the Wyre Forest, 1987 (Plant).

Flight: July to September in woodlands.

Larval F/ps: Polyphagous on deciduous trees and shrubs, including hawthorn*. April and May.

2299 Mouse Moth *Amphipyra tragopoginis* Clerck

V.C.H.: Very common throughout.

Post V.C.H.: Widespread, generally distributed and common.

Flight: July to September.

Larval F/ps: Polyphagous. April to June.

2300 Old Lady *Mormo maura* Linnaeus

V.C.H.: Scarce at Market Drayton and Calverhall. Common at Church Stretton.

Post V.C.H.: Widespread and fairly frequently recorded from throughout the county.

Flight: July and August. Gardens, wasteground, lakesides and river banks etc.

Larval F/ps: Polyphagous on deciduous trees and shrubs. September to May.

Notes: This species can often be found during the day roosting in sheds, outhouses and under bridges etc. and at night is attracted to *Buddleia* flowers. Ingrams (1922) states that this species ". . . simply swarmed . . ." at Marshbrook throughout August 1921 and that it varied in colour ". . . from sienna through browns to good purple."

2301 Bird's Wing *Dypterygia scabriuscula* Linnaeus

V.C.H.: Wyre Forest, June 1899 (Peed); Benthall Edge, 1905 and 1907 (Potts, 1906 and 1908) and Market Drayton, 1907 (Pendlebury, per Potts, 1908; Woodforde).

Post V.C.H.: Widespread and frequent in deciduous woodland and rough ground in the north-east and east of the county. It is interesting to note that Heath (1983, p. 161, map 76) shows a band of records from Merseyside, south-eastwards to Worcestershire. The north-eastern and eastern portions of Shropshire just overlap this band, creating a very clearly defined pattern of distribution within the county. The one exception is the record from Nesscliffe, 1937 (Hignett) but the species has not been seen in this area since that date. It is therefore possible that this individual was a vagrant.

Flight: Usually June and July with an occasional second brood in August and September, though this has not, to my knowledge, been recorded in Shropshire.

Larval F/ps: Polyphagous on low plants such as dock* and sorrel. July to August.

2302 Brown Rustic *Rusina ferruginea* Esper

V.C.H.: Generally distributed and common. Often found at thistle blossom (Newnham, 1901a).

Post V.C.H.: Fairly common in woods, heathlands and mosses throughout the county.

Flight: June and July.

Larval F/ps: Polyphagous on low plants, including dock*. August to May.

2303 Straw Underwing *Thalpophila matura* Hufnagel

V.C.H.: Church Stretton, not uncommon at sugar.

Post V.C.H.: Fairly common on rough grasslands, open woodlands, moorlands and heathlands throughout the county.

Flight: July and August.

Larval F/ps: Grasses. September to May.

2305 Small Angle Shades *Euplexia lucipara* Linnaeus

V.C.H.: Frequent throughout.

Post V.C.H.: Widespread and fairly common throughout. Mainly in woodlands, gardens and bracken dominated uplands.

Flight: June and July. There is an occasional partial second emergence in September but this has not, to my knowledge, been recorded in Shropshire.

Larval F/ps: Polyphagous, mainly on ferns. Newnham (1901a) noted that the adults were usually found in the vicinity of *Pteris aquilina*. August and September.

2306 Angle Shades *Phlogophora meticulosa* Linnaeus

V.C.H.: Common throughout.

Post V.C.H.: Widespread, generally distributed and common throughout.

Flight: Usually May to October in two protracted broods though outside Shropshire it has been caught in every month of the year.

Larval F/ps: Polyphagous, throughout the year. Often recorded on snowberry in Riley's garden in Wellington, though not on other, apparently suitable plants.

2311 Double Kidney *Ipimorpha retusa* Linnaeus

V.C.H.: Church Stretton, occasionally found as larvae on aspen (Newnham, 1901a).

Post V.C.H.: A very local and uncommon species. Recorded occasionally at Preston Montford Field Centre (R.I.S. trap, det. Nicklen and Riley). Also recorded at Cleobury Mortimer, 15.vii.1922 (two) (Woodward); Whixall Moss (Burrows, per Fielding, 1974a); Rednall, 1948 (Hignett) and once from the pre-1974 Shropshire/Flintshire border in 1949 by G. Smith (per B.R.C., Monkswood).

Flight: July to September in damp localities.

Larval F/ps: Aspen*, sallow and willow. April and May.

2312 The Olive *Ipimorpha subtusa* Denis & Schiffermüller

V.C.H.: Frequent at Church Stretton. Larvae are often found between spun leaves of poplar (Newnham, 1901a). Also Benthall, 1905 (Potts, 1906).

Post V.C.H.: Local and uncommon. Recorded from Maesbrook, 1941 (Hignett, per Pendlebury, 1942); Ironbridge, 1961 (Derry & Whitney); Preston Montford, 1968 (Heath); Monkhopton, 1970 (Whitney) and Woore, 1981 to 1983 (Holdsworth).

Flight: July to September in woodlands, gardens and damp localities.

Larval F/ps: Poplars*, including aspen. April and May.

2313 Angle-striped Sallow *Enargia paleacea* Esper

V.C.H.: Unrecorded.

Post V.C.H.: Outside the Wyre Forest, where it is fairly common (Evans), this species is very local and infrequently recorded. Even within the Wyre Forest Plant (pers. comm.) states that it is not universally distributed.: Whixall Moss, 1920 (Henstock); Quatford, 1960 (D'Arcy); Monkhopton, 1970 (Whitney) and Wellington, 1978 (Riley).

Flight: July to September in mature birch woodland.

Larval F/p: Birch. April to June.

2313i The Suspected *Parastichtis suspecta* Hübner

V.C.H.:   Common at sugar at Market Drayton (Woodforde, 1900f; Pendlebury, per Potts, 1908) and one record from Benthall Edge, 1906 (Potts, 1907).

Post V.C.H.:   Apart from the Wyre Forest, where it is common (Evans), this species is only infrequently noted from woodlands and heathlands. Recorded · from Rednall, 1948 (Hignett, per Pendlebury, 1950); Quatford, 1960 (D'Arcy); Whixall Moss, 1934 & 1972 (Rutherford) and 1985 (Hardwick) and Woore, 1980 and 1982 (Holdsworth).

Flight: July and August.

Larval F/ps: Birch and sallow. April and May.

2314 Dingy Shears *Parastichtis ypsillon* Denis & Schiffermüller

V.C.H.:   Frequent in damp places near willows at Church Stretton (Newnham, 1901a). Also Shrewsbury, 1897 (Cortissos, 1898) and Benthall, 1906 (Potts).

Post V.C.H.:   Very local and uncommon. Recorded only from Meole Brace, 1928 (Henstock); Whixall Moss, 1934 (Warren; Fielding, 1947a); Maesbrook, 1937 (Hignett); Preston Montford, 1968 and 1980 (Heath); Woore, 1971–1980 (Holdsworth) and Ludlow, 6.vii and 21.vii.1989 (R.I.S. trap, det. Riley).

Flight: June to August in damp localities.

Larval F/ps: Willow, poplar and sallow. April to June.

2315 Heart Moth *Dicycla oo* Linnaeus

V.C.H.:   Unrecorded.

Post V.C.H.:   One unconfirmed record from Meole Brace, 25.vi.1921 (Henstock, per Ingrams, 1922). The specimen cannot be traced.

Flight: June and July in open woodland where there are mature oaks.

Larval F/p: Oak. April to June.

Notes: This species is restricted to south-east England. If Henstock's record was genuine it possibly represents a vagrant.

2316 Lesser-spotted Pinion *Cosmia affinis* Linnaeus

V.C.H.:   Common at Shrewsbury (Stainton, 1857. Vol. 1: 259); rare at Church Stretton; (occasional at sugar near elms (Newnham, 1901a)) and Calverhall, 1909 (Thornewill, per Pendlebury, 1950).

Post V.C.H.:   Local and uncommon. Recorded from Calverhall, 1909 (Thornewill); Shrewsbury, 1913 (Pendlebury & Pendlebury, 1914); Oswestry, 1930 (Hignett, 1931); Ludlow, 1939 (Bretherton); Bridgnorth, 1970 (Wint); Preston Montford Field Centre, 1970 (R.I.S. trap, det. Nicklen); Pontesbury, 1970 (D. Smith); Bucknell, 1972 (Shephard) and Shirlett, 1977 (Whitney).

Flight: July and August, inhabiting woodlands and hedgerows.

Larval F/ps: English elm and wych elm. April to June.

Notes: With such an infrequently recorded species it is impossible to say how much it has been affected by Dutch elm disease.

2317 White-spotted Pinion *Cosmia diffinis* Linnaeus

V.C.H.:   Occasional at sugar near elms at Church Stretton.

Post V.C.H.:   Very local and uncommon. Recorded only from Pontesbury, 1973 (D. Smith) and Ironbridge, 1974 (Derry).

Flight: July to September in open woodland and moorland.

Larval F/ps: English elm and wych elm. April to June.

Notes: Nationally this species is known to be local and generally uncommon.

2318 The Dun-bar *Cosmia trapezina* Linnaeus

V.C.H.:   Generally common.

Post V.C.H.:   Widespread, generally distributed and common throughout.

Flight: July to September.

Larval F/ps: Polyphagous on deciduous trees and shrubs. Recorded in Shropshire on oak, hazel, hawthorn and birch. April to June.

2319 Lunar-spotted Pinion *Cosmia pyralina* Denis & Schiffermüller

V.C.H.:   Recorded only from Shrewsbury (Stainton, 1857. Vol. 1: 258) and Ragleth Wood near Church Stretton, at light in August 1894 (Newnham, 1901a).

Post V.C.H.:   Apart from Preston Montford Field Centre, where it is regularly recorded (though not every year) at the R.I.S. light trap (det. Riley), this species has only been noted at Shrewsbury, 1913 (Pendlebury and Pendlebury, 1914, and Pendlebury, 1915); Quatford, 1960 (D'Arcy) and Alveley, 1988 (Blunt).

Flight: July to August. Woodlands and hedgerows.

Larval F/ps: English elm, wych elm, hawthorn, blackthorn and apple. April to June.

2321 Dark Arches *Apamea monoglypha* Hufnagel

V.C.H.:   Common throughout.

Post V.C.H.:   Widespread, generally distributed and common, sometimes abundant.

Flight: June to August.

Larval F/ps: Roots and stem bases of grasses. August to June.

Notes: The melanic ab. *aethiops* Tutt is recorded frequently throughout the county. It was also noted in the V.C.H. (Newnham 1897a and 1908). Newnham (1901a and 1908) also recorded abs. *obscura* Tutt, *brunnea* Tutt and *infuscata* White at Church Stretton.

2322 Light Arches *Apamea lithoxylaea* Denis & Schiffermüller

V.C.H.:   Generally distributed and fairly common.

Post V.C.H.:   Widespread and common in rough grassy localities.

Flight: June to early August.

Larval F/ps: The natural foodplants are assumed to be grasses. September to May.

2323 Reddish Light Arches *Apamea sublustris* Esper

V.C.H.:   Not common. Recorded from Broseley, 1899 (Potts, per Cortissos, 1900) and Benthall, 1902 (Potts, 1903), Wyre Forest (Peed) and Church Stretton.

Post V.C.H.:   Unrecorded.

Flight: June and July. Probably mainly associated with limestone and sandstone grasslands.

Larval F/ps: Grasses. September to May (Heath, 1983).

Notes: Further investigation is required to ascertain this species' status in Shropshire. It is figured on Plate 11.

2325 Crescent Striped *Apamea oblonga* Haworth

V.C.H.: Two unconfirmed records, presumably of mistaken identity, from Church Stretton at rest in July 1897 and at sugar on 6.vii.1899 (Newnham, 1901a and 1908).

Post V.C.H.: Unrecorded.

Flight: June to early August in coastal localities.

Larval F/ps: Saltmarsh-grass, which is not present in Shropshire. September to June.

2326 Clouded-bordered Brindle *Apamea crenata* Hufnagel

V.C.H.: Frequent and general.

Post V.C.H.: Widespread and common in woodlands, gardens and heathland.

Flight: May to July.

Larval F/ps: Various grasses. August to April.

Notes: The melanic ab. *combusta* Haworth is common. This was also known to occur in Shropshire prior to publication of the V.C.H. (Newnham, 1897a). It was as common as the type in the Church Stretton district (Newnham, 1901a).

2327 Clouded Brindle *Apamea epomidion* Haworth

V.C.H.: Uncommon and local. Recorded from Calverhall, 1901 (Thornewill); Church Stretton 1899 & 1906 (Bradburne); Broseley and Wyre Forest (Woodforde, 1902c).

Post V.C.H.: Very local and infrequently noted. Recorded from Bromfield, 1955 (Norton); Broseley, 1968 (Whitney); Pontesbury, 1972 & 1974 (D. Smith); Shirlett, 1978 (Whitney) and Wellington, 1979 (Riley).

Flight: June and July in woodlands and gardens.

Larval F/ps: Various grasses. August to March.

2329 The Confused *Apamea furva britannica* Cockayne

V.C.H.: Broseley, 1899 (Potts, per Cortissos, 1900), Wyre Forest (Edwards) and the Longmynd where it comes to sugar and thistle blossoms (Newnham, 1901a and 1908). Newman (1869) also cites Shropshire for this species.

Post V.C.H.: Local and uncommon. Recorded only from Rodington, 1956 (Briggs); and Wellington, 1978 & 1979 (Riley, det. genitalia).

Flight: July and August, usually on upland moorland.

Larval F/ps: Rough meadow-grass and wood meadow-grass. September to June. Newnham (1908) records finding larvae at the base of grasses on the Longmynd.

Notes: This species is superficially very similar to *A. remissa* f. *obscura* Haworth. Skinner (1984) shows the diagnostic features.

2330 Dusky Brocade *Apamea remissa* Hübner

V.C.H.: Calverhall, 1895 (Thornewill); Market Drayton (Woodforde); Broseley (Potts) and Church Stretton.

Post V.C.H.: Widespread and fairly common in open woodlands and grassy localities.

Flight: June and July.

Larval F/ps: Various grasses. September to April.

Notes: F. *obscura* Haworth is the dominant form.

2331 Small Clouded Brindle *Apamea unanimis* Hübner

V.C.H.: Calverhall, once in 1901 and Church Stretton ". . . now and again in damp places . . ." (Newnham, 1901a).

Post V.C.H.: Widespread but not common outside the Wyre Forest. Recorded from Oswestry, 1928 (Hignett, 1931); Quatford, 1960 (D'Arcy); Pontesbury, 1974 (D. Smith); Wellington, 1979 (Riley); Woore, 1980 to 1983 (Holdsworth); Preston Montford Field Centre, 1970, 1971 and 1982 (R.I.S. trap det. Nicklen and Riley); Whixall Moss, 1985 (Hardwick) and Ludlow, 1989 (R.I.S. trap, det. Riley).

Flight: May to July in damp localities.

Larval F/ps: Various grasses. July to April. Does not feed after hibernation.

2332 Union Rustic *Apamea pabulatrix* Brahm

V.C.H.: Reared once in 1879 from a larva found near Church Stretton (Newnham, 1901a and 1908).

Post V.C.H.: Unrecorded.

Flight: July to August in mature woodlands.

Larval F/ps: Various grasses. September to May.

Notes: This species has not been recorded in Britain since 1935 and is now probably extinct. It is figured on Plate 11.

2333 Large Nutmeg *Apamea anceps* Denis & Schiffermüller

V.C.H.: Occasional at Church Stretton, scarce at Market Drayton and twice in the Wyre Forest (18 & 24.vi.1899).

Post V.C.H.: Recorded only from Meole Brace, 1928 (Henstock) and Rodington, 1954 and 1962 (Briggs). No specimens can be traced.

Flight: June and July in grassy localities.

Larval F/ps: Grasses. August to April.

2334 Rustic Shoulder-knot *Apamea sordens* Hufnagel

V.C.H.: Calverhall, abundant in 1895 only (Thornewill); Broseley (Potts) and Church Stretton, frequent.

Post V.C.H.: Very common in grassy places throughout the county.

Flight: May and June.

Larval F/ps: Grasses. August to March.

2335 Slender Brindle *Apamea scolopacina* Esper

V.C.H.: Generally rare and local. Found in most of the woods around Church Stretton (Newnham, 1897a).

Post V.C.H.: Not uncommon in the Wyre Forest (Evans) and the Ercall Woods (Riley). Occasional at Preston Montford Field Centre (R.I.S. trap, det. Riley). Other records from Oswestry, 1930 (Hignett, 1931); Quatford, 1960 (D'Arcy); Bridgnorth, 1970 (Wint); Pontesbury, 1977 (D. Smith); Shirlett, 1978 (Whitney); Woore, 1979 (Holdsworth) and Llanymynech, 22.vii.1989 (Townsend).

Flight: June to August in woodlands.

Larval F/ps: Various grasses. September to May.

2336 Double Lobed *Apamea ophiogramma* Esper

V.C.H.: Unrecorded.

Post V.C.H.: Regular at the R.I.S. trap at Preston Montford Field Centre (det. Riley). Other records from Quatford, 1960 (D'Arcy); Buildwas, 1968 (Whitney); Dawley, 1975 (Jacques); Dothill, 1976 (Riley); Monkhopton, 1977 (Whitney) and Woore, 1983 (Holdsworth).

Flight: June to August in woods, gardens and damp localities.

Larval F/p: Reed sweet-grass. August to June.

Notes on *Oligia strigilis* L., *O. versicolor* Borkhausen and *O. latruncula* Denis & Schiffermüller

These three species can only be confidently separated by means of genitalia examination. Sufficient samples have been taken to give a brief summary of their distributions within the county. Newman (1869) considered *O. latruncula* to be merely a form of *O. strigilis*. Newnham (1908) reflects this by omitting details of the former species. † indicates those records determined by examination of genitalia.

2337 Marbled Minor *Oligia strigilis* Linnaeus

V.C.H.: Common throughout the county.

Post V.C.H.: Common in grassy localities throughout the county.

Flight: May to July.

Larval F/ps: Inside the stems and roots of various grasses. Fully grown between March and May.

2338 Rufous Minor *Oligia versicolor* Borkhausen

V.C.H.: Unrecorded.

Post V.C.H.: Common at Preston Montford Field Centre (R.I.S. trap, det. Riley)†. Also recorded from Shirlett, 1969 (Whitney)†; Pontesbury, 1973 (D. Smith)†; Bucknell, 1976 (Shephard); Woore, 1984 (Holdsworth); Shirlett, 1980 (Whitney)†; Westhope and Clee St. Margaret, 1983 (Denman) and the Wyre Forest, 1987 (Plant)†.

Flight: June and July in grassy localities.

Larval F/ps: Unknown. Probably grasses. Autumn to spring.

2339 Tawny Marbled Minor *Oligia latruncula* Denis & Schiffermüller

V.C.H.: Unrecorded.

Post V.C.H.: Widespread and fairly common in grassy habitats throughout the county.

Flight: May to July.

Larval F/ps: Grasses. Late summer to May.

2340 Middle-barred Minor *Oligia fasciuncula* Haworth

V.C.H.: Common throughout.

Post V.C.H.: Common in damp localities throughout the county.

Flight: June and July. Often found at ragwort blossom in damp, grassy meadows.

Larval F/ps: Grasses. August to May.

2341 Cloaked Minor *Mesoligia furuncula* Denis & Schiffermüller

V.C.H.: Frequent throughout.

Post V.C.H.: Local but widespread and fairly common in grassy localities, particularly on sandy soils. Often found at ragwort blossom.

Flight: July to September.

Larval F/ps: Various grasses. Autumn to May.

2342 Rosy Minor *Mesoligia literosa* Haworth

V.C.H.:   Frequent throughout.

Post V.C.H.: Frequent in grassy localities throughout the county.

Flight: July and August.

Larval F/ps: Various grasses. Late summer to May or early June.

Notes: Various melanic forms approximating to f. *aethalodes* Richardson predominate in Shropshire.

Notes on the *Mesapamea* species.

Mesapamea secalis L. has recently been separated into two species by means of genitalia examination (Remm, 1983). It is not known how widespread the new *M. secalella* Remm is in Britain though it is assumed that it is well distributed. Only one study has been made of a population in Shropshire and the results are given here under *M. secalella*. The two species cannot be separated by means of superficial characters alone.

2343 Common Rustic *Mesapamea secalis* Linnaeus

V.C.H.:   Common throughout.

Post V.C.H.: Widespread and often abundant in grassy localities.

Flight: July and August.

Larval F/ps: Polyphagous on grasses and cereal crops.

2343a Lesser Common Rustic *Mesapamea secalella* Remm

V.C.H.:   Unrecorded.

Post V.C.H.: Genitalia examinations were made on a complete year's catch (1986) of *Mesapamea* species from the R.I.S. trap at Preston Montford Field Centre. Of 97 individuals examined seven were *M. secalella* (Riley and Southwood, 1988). *M. secalella* was also recorded in the Wyre Forest in 1987 (Plant), however no proportionate counts were made and further investigations are required to determine its exact status throughout Shropshire.

Flight: July, August and early September at Preston Montford.

Larval F/ps: Probably as *M. secalis*.

Notes: Good diagnostic notes are given in Jordan (1986) along with photographs of the genitalia.

2345 Small Dotted Buff *Photedes minima* Haworth

V.C.H.:   Generally frequent.

Post V.C.H.: Common in woodland openings and damp meadows throughout.

Flight: June to August. Often common at ragwort blossom.

Larval F/p: Tufted hair-grass* (Newnham, 1901a). August to June.

2350 Small Wainscot *Photedes pygmina* Haworth

V.C.H.:   Common but local around Market Drayton (Woodforde) and Ragleth Wood, Church Stretton, though the section of the wood where this species occurred was felled in 1901 (Newnham, 1901a).

Post V.C.H.: Fairly common in damp woodland and other damp localities throughout the county.

Flight: August and September.

Larval F/ps: Sedges, rushes and grasses. October to July.

Notes: Newnham (1901a) mentions var. *fluxa* Treitschke, in which the nervures of the forewings are fuscous, as frequent at Ragleth Wood, Church Stretton prior to 1901 (see V.C.H., above).

2352 Dusky Sallow *Eremobia ochroleuca* Denis & Schiffermüller

V.C.H.: Found occasionally at rest on flowers in dry stony localities around Church Stretton.

Post V.C.H.: Recorded only from Quatford, 1960 (D'Arcy).

Flight: July and August, preferring dry grassy habitats.

Larval F/ps: Grasses. May and June.

2353 Flounced Rustic *Luperina testacea* Denis & Schiffermüller

V.C.H.: Common throughout.

Post V.C.H.: Often very common in grassy places throughout the county.

Flight: August and September.

Larval F/ps: Polyphagous on grasses and cereal crops. September to June.

Notes on the *Amphipoea* species.

A. oculea L. was regarded as being the only "Ear Moth" by Newnham (1908). The four species now known to occur in Britain can only be distinguished confidently by means of genitalia examination. Of these four only two have been recorded in Shropshire. Further investigations are required to determine their distributions within the county but the records, as supplied, are given under each species. † denotes that the records have been checked by genitalia examination.

2357 Large Ear *Amphipoea lucens* Freyer

V.C.H.: Unrecorded.

Post V.C.H.: Recorded only from Bridgnorth, 1970 (Wint)†.

Flight: August and September. Possibly on moorland and the mosses of the north.

Larval F/ps: Moorland grasses. May to July.

2360 Ear Moth *Amphipoea oculea* Linnaeus

V.C.H.: Abundant at Calverhall (Thornewill) and frequent at Church Stretton. Also recorded at Broseley, 1897 (Potts, per Cortissos, 1898).

Post V.C.H.: Apart from Church Stretton (D. Smith) and the Wyre Forest (Evans; Plant) where it is frequent, this species has been recorded from Shrewsbury, 1913 (Pendlebury & Pendlebury, 1914); Benthall, 1914 (Potts, per Pendlebury, 1915); Oswestry, 1930 (Hignett, 1931); Much Wenlock, 12.ix.1954 (K. G. V. Smith, 1956); Pontesbury, 1970 (D. Smith); Broseley, 1970 and Shirlett, 1977 (Whitney); Woore, 1979 (Holdsworth) and Hopton Titterhill, 1982 (Hicks).

Flight: July to September, usually in damp localities.

Larval F/ps: Polyphagous, though mainly on grasses. April to June.

Notes: Newnham (1901a) stated that this species is often seen flying over thistles etc. in the hottest sunshine. Pendlebury & Pendlebury (1914) record ab. *erythrostigma* Haw. at Shrewsbury, 31.viii.1913.

2361 Rosy Rustic *Hydraecia micacea* Esper

V.C.H.: Shrewsbury (Stainton, 1857. Vol. 1: 198); common at Calverhall (Thornewill) and frequent at Market Drayton (Woodforde) and Church Stretton.

Post V.C.H.: Widespread and common throughout the county.

Flight: August to October in gardens, allotments, wasteground etc.

Larval F/ps: Polyphagous on low plants.

2362 Butterbur *Hydraecia petasitis* Doubleday

V.C.H.:	Unrecorded.
Post V.C.H.:	Only one record: Bridgnorth, 1970 (Wint).
Flight:	August and September along river banks and other wet habitats where the larval foodplant grows.
Larval F/p:	Butterbur. April to July.
Notes:	This species is easily overlooked and is probably more widespread than the current record suggest. The larval foodplant is common on the limestone of the Oswestry Uplands and the Wenlock Escarpment and also along the Lower Severn Valley.

2364 Frosted Orange *Gortyna flavago* Denis & Schiffermüller

V.C.H.:	Shrewsbury (Stainton, 1857. Vol. 1: 196-197); scarce at Market Drayton (Woodforde) and not rare around Church Stretton.
Post V.C.H.:	Widespread and fairly common throughout in overgrown gardens, allotments, wasteground, roadside verges etc.
Flight:	September and October.
Larval F/ps:	Inside the stems of many suitably large plants such as foxglove and thistle. April to August.

2367 Haworth's Minor *Celaena haworthii* Curtis

V.C.H.:	Scarce at Market Drayton (Woodforde, 1894); Oswestry, 1907 (Pendlebury, per Potts, 1908) and once on the Longmynd.
Post V.C.H.:	Local and scarce: Church Stretton, 1935 (Rylands) and Whixall Moss (Burrows, per Fielding 1974a), 14.ix.1929 (Hignett, 1931) and 1985 (Hardwick).
Flight:	August and September on wet moorland and the northern mosses.
Larval F/p:	Probably common cottongrass. April to July. This plant is found at both localities from which the moth has been recorded since V.C.H. times.

2368 The Crescent *Celaena leucostigma leucostigma* Hübner

V.C.H.:	One at sugar in September 1896 at Calverhall (Thornewill).
Post V.C.H.:	Local and scarce: Quatford, 1960 (D'Arcy) and Bucknell, 1970 (Shephard).
Flight:	July to September in wet localities such as damp moorland and woodland.
Larval F/ps:	The stems and roots of suitably large wetland plants such as yellow iris. March to July.

2369 Bulrush Wainscot *Nonagria typhae* Thunberg

V.C.H.:	Calverhall (Thornewill) and Soudley Pools, Church Stretton.
Post V.C.H.:	Frequently recorded from wet localities throughout the county.
Flight:	July to September.
Larval F/p:	Common reedmace*. May to September.
Notes:	The melanic ab. *fraterna* Treitschke was recorded as "rarer than the type" at Soudley Pools by Newnham (1908).

2371 Brown-veined Wainscot *Archanara dissoluta* Treitschke

V.C.H.: Unrecorded.

Post V.C.H.: A single record from the Edgemond district, 23.vii.1949 (Christie).

Flight: July to September in the vicinity of common reed.

Larval F/p: Common reed. April to July.

2375 Large Wainscot *Rhizedra lutosa* Hübner

V.C.H.: Unrecorded.

Post V.C.H.: Local and infrequent: Shrewsbury, 2.x.1913 (Pendlebury & Pendlebury, 1914) and 1923 (Wood-Taylor, 1941); Broseley, 1968 and Shirlett, 1977 (Whitney); Oswestry, 1949 (Hignett); Whixall Moss (Burrows, per Fielding, 1974a); Dothill, 1979 (Riley) and Woore, 1982 (Holdsworth).

Flight: August to October in the vicinity of common reed.

Larval F/p: Common reed. April to July.

2377 Fen Wainscot *Arenostola phragmitidis* Hübner

V.C.H.: Unrecorded.

Post V.C.H.: Two records from Rodington on 17.vii.1955 (Briggs).

Flight: July and August in the vicinity of common reed.

Larval F/ps: Common reed. April to June.

2379 Small Rufous *Coenobia rufa* Haworth

V.C.H.: One at Calverhall, August 1879 (Thornewill).

Post V.C.H.: Frequently recorded from the R.I.S. trap at Preston Montford Field Centre (det. Riley). Other records from Hodnet, 27.viii.1954 (K.G.V. Smith, 1956); Rodington, 1962 (Briggs); Shirlett, 1970 (Whitney); Whixall Moss, 1971 (Hull) and Woore, 1983 (Holdsworth).

Flight: July and August in marshy localities.

Larval F/ps: Either jointed or soft rush, which are both common throughout the county. (Sinker *et al.*, 1985). September to June.

2380 Treble-lines *Charanycia trigrammica* Hufnagel

V.C.H.: Fairly common at Shrewsbury (Stainton, 1857. Vol. 1: 215); Ford, 1907 (Pendlebury, per Potts, 1908); Calverhall (Thornewill); Market Drayton (Woodforde); Broseley (Potts) and Church Stretton.

Post V.C.H.: Common in the Wyre Forest (Evans). Otherwise widespread but local on rough ground and open woodlands.

Flight: May to July.

Larval F/ps: Polyphagous on low plants. June to April.

Notes: The melanic ab. *bilinea* Haworth was recorded in the Wyre Forest by Rea (Newnham, 1908) but has not been noted at any other locality in Shropshire.

2381 The Uncertain *Hoplodrina alsines* Brahm

V.C.H.: Scarce at Market Drayton (Woodforde), otherwise common.

Post V.C.H.: Widespread, generally distributed and common throughout the county.

Flight: June to August.

Larval F/ps: Polyphagous on low plants. September to April.

2382 The Rustic *Hoplodrina blanda* Denis & Schiffermüller

V.C.H.: Market Drayton, scarce (Woodforde); Broseley, frequent (Potts) and Church Stretton, where it was less common than *H. alsines*.

Post V.C.H.: Less frequently recorded than *H. alsines*, to which it bears a great superficial resemblance, but widespread and fairly common in a variety of habitats throughout the county.

Flight: July and August.

Larval F/ps: Polyphagous on low plants. September to May.

2387 Mottled Rustic *Caradrina morpheus* Hufnagel

V.C.H.: Shrewsbury (Stainton, 1857. Vol. 1: 217); scarce at Market Drayton (Woodforde) and frequent at Church Stretton.

Post V.C.H.: Widespread and fairly common over all but the highest parts of the county.

Flight: June to early August.

Larval F/ps: Polyphagous on low plants. August to November.

2389 Pale Mottled Willow *Caradrina clavipalpis* Scopoli

V.C.H.: Infrequent throughout. Damp woods and meadows (Newnham, 1901a).

Post V.C.H.: Infrequently recorded from gardens, wasteground etc. throughout the county. Rarely common.

Flight: May to September, though it could be found both earlier and later, in two broods.

Larval F/ps: Polyphagous on the seeds of grasses, cereals and other plants. Autumn to Spring.

2394 Anomalous Wainscot *Stilbia anomala* Haworth

V.C.H.: Unrecorded.

Post V.C.H.: Very local and uncommon. Recorded only from Church Stretton, 1959 (Knill-Jones) and Earl's Hill Nature Reserve, 1968 (Heath).

Flight: August and September on heathland and moorland.

Larval F/ps: Various moorland grasses. October to March.

2397 Small Yellow Underwing *Panemeria tenebrata* Scopoli

V.C.H.: Generally distributed, though more common in some areas than others. Common in damp meadows around Church Stretton.

Post V.C.H.: Widespread but local, inhabiting flowery meadows, grassland and roadside verges.

Flight: May and June. Diurnal and easily overlooked.

Larval F/p: Common mouse-ear chickweed*. June and July.

2399 Bordered Sallow *Pyrrhia umbra* Hufnagel

V.C.H.: Unrecorded.

Post V.C.H.: There is a single record of a larva which was reared through to the moth in 1948 by Hignett at Llanymynech. Unfortunately the foodplant was not cited (Pendlebury, 1956).

Flight: Late May to early August. Most likely to be found in limestone areas.

Larval F/p: Restharrow. July and August.

Notes: Heath (1983) states that this species is absent from most of the West Midlands and Central Wales. The record of a bordered sallow caught at Benthall, 16.ix.1926 (Potts, per Ingrams, 1927) is erroneous and refers to *X. togata* Esp.

2410 Marbled White Spot *Lithacodia pygarga* Hufnagel

V.C.H.: Recorded only from the Wyre Forest (Peed).

Post V.C.H.: Recorded only from Button Oak, Wyre Forest, 25.vi.1988 (Blunt).

Flight: May to July. Should be sought in woodlands and on heathland and moorland.

Larval F/ps: Various grasses such as purple moor-grass and false brome. July to September.

2418 Cream-bordered Green Pea *Earias clorana* Linnaeus

V.C.H.: Unrecorded.

Post V.C.H.: Ironbridge, 1961 (Derry & Whitney) and one unconfirmed record from the Wyre Forest (per Plant).

Flight: May to July with an occasional second brood in August.

Larval F/ps: Various sallows.

Notes: This species could be easily mistaken for the very common *Tortrix viridana* L. (Tortricidae) and therefore overlooked: *T. viridana* has grey hindwings whereas in *E. clorana* they are white.

2421 Scarce Silver-lines *Bena prasinana* Linnaeus

V.C.H.: Cloverley Park, once (Thornewill); Market Drayton, common some years (Woodforde) and Church Stretton, larvae not uncommon on the trunks of oak in July and August (Newnham, 1901a).

Post V.C.H.: Restricted to woodlands containing oak, but not uncommon in suitable habitats.

Flight: June to August.

Larval F/p: Oak. September to May.

2422 Green Silver-lines *Pseudoips fagana britannica* Warren

V.C.H.: Unrecorded.

Post V.C.H.: Frequently recorded from woodlands throughout the county.

Flight: June and July. The occasional second brood, occurring in August and September has not, to my knowledge, been recorded in Shropshire.

Larval F/ps: Many deciduous trees, including oak*. August and September.

2423 Oak Nycteoline *Nycteola revayana* Scopoli

V.C.H.: Unrecorded.

Post V.C.H.: One record from Candy Wood, April 1930 (Hignett, 1931) and one from Preston Montford Field Centre, 19.x.1987 (R.I.S. trap, det. Riley).

Flight: September to May in the vicinity of oaks.

Larval F/p: Oak. June and July.

2425 Nut-tree Tussock *Colocasia coryli* Linnaeus

V.C.H.: Recorded only from Church Stretton as larvae on sallow.

Post V.C.H.: Restricted to wooded areas. Local and uncommon outside the Wyre Forest: Munslow, 1969 and Willey and Shirlett, 1970 (Whitney); Pontesbury, 1974 (D. Smith); Stoke-on-Tern, 1976 (Littlewood); Ercall Woods, 1978 (Riley) and Blakeway Coppice, 1987 (Coleshaw).

Flight: April to June and July to September in two broods.

Larval F/ps: Hazel*, sallow*, beech and maple. June, July, September and October.

Notes: So far as I am aware the melanic ab. *melanotica* Haverkampf has not been recorded in Shropshire.

2434 Burnished Brass *Diachrysia chrysitis* Linnaeus

V.C.H.:   Common everywhere.

Post V.C.H.:   Widespread, generally distributed and common throughout.

Flight: June to September in two broods.

Larval F/ps: Nettle* and dock*. September to May and July and August.

2437 Golden Plusia *Polychrysia moneta* Fabricius

V.C.H.:   Unrecorded.

Post V.C.H.:   This species was first recorded at Shrewsbury on 20.vii.1913 (Pendlebury and Pendlebury, 1914). It is now widespread and frequently recorded from gardens thoughout the county.

Flight: June to August. Often attracted to *Buddleia* flowers.

Larval F/ps: Wild and cultivated species of *Delphinium*. September to April.

Notes: This species was unknown in Britain before 1890. It has spread rapidly since, possibly due to the popularity of its foodplant in gardens.

2439 Gold Spot *Plusia festucae* Linnaeus

V.C.H.:   General and occasional. The larvae were noted by Newnham (1901a) to fold leaves of yellow iris, in which it spins a whitish cocoon similar to a spider's web.

Post V.C.H.:   Regularly recorded from damp localities throughout the county though never common.

Flight: June and July. I have not received any records of the second, August and September, brood in Shropshire.

Larval F/ps: Various wetland plants including yellow iris*. The length of the larval stage in Shropshire cannot be established until the species' phenology here is understood.

2441 Silver Y *Autographa gamma* Linnaeus

V.C.H.:   Common throughout.

Post V.C.H.:   Widespread, generally distributed and common throughout the county.

Flight: An immigrant species which also breeds here and appears from Spring to Autumn.

Larval F/ps: Widely polyphagous, including potato*. Throughout the Summer and Autumn.

Notes: The diminutive ab. *gammina* Staudinger has been recorded occasionally from Dothill (Riley). Newnham (1901a) recorded a large, light-coloured form on the Longmynd which he thought "might well be a distinct species".

2442 Beautiful Golden Y *Autographa pulchrina* Haworth

V.C.H.:   General and frequent.

Post V.C.H.:   Frequently recorded from woodlands, wasteground and gardens through-out the county.

Flight: June and July.

Larval F/ps: Various low plants. August to May.

2443 Plain Golden Y *Autographa jota* Linnaeus

V.C.H.: General and frequent.

Post V.C.H.: Frequently recorded from woodlands, wasteground and gardens throughout the county.

Flight: June to early August.

Larval F/ps: Polyphagous, mainly on herbaceous plants, including nettle*. August to May.

2444 Gold Spangle *Autographa bractea* Denis & Schiffermüller

V.C.H.: Benthall Edge (Barrett) and Shrewsbury (Stainton, 1857. Vol. 1: 307).

Post V.C.H.: Fairly common in the Wyre Forest. Otherwise recorded, usually as singletons, from Rodington, 1955 and 1957 (Briggs); Minsterley, 1960 (D. Smith); Broseley, 1968 (Whitney); Pontesbury, 1971 (D. Smith); Dothill, 1973 (Riley); Shirlett, 1980 (Whitney) and Llanymynech, 22.vii.1989 (Townsend).

Flight: July and August. Wasteland, gardens and moorland.

Larval F/ps: Polyphagous on low plants. September to May.

2447 Scarce Silver Y *Syngrapha interrogationis* Linnaeus

V.C.H.: Four specimens flying over pinks at Church Stretton in June 1895 and 1896 (Newnham, 1896 & 1897a). Also noted from Shrewsbury (Newman, 1869).

Post V.C.H.: Recorded only once from Pontesbury, 1978 (D. Smith).

Flight: June to August on heather-clad moorland.

Larval F/ps: Heather and bilberry. September to June.

2449 Dark Spectacle *Abrostola trigemina* Werneburg

V.C.H.: Generally distributed. Often seen flying over *Lychnis* species, etc in the evening (Newnham, 1901a).

Post V.C.H.: Apart from the Wyre Forest, where it is not uncommon, it has been recorded from Shrewsbury, 1913 (Pendlebury and Pendlebury, 1914; Wood-Taylor, 1941); Rodington, 1956 & 1958 (Briggs); Minsterley, 1960 (D. Smith); Preston Montford Field Centre, 1967 (R.I.S. trap, det. Nicklen); Broseley, 1968 (Whitney); Pontesbury, 1969 (D. Smith); Shirlett, 1970 (Whitney); Rowton, 1976 (Littlewood) and Ludlow, 1980 (Norton).

Flight: June and July in gardens, wasteground etc.

Larval F/ps: Nettle and hop. August and September.

2450 The Spectacle *Abrostola triplasia* Linnaeus

V.C.H.: Generally distributed. Often seen flying over *Lychnis* species etc in the evening (Newnham, 1901a).

Post V.C.H.: Widespread and frequently recorded from woodlands, gardens and wasteground throughout.

Flight: May to July.

Larval F/p: Nettle*. July to September.

2451 Clifden Nonpariel *Catocala fraxini* Linnaeus

South (1961) states that this rare immigrant to Britain was noted in Shropshire in 1872. No further details of this record are available.

2452 Red Underwing *Catocala nupta* Linnaeus

V.C.H.: Unrecorded in the V.C.H. but noted by Blatch (1886) from the Wyre Forest.

Post V.C.H.: Frequently recorded from many of the larger woodlands throughout the county.

Flight: August and September.

Larval F/ps: Poplar* and willow.

2455 Dark Crimson Underwing *Catocala sponsa* Linnaeus

V.C.H.:   Unrecorded.

Post V.C.H.:   Two unconfirmed records from Buildwas power station during August and September 1942 (Mason, per Pendlebury, 1943). These were almost certainly *C. nupta* as *C. sponsa* has never been recorded outside south-eastern England and the New Forest, Hampshire.

Flight: August and September in oak woodland.

Larval F/p: Oak. April to June.

2462 Mother Shipton *Callistege mi* Clerck

V.C.H.:   Very common around Church Stretton on rough ground and in clover fields. Also recorded from the Wyre Forest (Blatch, 1886).

Post V.C.H.:   Widespread and fairly common in open woodlands, heathland and rough fields throughout.

Flight: May and June. Diurnal, flying in bright sunshine.

Larval F/p: Clover*. July to September.

Notes: Potts (per Ingrams, 1926) records an individual from near Benthall Hall, June 1925, approaching ab. *extrema* Haas in which there is a heavy white suffusion over all the wings, obliterating most of the usual markings.

2463 Burnet Companion *Euclidia glyphica* Linnaeus

V.C.H.:   Frequent in western parts. Also recorded from the Wyre Forest (Blatch, 1886).

Post V.C.H.:   Widely distributed and frequent in woodland rides and clearings. Occasionally recorded from more open habitats such as the old heather-clad pit workings around Dawley, most of which have unfortunately now disappeared.

Flight: May and June. Diurnal, flying in the sunshine.

Larval F/ps: Red clover* and other clovers and trefoils. July and August.

2464 The Alchymist *Cetaphia alchymista* Denis & Schiffermüller

V.C.H.:   Unrecorded.

Post V.C.H.:   A single specimen was recorded flying along a field hedge at Cleobury Mortimer on 20-iv-1922 by Comm. J.C. Woodward (Woodward, 1922a and 1922b). This is one of only 15 British records of this scarce immigrant.

Flight: May to July, inhabiting woodland.

Larval F/ps: Oak and occasionally elm. July and August. The larva has only been recorded twice in Britain, and never in Shropshire.

2466 The Blackneck *Lygephila pastinum* Treitschke

V.C.H.:   Unrecorded.

Post V.C.H.:   Recorded only from the Wyre Forest where it is locally common (Evans).

Flight: June and July along damp woodland edges and rides and other wet localities.

Larval F/p: Tufted vetch. August to May.

Notes: The larval foodplant is fairly common throughout (Sinker *et al.*, 1985) but Shropshire is on the northern edge of *L. pastinum*'s range in Britain. This accounts for its localised distribution in the county.

2469 The Herald *Scoliopteryx libatrix* Linnaeus

V.C.H.: Generally common. Larvae often found on sallow and willow (Newnham, 1901a).

Post V.C.H.: Fairly common in woodlands, gardens and damp localities throughout.

Flight: July to June with a period of hibernation over the coldest months when it can be found in sheds, coal bunkers, outhouses etc.

Larval F/ps: Sallow*, willow*, osier and poplar. June to August.

Notes: A female with a very dark ground colour and the usual markings very well developed was recorded by Melvill in 1916. No locality is cited (Ingrams, 1917).

2470 Small Purple-barred *Phytometra viridaria* Clerck

V.C.H.: Calverhall, common (Thornewill); Market Drayton, frequent (Woodforde) and Church Stretton, common and sometimes abundant on the Ragleth (Newnham, 1901a).

Post V.C.H.: Recorded from heathlands, open woodlands and woodland rides throughout the county, usually on calcareous or neutral soils. However there are records from the acid mosses of Whixall and Wem. Rarely common and easily overlooked.

Flight: May to July, usually diurnal, flying in bright sunshine.

Larval F/ps: Milkworts and lousewort. July to September.

2473 Beautiful Hook-tip *Laspeyria flexula*. Denis & Schiffermüller

V.C.H.: Unrecorded.

Post V.C.H.: Recorded only from Bromfield, 1953 and 1978 (Norton) and the Wyre Forest, 1986 (Plant) and 1988 (Taylor, per Plant).

Flight: July and August. Woodlands, gardens and orchards.

Larval F/ps: Lichens growing on various trees including hawthorn, blackthorn, spruce, larch and apple.

Notes: Shropshire is on the north-western edge of this species' known British range. This accounts for its very localised distribution in the county.

2474 Straw Dot *Rivula sericealis* Scopoli

V.C.H.: Unrecorded.

Post V.C.H.: Fairly common in damp woodlands, meadows, mosses and the wetter parts of heathland throughout the county.

Flight: June to early August. The second brood which occasionally occurs in southern England during August and September (Skinner, 1984) has not, to my knowledge, been recorded in Shropshire. The adults can often be found on ragwort blossoms during the day, though they do not feed (Heath, 1983).

Larval F/ps: False-bromes. August to May.

Notes: The lack of records in the V.C.H. may be due to the belief that this species belonged to the Pyralidae which was not covered by that publication.

2475 Waved Black *Parascotia fuliginaria* Linnaeus

V.C.H.: Unrecorded.

Post V.C.H.: A single diminutive male was caught in the R.I.S. trap at Ludlow on 17.ix.1989 (det. Riley). This constitutes the only Shropshire record and, due to the late date of capture, may also represent a partial second emergence for the long dry summer of that year. There is a single record from the Wyre Forest, 6.viii.1988 (Plant). Although the specimen was caught 50 yards into

Worcestershire, it was felt worth recording as the species is almost certainly found in the Shropshire portion of the Forest.

Flight: June and July in damp woodland.

Larval F/ps: Various fungi growing on old or rotting timber. August to June.

2476 Beautiful Snout *Hypena crassalis* Fabricius

V.C.H.: Unrecorded in the V.C.H. but Woodforde (1902c) cites this species as fairly common at Market Drayton in 1902.

Post V.C.H.: Local and generally uncommon outside the Wyre Forest. Recorded from Caughley Woods, 20.vi.1915 (Potts, per Ingrams, 1917); Wrekin, 1953, larvae on bilberry (K.G.V. Smith, 1954); Stoke-on-Tern, 1976 (Littlwood); Shirlett, 1977 (Whitney) and the Ercall Woods, 1979 (Riley).

Flight: June and July in woodlands.

Larval F/p: Bilberry*. August to September.

Notes: There is evidence to suggest that *H. crassalis* is fairly mobile as it is regularly recorded away from its known foodplant (Riley, 1986c). It is also stated by continental authors to feed on heather. It is therefore possible that it may extend its range within the county by means of migration, even into what appear to be unsuitable habitats. The record from Stoke-on-Tern also suggests that it is migratory as there is no known colony for some distance from this locality.

2477 The Snout *Hypena proboscidalis* Linnaeus

V.C.H.: General and common.

Post V.C.H.: Widespread, generally distributed and common throughout the county.

Flight: Late June to early October in two broods.

Larval F/p: Nettle*. October to May and July and August.

2480 Buttoned Snout *Hypena rostralis* Linnaeus

V.C.H.: Recorded from the Wyre Forest (Edwards).

Post V.C.H.: This species has become much scarcer nationally in recent years. It has not been recorded from the Wyre Forest since V.C.H. times and is now probably extinct in Shropshire.

Flight: August to early June, hibernating from November to March. Hedgerows and rough ground where wild hop grows.

Larval F/p: Hop. June and July.

Notes: Plant (1987) suggests searching for hibernating adults during the winter months. It is stated that they can easily be found in dry sheltered places such as outhouses, coalbunkers etc in the vicinity of hop. Although the author had not found adults in hollow trees there is no reason to suppose these are not used as overwintering quarters. The moth seldom comes to light.

2482 White-line Snout *Schrankia taenialis* Hübner

V.C.H.: Unrecorded.

Post V.C.H.: One unconfirmed record from Bomere Pool. This note came from the Biological Records Centre at Monkswood Experimental Station but no date or recorder's name is known. Shropshire is well outside the known range for this species and I suspect that the record is attributable to *S. costaestrigalis* Steph.

Flight: July and August. Damp woodland, heathland and hedgerows.

Larval F/ps: Unknown.

2484 Pinion-streaked Snout *Schrankia costaestrigalis* Stephens

V.C.H.: Local. Recorded only from Market Drayton where it was common (Woodforde, 1900f; Pendlebury, 1950).

Post V.C.H.: Very local and generally uncommon but easily overlooked. Recorded from Minsterley, 1960 and Pontesbury, 1973 (D. Smith); Whixall Moss, 1985 (Hardwick); Wyre Forest, 1964 (Evans) and 1987 (Plant) and Llanymynech, 22.vii.1989 (Townsend).

Flight: June to August. The second brood which sometimes occurs in southern England has not, to my knowledge, been recorded in Shropshire.

Larval F/ps: Unknown, though Woodforde reared this species in captivity on wild thyme (Newnham, 1908).

2485 Marsh Oblique-barred *Hypenodes humidalis* Doubleday

V.C.H.: Unrecorded.

Post V.C.H.: Frequently recorded from Whixall Moss.

Flight: June to early August with a smaller second generation in September. Inhabits mosses and boggy moorlands.

Larval F/ps: Unknown.

2488 Common Fan-foot *Pechipogo strigilata* Linnaeus

V.C.H.: Unrecorded.

Post V.C.H.: Recorded only from the Wyre Forest, 1960 (Evans), 1970 (Scott) and 1984 and 1988 (Plant). Plant's specimens were exhibited at the annual exhibition of the B.E.N.H.S. in 1984.

Flight: May and June in woodland.

Larval F/ps: Dead leaves and birch catkins. July to April.

Notes: This much-decreased species is now rarely recorded outside Hampshire, Sussex and Kent. For this reason it is important to investigate the Wyre Forest locality fully. *P. strigilata* can easily be mistaken for the more common *H. tarsipennalis* Tr. Skinner (1984) discusses the diagnostic features.

2489 The Fan-foot *Herminia tarsipennalis* Treitschke

V.C.H.: Not rare at Market Drayton. Apparently not noted elsewhere.

Post V.C.H.: Widespread, generally distributed and common.

Flight: June and July.

Larval F/ps: Dead leaves of many tree species. August to October.

2492 Small Fan-foot *Herminia grisealis* Denis & Schiffermüller

V.C.H.: Common in many damp woods.

Post V.C.H.: Common in woodland, mature gardens and rough ground throughout the county.

Flight: June to August.

Larval F/ps: Oak and alder. August to October.

Appendix I — Inventory of Microlepidoptera

The microlepidoptera have been largely ignored in Shropshire; the V.C.H. omitted them completely and the only resident lepidopterist to record them seriously was J. Hignett from the late 1920s to the late 1940s. Consequently the list of species for the county was very poor and most were represented on the strength of single records. This told us nothing about the species' distribution and frequency in Shropshire and, consequently, it was intended at the outset of this project to deal only with the macrolepidoptera. However, in the course of collecting data on the latter group I received many lists of microlepidoptera from visiting entomologists who have collected in Shropshire from time to time. Some of these were extensive and several covered concurrent seasons at certain localities (e.g. C. W. Plant, Wyre Forest, 1981–1988). After approaching the country's leading authorities on the various microlepidopteron families for further Shropshire records, and collating these with data collected from the Shropshire Biological Records Centre and the Rothamsted Insect Survey light trap at Preston Montford Field Centre, it was felt that a species inventory should be appended.

Although the amount of distributional data I am able to present is less than that for the macrolepidoptera, and few historical comparisons are possible, this list will form the corner stone for future study and will encourage more interest in the group amongst resident lepidopterists. Also I have found that British recorders of certain families (e.g. M. Parsons, recorder for the Oecophoridae) have no records at all for Shropshire. The list therefore provides much valuable data for increasing our knowledge of the national distribution of these groups.

The nomenclature complies with Bradley and Fletcher (1986) as amended by Emmet (1987) and Agassiz (1988). English names do not exist for most of the microlepidoptera (a fact that may discourage some newcomers to the group) but I have included those which are either in common use or refer to agricultural or horticultural pest species.

The author has relied heavily on input from visiting entomologists to make the microlepidoptera inventory as comprehensive as possible. A list of contributors is given in the acknowledgements.

The main single contributor was J. Hignett, whose records are extracted from *The Record of Bare Facts* (later summarised by Pendlebury (1950)). It has not always been possible to verify the identifications but, for the sake of literary consistency, the author felt that all previously published records should be included. Any doubts which exist about the validity of certain records are explained in a cautionary note.

FAMILY: MICROPTERIGIDAE

1. *Micropterix tunbergella* **Fabricius** Candy Wood and Llynclys, 1930 (Hignett); Hope Dale, 13.v.1976 (Langmaid) and Heath (1976) p. 152.
3. *Micropterix aureatella* **Scopoli** Candy Wood, 1929 (Hignett); Whixall Moss, 28.v.1939 (Warren) and 1981–87 (Hardwick and McWilliam); Wyre Forest, 1981–87 (Blunt; Plant) and Heath (1976) p. 153.
4. *Micropterix aruncella* **Scopoli** Oswestry, 1930 (Hignett).
5. *Micropterix calthella* **Linnaeus** Shrewsbury, 1912, on *Ranunculus auricomus* (Melvill); Oswestry, 1930 (Hignett); Ironbridge, 15.v.1976 (Langmaid); Whixall Moss, 1981–87 (Hardwick and McWilliam) and Heath (1976) pp. 154–155.

FAMILY: ERIOCRANIIDAE

6. *Eriocrania subpurpurella* **Zeller** Candy Wood, 1930 (Hignett); Whixall Moss, 31.vii.1986 (Langmaid), 30.v.1987, mines in *Quercus* (Pelham-Clinton) and 1981–87 (Hardwick and McWilliam); Colemere, 30.v.1987, mines in *Quercus* (Langmaid); Pike's End Moss, 30.v.1987 (Pelham-Clinton); Preston Montford, April & May 1987 (R.I.S. trap, det. Riley) and Hodnett, 30.vi.1988, a few vacated mines in *Quercus* (Langmaid and Pelham-Clinton).
10. *Eriocrania salopiella* **Stainton** Near Shrewsbury, April 1853 (Salt). A "wet place among birches" near Shrewsbury is the type locality for this species which was first

described by Stainton in 1854 (Stainton, 1854). Further details are described by Heath (1976) pp. 162–163. Hignett recorded this species at Whixall Moss in 1931 but no confirmatory specimens are available.

12. *Eriocrania sangii* **Wood**   Whixall Moss, 1981–87 (Hardwick and McWilliam).
13. *Eriocrania semipurpurella* **Stephens**   Whixall Moss, 1.v.1931 (Hignett) and 28.v.1939 (Warren).

FAMILY: NEPTICULIDAE

19. *Bohemannia quadrimaculella* **Boheman**   Rednal, 1948 (Hignett).
19i. *Bohemannia pulverosella* **Stainton**   Heath (1976) pp. 202–203.
23. *Ectoedemia argyropeza* **Zeller**   Walcott Park, larvae on *P. tremula* (Burkhill) and Whixall Moss, 1981–85 (Hardwick).
25. *Ectoedemia intimella* **Zeller**   Whixall Moss, 1981–85 (Hardwick).
28. *Ectoedemia angulifasciella* **Stainton**   Prees Heath (Burrows, per Fielding, 1974b) and Heath (1976) pp. 192–193.
29. *Ectoedemia atricollis* **Stainton**   Heath (1976) p. 193.
34. *Ectoedemia occultella* **Linnaeus**   Prees Heath (Burrows, per Fielding, 1974b); Walcott Park, 1930 (Burkhill); Llynclys, 1948 (Hignett); Whixall Moss, 1930 (Hignett) and 1981–85 (Hardwick); Wyre Forest, 1981–87 (Plant); Brown Moss, 21.v.1988 (Hardwick) and Heath (1976) p. 197.
37. *Ectoedemia albifasciella.* **Heinemann**   Heath (1976) p. 199 and Ironbridge, 17.ix.1980 (Emmet).
38. *Ectoedemia subbimaculella* **Haworth**   Nesscliffe, 9.vi.1932 (Hignett); Wyre Forest, 1981–87 (Plant) and Bayston Hill, 21.xi.1987, several mines in *Quercus* (Langmaid).
39. *Ectoedemia heringi* **Toll**   Heath (1976) pp. 200–202 and Bayston Hill, 21.xi.1987, a few mines in *Quercus* (Langmaid and Pelham-Clinton).
42. *Fomoria septembrella* **Stainton**   Prees Heath (Burrows, per Fielding, 1974b); Heath (1976) pp. 204–205 and Ironbridge, 17.ix.1980 (Emmet).
46. *Trifurcula immundella* **Zeller**   Prees Heath (Burrows, per Fielding, (1974b); Nesscliffe, July 1931 (Hignett); Heath (1976) pp. 210–211 and Preston Montford, August 1988, one (R.I.S. trap, det. Dunn).
48. *Trifurcula cryptella* **Stainton**   Candy Wood, 1930 (Hignett).
50. *Stigmella aurella* **Fabricius**   Heath (1976) pp. 214–215; Wyre Forest, 1981–87 (Plant) and Bayston Hill, 21.xi.1987, a few mines in *Rubus fruticosa* (Langmaid and Pelham-Clinton).
63. *Stigmella marginicolella* **Stainton**   Heath (1976) p. 224; Ironbridge, 17.ix.1980 (Emmet) and Wyre Forest, 1988 (Plant).
67. *Stigmella plagicolella* **Stainton**   Wyre Forest, 1981–87 (Plant) and Heath (1976) pp. 226-228.
68. *Stigmella salicis* **Stainton**   Prees Heath (Burrows, per Fielding, 1974b); Heath (1976) p. 228–229 and Whixall Moss, 31.vii.1976, a few mines in *Salix atrocinerea* (Langmaid and Pelham-Clinton).
70. *Stigmella obliquella* **Heinemann**   Shrewsbury, 21.xi.1987, many vacated mines in *Salix fragilis* (Langmaid and Pelham-Clinton) and Preston Montford, August 1988, one (R.I.S. trap, det. Dunn).
72. *Stigmella myrtillella* **Stainton**   A single larva in a leaf of *Vaccinium myrtillus* at Burwarton, 22.ix.1889 (Bankes, 1889).
73. *Stigmella trimaculella* **Haworth**   Heath (1976) p. 231.
75. *Stigmella floslactella* **Haworth**   Oswestry, 1930 (Hignett); Heath (1976) pp. 232–233 and Harley, 1.viii.1986, a few mines on *Corylus* (Pelham-Clinton).
77. *Stigmella tityrella* **Stainton**   Wyre Forest, 1981–87 (Plant) and Heath (1976) p. 233.
78. *Stigmella pomella* **Vaughan**   Oswestry, 1930 (Hignett).
79. *Stigmella perpygmaella* **Doubleday**   Heath (1976) pp. 234–235.
80. *Stigmella ulmivora* **Fologne**   Heath (1976) p. 307.
81. *Stigmella hemargyrella* **Koller**   Candy Wood, 1932 (Hignett) and Heath (1976) p. 236.

83. *Stigmella atricapitella* **Haworth** Heath (1976) p. 239 and Wyre Forest, 1988 (Plant).
84. *Stigmella ruficapitella* **Haworth** Bayston Hill, 21.xii.1987, one vacated mine in *Quercus* (Langmaid and Pelham-Clinton) and Wyre Forest, 1988 (Plant).
86. *Stigmella roborella* **Johansson** Heath (1976) pp. 241–243.
87. *Stigmella svenssoni* **Johansson** Bayston Hill, 21.xi.1987, one mine in *Quercus* (Langmaid and Pelham-Clinton).
92. *Stigmella anomalella* **Goeze** **Rose Leaf Miner** Heath (1976) pp. 246–247.
93. *Stigmella centifoliella* **Zeller** Candy Wood, 1930 (Hignett) and Wyre Forest, 1981–87 (Plant).
95. *Stigmella viscerella* **Stainton** Heath (1976) pp. 248–249.
97. *Stigmella malella* **Stainton** **Apple Pygmy** Heath (1976) p. 249.
99. *Stigmella hybnerella* **Hübner** Heath (1976) p. 251.
100. *Stigmella oxyacanthella* **Stainton** Heath (1976) p. 252.
103. *Stigmella nylandriella* **Tengström** Wyre Forest, 1981–87 (Plant).
108. *Stigmella crataegella* **Klimesch** Heath (1976) p. 258; Whixall Moss (Burrows, per Fielding, 1974a) and Worfield, 10.ix.1978, many empty mines on *Crataegus*, and Harley, 1.viii.1986, one mine on *Crataegus* (Pelham-Clinton).
110. *Stigmella betulicola* **Stainton** Leaf mines in birch at an army training ground near Shrawardine, 1980 (Finch); Whixall Moss, 1981–85 (Hardwick) and 1.vii.1988, a few tenanted mines in birch (Langmaid and Pelham-Clinton) and Heath (1976) pp. 259–260.
111. *Stigmella microtheriella* **Stainton** Wyre Forest, 1981–87 (Plant); Heath (1976) p. 260 and Harley, 9.viii.1986, many mines in *Corylus* (Langmaid and Pelham-Clinton).
112. *Stigmella luteella* **Stainton** Heath (1976) p. 261.
114. *Stigmella glutinosae* **Stainton** Ironbridge, 17.ix.1980 (Emmet).
115. *Stigmella alnetella* **Stainton** Prees Heath (Burrows, per Fielding, 1974b).
116. *Stigmella lapponica* **Wocke** Several vacated mines in birch at Whixall Moss, 1.vii.1988 (Langmaid and Pelham-Clinton).
117. *Stigmella confusella* **Wood** Whixall Moss, 31.vii.1986, a few mines in *Betula* (Langmaid and Pelham-Clinton).

FAMILY: OPOSTEGIDAE

119. *Opostega salaciella* **Treitschke** Candy Wood, 1929 (Hignett).
120. *Opostega crepusculella* **Zeller** Dolgoch, 1946 (Hignett).

FAMILY: TISCHERIIDAE

123. *Tischeria ekebladella* **Bjerkander** Candy Wood, 1931 (Hignett) and Wyre Forest, 1981–87 (Plant).
124. *Tischeria dodonaea* **Stainton** Whixall Moss, 1931 (Hignett).
125. *Tischeria marginea* **Haworth** Candy Wood, 1947 (Hignett) and Heath (1976) pp. 274–275.

FAMILY: INCURVARIIDAE

128. *Phylloporia bistrigella* **Haworth** Whixall Moss, 1930 (Hignett); 1981–85 (Hardwick and McWilliam) and Heath (1976) pp. 278–279.
129. *Incurvaria pectinea* **Haworth** Whixall Moss, 1948 (Hignett).
130. *Incurvaria masculella* **Denis & Schiffermüller** Oswestry, 1930 (Hignett); Ercall Heath, 20.v.1947 (E. S. Lewis) and Whixall Moss, 1981–85 (Hardwick and McWilliam).
138. *Lampronia fuscatella* **Tengström** Whixall Moss, 11.iv.1987, three tenanted galls on *Betula* (Langmaid and Pelham-Clinton).
140. *Nematopogon swammerdamella* **Linnaeus** Brown Moss, 14.v.1937 and Loynton Moss, 18.v.1944, 10.v.1945 and 13.vi.1946 (E. S. Lewis); Heath (1976) pp. 280–281; Pike's End Moss, 30.v.1987 (Pelham-Clinton); Whixall Moss, 14.v.1937 (E. S. Lewis) and 1981–85 (Hardwick and McWilliam) and Colemere, 30.v.1987 (Langmaid and Pelham-Clinton).

141. *Nematopogon schwarziellus* **Zeller**   Oswestry, 1930 (Hignett); Heath (1976) pp. 289–290 and Whixall Moss and Pike's End Moss, 30.v.1987 (Pelham-Clinton).

146. *Nemophora cupriacella* **Hübner**   Llanforda, 10.vi.1931 (Hignett).

148. *Nemophora degeerella* **Linnaeus**   Bromfield, 1.viii.1955 (Norton); Stoke-on-Tern, 1978 (Littlewood); Clee St. Margaret, 5.viii.1984 (Denman); Brown Moss, 22.viii.1984 and Preston Montford Field Centre, 17 & 18.viii.1982, mines in *Populus*, and 22.viii.1984 (at M.V.) (Finch); Whixall Moss (Burrows, per Fielding, 1974a), 1930 (Hignett) and 1981–85 (Hardwick); Hawk Lake, 1981–85 (Hardwick); Wyre Forest, 1959 (Manchester Museum), 1976 (S.B.R.C.) and 1981–87 (Plant) and Hodnett, 30.vi.1988 (two) and Whixall Moss, 1.vii.1988 (one) (Langmaid and Pelham-Clinton).

150. *Adela reaumurella* **Linnaeus**   Mile House Lane, 1929 (Ingrams); Llanymynech and Oswestry, 1930 (Hignett); Ercall Heath, 10.v.1944 (E. S. Lewis); Shrewsbury, 8.v.1945 (Lloyd); Hodnet and Hopley Coppice, 4.vi.1974 (Pelham-Clinton); Wyre Forest, 1981–87 (Plant); Whixall Moss, 1981–88 (Hardwick and McWilliam) and Brown Moss, 21.v.1988 (Hardwick).

151. *Adela croesella* **Scopoli**   Heath (1976) p. 298; Whixall Moss, 23.vi.1962 (Taylor) and 2.vii.1977 (Warren) and Wenlock Edge, 13.vi.1989 (Coleshaw).

152. *Adela rufimitrella* **Scopoli**   Halston, 2.vi.1932 (Hignett).

153. *Adela fibulella* **Denis & Schiffermüller**   Whixall Moss, (Burrows, per Fielding, 1974a); Mile House Lane, 1929 (Ingrams); Oswestry, 1929 (Hignett); Clun Forest, 16.vi.1942 (City of Birmingham Museum); Heath (1976) p. 299; Wyre Forest, 23.vi.1929 (City of Birmingham Museum) and 1981–87 (Plant) and Llanymynech, 29.v.1989 (Townsend).

FAMILY: HELIOZELIDAE

154. *Heliozela sericiella* **Haworth**   Middleton, 1944 (Hignett); Whixall Moss, 1981–87 (Hardwick and McWilliam) and Ironbridge, larval mines 17.ix.1980 (Emmet).

156. *Heliozela resplendella* **Stainton**   Ironbridge, larval mines 17.ix.1980 (Emmet).

157. *Heliozela hammoniella* **Sorhagen**   Candy Wood, 5.viii.1931 (Hignett) and Whixall Moss 1981–85 (Hardwick) and 31.vii.1986, a few mines in *Betula* (Langmaid and Pelham-Clinton).

158. *Antispila pfeifferella* **Hübner**   Llanymynech, 1930 (Hignett).

FAMILY: PSYCHIDAE

175. *Narycia monilifera* **Geoffroy**   Whixall Moss, 11.iv.1987, a few old cases (Langmaid and Pelham-Clinton).

177. *Dahlica inconspicuella* **Stainton Lesser Lichen Case-bearer**   Aston, 1948 (Hignett); Wrekin, 12.v.1951 (Warren) and Heath (1985) pp. 134–135.

181. *Taleporia tubulosa* **Retzius**   Prees Heath (Burrows, per Fielding, 1974b); Nesscliffe, 1931 (Hignett); Heath (1985) pp. 136–137; Wyre Forest, 1981–87 (Plant); Whixall Moss, 1931 (Hignett) and 21.v.1988 (McWilliam) and Brown Moss, 1986–88 (McWilliam; Hardwick).

185. *Luffia ferchaultella* **Stephens**   Whixall Moss, 31.vii.1986, a few old cases (Langmaid and Pelham-Clinton).

186. *Psyche casta* **Pallas**   Heath (1985) pp. 143–144; Hodnet, 4.vi.1974 (Pelham-Clinton); Wyre Forest, 1981–87 (Plant) and Whixall Moss 1981–88 (Hardwick, Langmaid and Pelham-Clinton).

191. *Acanthopsyche atra* **Linnaeus**   Hignett (1931) recorded the larval cases of this species as very common at Whixall Moss. Although no confirmatory specimens remain, the fact that this species is known to occur across Shropshire's northern border into Cheshire (Heath, 1976) suggests these records may be valid.

195. *Sterrhopterix fusca* **Haworth**   Heath (1985) pp. 150–151 and Whixall Moss, 1930 (Hignett), 1976 (Warren), 1981–85 (Hardwick) and 30.v.1987 and 1.vii.1988, many larvae on *Betula* and a few on *Quercus* (Langmaid and Pelham-Clinton).

FAMILY: TINEIDAE

215. *Nemapogon granella* **Linnaeus   Corn Moth**   Oswestry, 1933 (Hignett). Although there are no confirmatory specimens, this species has been recorded from most of the English counties south of, and including, Cheshire, Staffordshire and Nottinghamshire (Heath, 1985).

216. *Nemapogon cloacella* **Haworth   Cork Moth**   Oswestry, 1930 (Hignett); Heath (1985) p. 174; Whixall Moss (Burrows, per Fielding, 1974b), 1981–85 (Hardwick) and 31.vii.1986 (Langmaid and Pelham-Clinton); Preston Montford, June 1986 (one) and 1987 (one) (R.I.S. trap, det. Dunn) and Wyre Forest, 1981–87 (Plant).

220. *Nemapogon clematella* **Fabricius**   Whixall Moss (Burrows, per Fielding, 1974a) and Oswestry, 1930 (Hignett).

223. *Nemaxera betulinella* **Fabricius**   Llanforda, 1929 (Hignett) and Heath (1985) p. 183.

224. *Triaxomera parasitella* **Hübner**   Rednal, 1933 (Hignett) and Heath (1985) p. 184.

225. *Triaxomera fulvimitrella* **Sodoffsky**   Oswestry, 1948 (Hignett).

227. *Monopis laevigella* **Denis & Schiffermüller**   Oswestry, 1930 (Hignett) and Whixall Moss, 1981–85 (Hardwick).

228. *Monopis weaverella* **Scott**   Whixall Moss, 1981–85 (Hardwick).

234. *Trichophaga tapetzella* **Linnaeus   Tapestry Moth**   Shrewsbury, 1899 (Cortissos) and Oswestry, 1930, common (Hignett).

237. *Niditinea fuscella* **Linnaeus   Brown-dotted Clothes Moth**   Oswestry, 1930 (Hignett).

240. *Tinea pellionella* **Linnaeus**   Oswestry, 1948 (Hignett) and Bucknell, 1971 and 1973 (Shephard).

242. *Tinea translucens* **Meyrick**   Oswestry, 1930 (Hignett).

245. *Tinea pallescentella* **Stainton**   Oswestry, 1930 (Hignett).

246. *Tinea semifulvella* **Haworth**   Candy Wood, 13.vii.1931 (Hignett); Heath (1985) p. 204 and Preston Montford, 1986, 1987 and 1988 (R.I.S. trap, det. Dunn; Riley).

247. *Tinea trinotella* **Thunberg**   Oswestry, 1930 (Hignett) and Preston Montford, June 1986, one (R.I.S. trap, det. Dunn), May and June (three) and August (two) 1987 and August 1988, one (R.I.S. trap, det. Riley). The second brood is only usually recorded in southern England.

250i. *Oinophila v-flava* **Haworth   Yellow V Moth**   Oswestry, "In centre of town 1929, one specimen" (Hignett, 1931).

FAMILY: OCHSENHEIMERIIDAE

251. *Ochsenheimeria mediopectinellus* **Haworth**   One record from an army training ground near Shrawardine, 18.viii.1984 (Finch) and Heath (1985) pp. 209–210.

FAMILY: LYONETIIDAE

254. *Leucoptera laburnella* **Stainton**   Oswestry, 1930, abundant (Hignett); Heath (1985) p. 215 and Shrewsbury, 29.vii.1986, a few at M.V. (Langmaid and Pelham-Clinton).

256. *Leucoptera spartifoliella* **Hübner**   Nesscliffe, 30.vii.1931 (Hignett) and a colony on broom at Earl's Hill, N.N.R., July 1980 (Finch).

260. *Leucoptera malifoliella* **Costa   Pear Leaf Blister Moth**   Heath (1985) p. 221 and Worfield, 10.ix.1978, a few mines on *Crataegus* (Pelham-Clinton).

263. *Lyonetia clerkella* **Linnaeus   Apple Leaf Miner**   Candy Wood, 1929 (Hignett); Heath (1985) pp. 224–225; Colemere, 30.v.1987, several mines on *Crataegus* and *Malus* (Langmaid and Pelham-Clinton); Shrewsbury, 30.vi.1988, one at M.V. (Langmaid and Pelham-Clinton) and Brown Moss, 9.ix.1989 (Hardwick).

FAMILY: BUCCULATRICIDAE

265. *Bucculatrix cristatella* **Zeller**   Bwlch, June 1931 (Hignett).

266. *Bucculatrix nigricomella* **Zeller**   Whitehaven, 1944 (Hignett) and Wyre Forest 25.viii.1986 (Plant).

271. *Bucculatrix albedinella* **Zeller**   Ironbridge, larval mines 17.ix.1980 (Emmet).
272. *Bucculatrix cidarella* **Zeller**   Prees Heath (Burrows, per Fielding, 1974b); Rednal, 1948 (Hignett); Hopesay, 14.ix.1981, larva on *Alnus* (Langmaid); Whixall Moss, 15.ix.1981, larva on *Alnus* (Langmaid) and Heath (1985) pp. 234–235.
274. *Bucculatrix ulmella* **Zeller**   Heath (1985) pp. 236–237 and Brown Moss, 9.ix.1989 (Hardwick).
275. *Bucculatrix bechsteinella* **Bechstein & Scharfenberg**   Knockin, 1948 (Hignett).

FAMILY: GRACILLARIIDAE

281. *Caloptilia populetorum* **Zeller**   Llanforda, 1929 (Hignett).
282. *Caloptilia elongella* **Linnaeus**   Prees Heath (Burrows, per Fielding, 1974b); Candy Wood, 1929 (Hignett); Mary Knoll Valley, 11.x.1966 (Warren); Heath (1985) pp. 258–259; Whixall Moss (Burrows, per Fielding, 1974a), 31.vii.1986, a few larvae on *Alnus glutinosa* (Langmaid and Pelham-Clinton); Preston Montford, April (two) and July (two) 1988 (R.I.S. trap, det. Dunn) and Brown Moss, 9.ix.1989 (Hardwick).
283. *Caloptilia betulicola* **Hering**   Heath (1985) p. 258 and Whixall Moss, 15.ix.1981, larva on birch (Langmaid) and 31.viii.1986 (Langmaid and Pelham-Clinton).
286. *Caloptilia alchimiella* **Scopoli**   One unconfirmed record from Candy Wood, 1930 (Hignett) and Preston Montford, June 1988, one (R.I.S. trap, det. Dunn).
287. *Caloptilia robustella* **Jäckh**   Wyre Forest, 1981–87 (Plant) and Preston Montford, July 1987, two (R.I.S. trap, det. Riley).
288. *Caloptilia stigmatella* **Fabricius**   Whixall Moss (Burrows, per Fielding, 1974a), 10.iv.1931 (Hignett), 15.ix.1981, larvae on sallow (Langmaid) and 1981–85 (Hardwick); Heath (1985) p. 266; Preston Montford, October 1987, one (R.I.S. trap, det. Riley) and July to December 1988 (R.I.S. trap, det. Dunn and Riley); Ironbridge, 11.vii.1990, larval feedings on *Salix* sp. and Brown Moss, 11.vii.1990, cone on *Salix* sp. (Palmer).
293. *Caloptilia syringella* **Fabricius**   Oswestry, 1930 (Hignett); Llanymynech, 9.vii.1963 (Warren) and Heath (1985) pp. 270-271.
294. *Aspilapteryx tringipennella* **Zeller**   Llanforda, 1930 (Hignett) and Heath (1985) pp. 271-272.
296. *Calybites phasianipennella* **Hübner**   Oswestry, 1929 (Hignett) and Whixall Moss, 15.ix.1981, larvae on *Polygonum pessicaria* and *Rumex acetosella* (Langmaid).
297. *Calybites auroguttella* **Stephens**   Wolfshead, 1944 (Hignett); Ironbridge, 17.ix.1980 (Emmet) and Wyre Forest, 1981–87 (Plant).
301. *Parornix betulae* **Stainton**   Whixall Moss, 1930 (Hignett), 15.ix.1981, larvae on *Betula* (Langmaid) and 1981–85 (Hardwick) and Heath (1985) pp. 278–279.
303. *Parornix anglicella* **Stainton**   Oswestry, 1930 (Hignett); Worfield, 10.ix.1978, spinnings on *Crataegus* (Pelham-Clinton); Hopesay, 1981 (Langmaid); Whixall Moss, 1981–85 (Hardwick); Heath (1985) pp. 280–282; Harley, 1.viii.1986 (Pelham-Clinton); Wyre Forest, 1981–87 (Plant); Preston Montford, June 1988, three (R.I.S. trap, det. Dunn) and Wem, 10.vii.1990, spinnings on hawthorn (Palmer).
304. *Parornix devoniella* **Stainton**   Oswestry, 1930 (Hignett); Ironbridge, 17.ix.1980 (Emmet); Hopesay, 1981, larvae on *Corylus* (Langmaid); Harley, 1.viii.1986, one mine on *Corylus* (Pelham-Clinton) and Preston Montford, August 1987, two (R.I.S. trap, det. Dunn).
305. *Parornix scoticella* **Stainton**   Oswestry, 1929 (Hignett) and Heath (1985) pp. 283–284.
308. *Parornix finitimella* **Zeller**   Hopesay, 1981, larvae on *Prunus* (Langmaid).
309. *Parornix torquillella* **Zeller**   One unconfirmed record from Candy Wood, 1929 (Hignett). Other records from Hopesay, 1981, larvae on *Prunus* (Langmaid); Heath (1985) pp. 287–288 and Preston Montford, May to July 1987 (R.I.S. trap, det. Dunn).
310. *Callisto denticulella* **Thunberg**   Oswestry, 1929 (Hignett) and Heath (1985) pp. 289–290.
313. *Acrocercops brongniardella* **Fabricius**   Wyre Forest, 1981–87 (Plant).

315. *Phyllonorycter harrisella* **Linnaeus**   Oswestry, 1930 (Hignett); Whixall Moss, 1981–85 (Hardwick and McWilliam); Heath (1985) p. 306 and Wyre Forest, 1981–87 (Plant).

317. *Phyllonorycter heegeriella* **Zeller**   Ironbridge, 17.ix.1980 (Emmet); Bayston Hill, 25.xii.1985 and 21.xi.1987, mines in *Quercus* (Langmaid and Pelham-Clinton) and Preston Montford, August 1987, one (R.I.S. trap, det. Dunn).

320. *Phyllonorycter quercifoliella* **Zeller**   Oswestry, 1930 (Hignett); Hopley Coppice, 4.vi.1974 (Pelham-Clinton); Heath (1985) p. 311; Whixall Moss, 31.vii.1986 (Langmaid and Pelham-Clinton); Wyre Forest, 1981–87 (Plant) and Preston Montford, May to September 1987 (five) and 1988 (five) (R.I.S. trap, det. Dunn).

321. *Phyllonorycter messaniella* **Zeller**   Maesbury, 1948, abundant (Hignett); Heath (1985) pp. 312–313; Whixall Moss, 31.vii.1986 (Langmaid and Pelham-Clinton) and Wyre Forest, 1981–87 (Plant).

322. *Phyllonorycter muelleriella* **Zeller**   Wyre Forest, 1981–87 (Plant).

323. *Phyllonorycter oxyacanthae* **Frey**   Harley, 9.viii.1986, one mine in *Crataegus* (Langmaid and Pelham-Clinton); Wyre Forest, 1981–87 (Plant) and Brown Moss, 9.ix.1989 (Hardwick).

324. *Phyllonorycter sorbi* **Frey**   Whixall Moss, 1981–85 (Hardwick); Wyre Forest, 1981–87 (Plant) and Hodnett, 30.vi.1988, two mines in *Sorbus aucuparia* (Langmaid and Pelham-Clinton). Also represented from Shropshire in the H. Heal collection (Irish national collection, Dublin) (Emmet, pers. comm.).

325. *Phyllonorycter mespilella* **Hübner**   Oswestry, 1930 (Hignett). The record in Heath (1985) has subsequently been deemed incorrect (Emmet, pers. comm.).

326. *Phyllonorycter blancardella* **Fabricius**   Oswestry, 1930 (Hignett); Heath (1985) pp. 318–319; Preston Montford, July 1986,one (R.I.S. trap, det. Dunn) and Wyre Forest, 1981–87 (Plant).

329. *Phyllonorycter spinicolella* **Zeller**   Albynes, 1918 (Pitt); Oswestry, 1930 (Hignett); Hopedale, 14.ix.1981, larvae on *Prunus* (Langmaid) and Heath (1985) pp. 322–323.

332. *Phyllonorycter corylifoliella* **Hübner**   Worfield, 10.ix.1978, a few mines on *Crataegus* (Pelham-Clinton); Heath (1985) pp. 327–328 and Wyre Forest, 1981–87 (Plant).

333. *Phyllonorycter viminiella* **Sircom**   Llanforda and Oswestry, 6.v.1931 (Hignett); Heath (1985) pp. 328–329 and Wyre Forest, 1981–87 (Plant).

335. *Phyllonorycter salicicolella* **Sircom**   One unconfirmed record from Oswestry, 1930 (Hignett). Also Heath (1985) pp. 330–331.

337. *Phyllonorycter hilarella* **Zetterstedt**   Llynclys, 1930 (Hignett); Hopedale, 1971, larvae on *Salix caprea* (Langmaid); Heath (1985) p. 332 and Preston Montford, June 1987, one (R.I.S. trap, det. Riley).

338. *Phyllonorycter cavella* **Zeller**   Oswestry, 1930 (Hignett); Hopley Coppice, 4.vi.1974 (Pelham-Clinton) and Heath (1985) p. 333.

340. *Phyllonorycter scopariella* **Zeller**   Prees Heath (Burrows, per Fielding, 1974b); Oswestry, 1949 (Hignett) and Heath (1985) pp. 334–335.

341. *Phyllonorycter maestingella* **Müller**   Candy Wood, 1930 (Hignett); Cuckoopen Coppice, 1963 (Warren); Hopedale, 13.v.1976 (Langmaid); Heath (1985) pp. 336–337; Wyre Forest, 1981–87 (Plant) and Brown Moss, 1986 & 1987 (McWilliam).

342. *Phyllonorycter coryli* **Nicelli Nut Leaf Blister Moth**   Oswestry, 1948 (Hignett); Hopesay, 14.ix.1981, mines on *Corylus* (Langmaid); Heath (1985) pp. 337–338; Harley, 1.viii.1986, mines on *Corylus* (Pelham-Clinton); Wyre Forest, 1981–87 (Plant) and Brown Moss, 9.ix.1989 (Hardwick).

344. *Phyllonorycter strigulatella* **Zeller**   One unconfirmed record from Aston, 1930 (Hignett). Changes in subsequent nomenclature cast some doubt on its validity.

345. *Phyllonorycter rajella* **Linnaeus**   Oswestry, 1930 (Hignett); Hopesay, 14.ix.1981 (Langmaid); Heath (1985) pp. 340–341; Whixall Moss, 15.ix.1981 (Langmaid), 1981–85 (Hardwick) and 31.vii.1986, one mine in *Alnus glutinosa* (Langmaid and Pelham-Clinton) and Wyre Forest, 1981–87 (Plant).

347. *Phyllonorycter anderidae* **Fletcher**   Prees Heath and Whixall Moss (Burrows, per Fielding, 1974a & b); Heath (1985) pp. 342–343 and Whixall Moss, 1981–87 (Hardwick).

351. *Phyllonorycter lautella* **Zeller**   Hopedale, 13.v.1976 (Langmaid) and Heath (1985) pp. 341–346.
352. *Phyllonorycter schreberella* **Fabricius**   Heath (1985) pp. 346–347.
353. *Phyllonorycter ulmifoliella* **Hübner**   Oswestry, 1.v.1931 (Hignett); Heath (1985) pp. 347–348; Whixall Moss, 1981–85 (Hardwick) and 31.vii.1986 and 1.vii.1988, a few mines in *Betula* (Langmaid and Pelham-Clinton) and Wyre Forest, 1981–87 (Plant).
354. *Phyllonorycter emberizaepenella* **Bouché**   Heath (1985) pp. 348–349; Wyre Forest, 1981–87 (Plant) and Brown Moss, 9.ix.1989 (Hardwick).
356. *Phyllonorycter tristrigella* **Haworth**   Aston, 1948 (Hignett) and Heath (1985) p. 350.
357. *Phyllonorycter stettinensis* **Nicelli**   Sweeney, 1930 (Hignett); Heath (1985) p. 351; Whixall Moss, 15.ix.1981 and 31.vii.1986, a few mines in *Alnus glutinosa* (Langmaid and Pelham-Clinton) and Wyre Forest, 1981–87 (Plant).
358. *Phyllonorycter froelichiella* **Zeller**   Whixall Moss, 15.ix.1981, mines in *Alnus* (Langmaid) and Heath (1985) pp. 352–353.
359. *Phyllonorycter nicellii* **Stainton**   Llynclys, 1930 (Hignett); Heath (1985) pp. 352–353; Wyre Forest, 1981–87 (Plant) and Brown Moss, 9.ix.1989 (Hardwick).
360. *Phyllonorycter kleemannella* **Fabricius**   Shrawardine army training ground, 14.viii.1982 (Finch); Whixall Moss, 1981–85 (Hardwick) and Heath (1985) pp. 352–354.
361. *Phyllonorycter trifasciella* **Haworth**   Heath (1985) p. 355; Wyre Forest, August 1988, common as larval mines (Plant) and Brown Moss, 9.ix.1989 (Hardwick).
362. *Phyllonorycter acerifoliella* **Zeller**   Oswestry, 1930 (Hignett) and Harley, 1.viii.1986, a few mines on *Acer campestre* (Pelham-Clinton).
364. *Phyllonorycter geniculella* **Ragonot**   Heath (1985) pp. 357–358; Preston Montford, July 1987 and August 1988 (R.I.S. trap, det. Riley) and Brown Moss, 9.ix.1989 (Hardwick).
368. *Phyllocnistis unipunctella* **Stephens**   Aston, 1930 (Hignett); Ironbridge, 17.ix.1980 (Emmet) and Preston Montford, 17.viii.1982, mines on *Populus* (Finch).

FAMILY: CHOREUTIDAE

385. *Anthophila fabriciana* **Linnaeus**   Shrewsbury, 1905 (Melvill); Oswestry, 1930 (Hignett); Bomere, Sweatmere and Fenemere, Sept. and Oct. 1979 (Shephard); Neenton, 18.vi.1969 (Pelham-Clinton); Hawk Lake, 1981–85 (Hardwick) Heath (1985) pp. 391–392; Colemere, 3.x.1979 (Shephard) and 30.v.1987, many (Langmaid and Pelham-Clinton); Wyre Forest, 1981–87, very common (Plant); Whixall Moss, 1981–88 (Hardwick, McWilliam, Langmaid, Pelham-Clinton and Burrows); Hodnet, 30.vi.1988, several (Landmaid and Pelham-Clinton) and Brown Moss, 1986 and 1987 (McWilliam) and 21.v.1988 and 9.ix.1989 (Hardwick).
387. *Choreutis sehestediana* **Fabricius**   Wyre Forest, 1981–87 (Plant).
388. *Choreutis myllerana* **Fabricius**   Whixall Moss, 4.vi.1931 (Hignett); Brown Moss, 24.vii.1938 (Warren) and Wyre Forest, 1981–87 (Plant).

FAMILY: GLYPHIPTERIGIDAE

391. *Glyphipterix simpliciella* **Stephens**   Oswestry, 1930 (Hignett); Hawk Lake, 1981–85 (Hardwick); Heath (1985) pp. 401–402; Whixall Moss, 21.v.1988 (McWilliam); Wyre Forest, 1988 (Plant) and Brown Moss, 21.v.1988 (Hardwick).
395. *Glyphipterix haworthana* **Stephens**   Whixall Moss, 10.vi.1932 (Hignett).
396. *Glyphipterix fuscoviridella* **Haworth**   Oswestry, 1930 (Hignett); Wyre Forest, 1981–87 (Plant); Whixall Moss, 1981–88 (Hardwick) and Brown Moss, 21.v.1988 (Hardwick).
397. *Glyphipterix thrasonella* **Scopoli**   Llanymynech, 1950 (Hignett).

FAMILY: YPONOMEUTIDAE

401. *Argyresthia laevigatella* **Herrich-Schäffer**   Llanymynech, 6.vii.1963 (Warren).
410. *Argyresthia brockeella* **Hübner**   Candy Wood, 1929 (Hignett); Whixall Moss, 1929

(Hignett), 2.vii.1939 (Warren), 1981–85 (Hardwick) and 31.vii.1986 and 1.vii.1988 (Langmaid and Pelham-Clinton); Brown Moss, 1986 & 1987 (McWilliam) and Preston Montford, June and July 1987 and 1988 (R.I.S. trap, det. Dunn).

411. *Argyresthia goedartella* **Linnaeus** Candy Wood, 1930 (Hignett); Whixall Moss, 1930 (Hignett); 15.ix.1981 (Langmaid), 1981–85 (Hardwick) and 31.vii.1986 (Langmaid); Harley, 9.viii.1986 (Langmaid and Pelham-Clinton); Wyre Forest, 1981–87 (Plant); Preston Montford, 18.viii.1982 and 18–20.viii.1984 (Finch) and 1986 & 1987 (R.I.S. trap, det. Dunn) and Brown Moss 1986 and 1987 (McWilliam).

412. *Argyresthia pygmaeella* **Denis & Schiffermüller** Rednal, 1948 (Hignett); Ashes Hollow, May 1976, larvae on *Salix caprea* (Langmaid); Whixall Moss, 1981–85 (Hardwick) and Preston Montford, July 1987 (R.I.S. trap, det. Riley).

413. *Argyresthia sorbiella* **Treitschke** Oswestry, 1929 (Hignett) and Preston Montford, July 1987, one (R.I.S. trap, det. Dunn).

415. *Argyresthia retinella* **Zeller** Llynclys, 1929 (Hignett); Whixall Moss, 1930 (Hignett), 1981–85 (Hardwick) and 31.vii.1986 and 1.vii.1988 (Langmaid and Pelham-Clinton); Brown Moss, 1986 & 1987 (McWilliam); Hodnett, 30.vi.1988, one (Langmaid and Pelham-Clinton) and Preston Montford, July 1988, one (R.I.S. trap, det. Dunn).

417. *Argyresthia mendica* **Haworth** Llanforda, 1929 (Hignett).

418. *Argyresthia conjugella* **Zeller** **Apple Fruit Moth** Oswestry, 1930 (Hignett) and Bomere, 22.viii.1984 (Finch).

419. *Argyresthia semifusca* **Haworth** Oswestry, 1929 (Hignett).

421. *Argyresthia bonnetella* **Linnaeus** Oswestry, 1929 (Hignett); Ashes Hollow, May 1976, larvae on hawthorn (Langmaid); Whixall Moss, 1981–85 (Hardwick) and Preston Montford, June 1988, one (R.I.S. trap, det. Riley).

422. *Argyresthia albistria* **Haworth** Oswestry, 1932 and Rednal, 1948 (Hignett) and Wyre Forest, 1981–87 (Plant).

423. *Argyresthia semitestacella* **Curtis** Oswestry, 1929 (Hignett).

424. *Yponomeuta evonymella* **Linnaeus** **Bird-cherry Ermine** Oswestry, 1930, larvae on *Prunus* (Hignett); Whixall Moss, 1981–85 (Hardwick); Wyre Forest, 1988 (Plant) and Preston Montford, 1986, 1987 and 1988 (R.I.S. trap, det. Riley).

425. *Yponomeuta padella* **Linnaeus** **Orchard Ermine** Shrewsbury, 1897 (Cortissos); Llynclys, 1930 (Hignett); Bromfield, 1.viii.1955 (Norton); Dothill, 18.vii.1976 (Riley); Clee St. Margaret, 5.viii.1984 (Denman); Preston Montford, 2.viii.1979 and August 1987 and 1988 (R.I.S. trap, det. Riley) and Wem, 10.vii.1990, larval spinnings on hawthorn (Palmer).

427. *Yponomeuta cagnagella* **Hübner** **Spindle Ermine** Oswestry, 1930 (Hignett) and Preston Montford, July 1987, one (R.I.S. trap, det. Riley).

430. *Yponomeuta plumbella* **Denis & Schiffermüller** Kinnerley, 1948 (Hignett).

436. *Pseudoswammerdamia combinella* **Hübner** Oswestry, 1930 (Hignett).

437. *Swammerdamia caesiella* **Hübner** Llynclys, 1929(Hignett); Whixall Moss, 1930 (Hignett) and 31.vii.1986, a few (Langmaid and Pelham-Clinton) and Preston Montford, July 1987 (one) and June 1988 (one) (R.I.S. trap, det. Dunn).

438. *Swammerdamia pyrella* **Villers** Oswestry, 1930 (Hignett) and Whixall Moss, 1981–85 (Hardwick).

441. *Paraswammerdamia lutarea* **Haworth** Oswestry, 1930 (Hignett) and Whixall Moss, 1981–85 (Hardwick).

442. *Cedestis gysseleniella* **Zeller** Candy Wood, 1930 (Hignett).

443. *Cedestis subfasciella* **Stephens** Knockin, 1948 (Hignett).

444. *Ocnerostoma piniariella* **Zeller** Shrewsbury, 1897 (Cortissos) and Candy Wood, 1930 and Knockin, 1948 (Hignett).

449. *Prays fraxinella* **Bjerkander** Oswestry, 1930 (Hignett) and Colemere, 30.v.1987, a few larvae on *Fraxinus* (Langmaid and Pelham-Clinton).

450. *Scythropia crataegella* **Linnaeus** **Hawthorn Moth** Four at Preston Montford, June 1987 (R.I.S. trap, det. Dunn).

452. *Ypsolopha nemorella* **Linnaeus** Single specimens have been recorded from the Ercall Woods, 10.vii.1976 (Riley) and Llanymynech, 23.vii.1989 (Townsend. Det. confirmed Riley).

151

453. *Ypsolopha dentella* **Fabricius** **Honeysuckle Moth** Oswestry, 1930 (Hignett).
455. *Ypsolopha scabrella* **Linnaeus** Oswestry and Rednall, 1948 (Hignett); Preston Montford, August 1987 (two) and 1988 (one) (R.I.S. trap, det. Riley) and Wyre Forest, 1988 (Plant).
456. *Ypsolopha horridella* **Treitschke** Edgerley, 1948 (Hignett).
459. *Ypsolopha sylvella* **Linnaeus** Kinnerley and Aston, 1948 (Hignett) and Brown Moss, 9.ix.1989 (Hardwick).
460. *Ypsolopha parenthesella* **Linnaeus** Oswestry, 1930 (Hignett); Mary Knoll Valley, 11.x.1976 (Warren); Whixall Moss, 1981–85 (Hardwick) and 31.vii.1986, two (Langmaid and Pelham-Clinton); Wyre Forest, 1981–87 (Plant) and Brown Moss, 1986 & 1987 (McWilliam).
461. *Ypsolopha ustella* **Clerck** Prees Heath (Burrows, per Fielding, 1974b); Oswestry, 1930 (Hignett); Wellington, 29.vii.1976 (Riley); Whixall Moss, 1981–85 (Hardwick) and 31.vii.1986, one (Langmaid and Pelham-Clinton); Wyre Forest, 1981–87 (Plant); Preston Montford, November 1987, one (R.I.S. trap, det. Riley); Brown Moss, 9.ix.1989 (Hardwick) and Llanymynech, 23.vii.1989, one (Townsend. Det. confirmed Riley).
462. *Ypsolopha sequella* **Clerck** Candy Wood, 1930 (Hignett) and Ellesmere, 11.vii.1963 (Warren).
463. *Ypsolopha vittella* **Linnaeus** Candy Wood, 1930 (Hignett).
464. *Plutella xylostella* **Linnaeus** **Diamond-back Moth** Frequent and sometimes common at R.I.S. traps at Preston Montford, Rowton and Stoke-on-Tern (Riley). Also recorded from Oswestry, 1930 (Hignett); Cosford, 1976 (Riley); Wellington, most years (Riley); Whixall Moss, 1981–87 (Burrows, Hardwick and McWilliam) and Shrewsbury, 30.vi.1988, one at M.V. (Langmaid and Pelham-Clinton). Appears to prefer open situations.
465. *Plutella porrectella* **Linnaeus** Oswestry, 1929 (Hignett).
467. *Rhigognostis annulatella* **Curtis** Hignett recorded this species at Penylan Lane, Oswestry, in 1929. Nationally it is a very local species, found, at its closest point to Shropshire, in northern Wales and Lancashire (Anon., 1978). As there are no confirmatory specimens this record should be treated with caution.
470. *Orthotaelia sparganella* **Thunberg** Aston, 1948 (Hignett).

FAMILY: EPERMENIIDAE

478. *Phaulernis fulviguttella* **Zeller** Whixall Moss, 1930 (Hignett) and 31.vii.1986, one (Langmaid and Pelham-Clinton).
483. *Epermenia chaerophyllella* **Goeze** Whixall Moss (Burrows, per Fielding, 1974a); Candy Wood, 1930 (Hignett) and Hodnett, 30.vi.1988, several larval feedings in *Heracleum* (Langmaid and Pelham-Clinton).

FAMILY: SCHRECKENSTEINIIDAE

485. *Schreckensteinia festaliella* **Hübner** Candy Wood, 1929 (Hignett); Wyre Forest, 1981–87 (Plant) and Preston Montford, May 1988 (R.I.S. trap, det. Dunn).

FAMILY: COLEOPHORIDAE

490. *Coleophora lutipennella* **Zeller** Oswestry, 1930 (Hignett). However, at this date *C. lutipennella* and *C. flavipennella* Dup. had not been separated. Hignett's record could, therefore, be either species.
491. *Coleophora gryphinipennella* **Hübner** Llanforda, 1930 (Hignett) and Preston Montford, June 1988, one (R.I.S. trap, det. Dunn).
492. *Coleophora flavipenella* **Duponchel** One tapped from an oak tree at Ironbridge, 11.vii.1990 and one female disturbed from oak at Brown Moss on the same day. Both were recorded by R. M. Palmer and the identifications were confirmed by examination of the genitalia.

493. *Coleophora serratella* **Linnaeus**   Shrawardine army training ground, July 1980, larval cases on *Betula pendula* (Finch); Whixall Moss, 1930 (Hignett), 1981, 1986 and 1988, larval cases on *Alnus* and *Betula* (Langmaid and Pelham-Clinton) and 1981–88 (Hardwick; McWilliam) and Brown Moss, 21.v.1988 and 9.ix.1989 (Hardwick).
494. *Coleophora coracipennella* **Hübner**   One unconfirmed record from Oswestry, July 1931 (Hignett). Also Whixall Moss, 1981–85 (Hardwick).
495. *Coleophora spinella* **Schrank   Apple & Plum Case-bearer**   Pike's End Moss, 30.v.1987, a few cases on *Crataegus* (Langmaid and Pelham-Clinton).
496. *Coleophora milvipennis* **Zeller**   Whixall Moss, larval cases on *Betula*, 15.ix.1981 (Langmaid), 11.iv.1987 (one case) and 1.vii.1988 (two cases) (Langmaid and Pelham-Clinton).
498. *Coleophora alnifoliae* **Barasch**   Whixall Moss, 15.ix.1981 (Langmaid).
499. *Coleophora limosipennella* **Duponchel**   Whixall Moss, 1931 (Hignett).
504. *Coleophora viminetella* **Zeller**   Llanymynech Hills, 1929 (Hignett) and Whixall Moss, larvae on *Salix atrocinerea*, 15.ix.1981 and 1986 (Langmaid and Pelham-Clinton) and 1981–87 (Hardwick and McWilliam).
510. *Coleophora juncicolella* **Stainton**   Three at Preston Montford, June 1987 (R.I.S. trap, det. Dunn).
511. *Coleophora orbitella* **Zeller**   Whixall Moss, two larval cases on *Betula*, 1.vii.1988 (Langmaid and Pelham-Clinton).
516. *Coleophora trifolii* **Curtis**   Preston Montford, June 1988, one (R.I.S. trap, det. Dunn).
518. *Coleophora mayrella* **Hübner**   Whixall Moss, 1981–85 (Hardwick) and Preston Montford, June and July 1986, 1987 and 1988 (R.I.S. trap, det. Dunn).
519. *Coleophora deauratella* **Zeller**   Preston Montford, June 1988, one (R.I.S. trap, det. Dunn).
522. *Coleophora lineola* **Haworth**   Shrewsbury (Stainton, 1859, p. 248).
525. *Coleophora solitariella* **Zeller**   "Near Shrewsbury" (Stainton, 1859, p. 118).
526. *Coleophora laricella* **Hübner   Larch Case-bearer**   Llanymynech Hills, 1932 (Hignett).
530. *Coleophora lixella* **Zeller**   Sturt Common, 18.vi.1971 (Warren).
532. *Coleophora albidella* **Denis & Schiffermüller**   Whixall Moss, larval case on *Salix* sp. 15.ix.1981 (Langmaid) and Preston Montford, 1986 & 1987 (R.I.S. trap, det. Dunn).
533. *Coleophora anatipennella* **Hübner   Pistol Case-bearer**   Shrawardine army training ground, July 1980 (Finch).
534. *Coleophora currucipennella* **Zeller**   Whixall Moss (Burrows, per Fielding, 1974a) and Oswestry, 1931 (Hignett).
536. *Coleophora ibipennella* **Zeller**   Whixall Moss, 1981–85 (Hardwick).
537. *Coleophora palliatella* **Zincken**   Wyre Forest, 1986 (Plant) and Preston Montford, July 1988, one (R.I.S. trap, det. Dunn).
541. *Coleophora pyrrhulipennella* **Zeller**   Whixall Moss, 1981–85 (Hardwick).
544. *Coleophora albicosta* **Haworth**   Llynclys, 1930 (Hignett); Wyre Forest, 1986 (Plant) and Preston Montford, June 1988, five (R.I.S. trap, det. Dunn).
546. *Coleophora genistae* **Stainton**   Llanymynech Hills, 1929 and 1947 (Hignett).
547. *Coleophora discordella* **Zeller**   Llanforda, 12.vii.1931 (Hignett) and Whixall Moss, 1981–85 (Hardwick and McWilliam).
555. *Coleophora follicularis* **Vallot**   Llanymynech Hills, 1929 (Hignett) and Hawk Lake, 1981–85 (Hardwick).
560. *Coleophora paripennella* **Zeller**   Whixall Moss, 1981–87 (Hardwick and McWilliam).
564. *Coleophora virgaureae* **Stainton**   Llynclys, 1948 (Hignett).
572. *Coleophora vestianella* **Linnaeus**   Gobowen, 12.vii.1932 and 1947 (Hignett). The nomenclature of this species and *C. saxicolella* Dup. have been greatly confused. *C. saxicolella* is far more widespread than *C. vestianella*, therefore Hignett's record may be attributable to the former species.
578. *Coleophora murinipennella* **Duponchel**   Llanymynech Hills, 12.vi.1932 and Wolfshead, 1947 (Hignett).
582. *Coleophora glaucicolella* **Wood**   Whixall Moss, 1981–85 (Hardwick).

584. *Coleophora alticolella* **Zeller**   Whixall Moss, 1981–87 (Hardwick and McWilliam) and Wyre Forest, 1981–87, common (Plant).

587. *Coleophora caespititiella* **Zeller**   Llanforda, 1929 (Hignett) and Preston Montford, June 1986, one (R.I.S. trap, det. Dunn).

FAMILY: ELACHISTIDAE

590. *Perittia obscurepunctella* **Stainton**   Wolfshead, 1948 (Hignett) and Hopedale, 13.v.1976 (Langmaid).

592. *Stephensia brunnichella* **Linnaeus**   Candy Wood, August 1931 (Hignett).

594. *Elachista gleichenella* **Fabricius**   Llynclys, 1947 (Hignett).

595. *Elachista biatomella* **Stainton**   Candy Wood, 1931 (Hignett).

597. *Elachista atricomella* **Stainton**   Babbin's Wood, 1931 (Hignett); Wyre Forest, 1981–87 (Plant) and Preston Montford, June and July 1987 (R.I.S. trap, det. Dunn).

598. *Elachista kilmunella* **Stainton**   Whixall Moss, 1931 (Hignett), 28.v.1939 (Warren) and 1981–85 (Hardwick).

600. *Elachista luticomella* **Zeller**   Candy Wood, 1929 (Hignett).

601. *Elachista albifrontella* **Hübner**   Oswestry, 1930 (Hignett); Wyre Forest, 1981–87 (Plant) and Whixall Moss, 1981–85 (Hardwick) and 21.v.1988 (McWilliam).

606. *Elachista humilis* **Zeller**   Candy Wood, 1930 (Hignett).

607. *Elachista canapennella* **Hübner**   Oswestry, 1930 (Hignett); Whixall Moss, 1981–85 (Hardwick); Shrewsbury, 29.vii.1986 (Langmaid); Wyre Forest, 1981–87 (Plant) and Preston Montford, June to August 1986, 1987 and 1988 (R.I.S. trap, det. Dunn).

608. *Elachista rufocinerea* **Haworth**   Oswestry, 1930 (Hignett); Hopedale, 13.v.1976 (Langmaid); Whixall Moss, 1981–88 (Hardwick; McWilliam) and Brown Moss, 21.v.1988 (Hardwick).

609. *Elachista cerusella* **Hübner**   Ellesmere, 23.vii.1932 and Rednal, 1948 (Hignett) and Preston Montford, August 1987, two (R.I.S. trap, det. Dunn).

610. *Elachista argentella* **Clerck**   Oswestry, 1930 (Hignett); Hopley Coppice, 4.vi.1974 (Pelham-Clinton); Whixall Moss, 1981–85 (Hardwick); Wyre Forest, 1981–87 (Plant) and Preston Montford, 1986, 1987 and 1988 (R.I.S. trap. Riley; Dunn).

611. *Elachista triatomea* **Haworth**   Llanymynech Hills, 1930 (Hignett).

613. *Elachista subocellea* **Stephens**   Llanymynech, 6.vii.1963 (Warren) and Preston Montford, June 1988, two (R.I.S. trap, det. Dunn).

615. *Elachista dispunctella* **Duponchel**   Albynes, 23.iii.1918 (Pitt); Candy Wood, 1929 (Hignett) and Bucknell, July 1972 (Shephard).

620. *Elachista gangabella* **Zeller**   Llynclys, 1947 (Hignett).

630. *Biselachista albidella* **Nylander**   Whixall Moss, June 1931 (Hignett) 28.viii.1978 (Langmaid) and 1981–85 (Hardwick).

631. *Cosmiotes freyerella* **Hübner**   One unconfirmed record from Oswestry, 1931 (Hignett).

FAMILY: OECOPHORIDAE

638. *Denisia augustella* **Hübner**   Oswestry, 1948 (Hignett). However, only two or three genuine British examples of *D. augustella* exist. Most specimens are attributable to *D. albimaculea* Haw. and this is probably the case with Hignett's record (Emmet, pers. comm.).

640. *Batia lunaris* **Haworth**   Wyre Forest, 1981–87 (Plant).

641. *Batia lambdella* **Donovan**   Two at Preston Montford, July 1987 (R.I.S. trap, det. Dunn).

642. *Batia unitella* **Hübner**   Shrewsbury, 30.vii.1986 (Langmaid and Pelham-Clinton) and Wyre Forest, 1981–87 (Plant).

644. *Borkhausenia fuscescens* **Haworth**   Candy Wood, 1948 (Hignett).

645. *Borkhausenia minutella* **Linnaeus**   Whixall Moss, 1930 (Hignett).

647. *Hofmannophila pseudospretella* **Stainton** Brown House-moth   Oswestry, 1930 (Hignett); Bucknell, 1971 & 1973 (Shephard); Ercall Woods, June 1975 (Riley); Whixall Moss, 1981–85 (Hardwick); Wyre Forest, 1981–87 (Plant) and Preston Montford, 1987 and 1988, several (R.I.S. trap, det. Riley).

648. *Endrosis sarcitrella* **Linnaeus White-shouldered House-moth** Shrewsbury, 1898 (Cortissos); Ercall Woods, 17.viii.1976 (Riley); Wyre Forest, 1981–87 (Plant); Whixall Moss, 1.vii.1988 (Langmaid and Pelham-Clinton); Preston Montford, 22.viii.1984 (Finch) and 1986, 1987 and 1988 (R.I.S. trap, det. Riley and Dunn) and Wem, 10.vii.1990 (Palmer).

649. *Esperia sulphurella* **Fabricius** Shrewsbury, 1897 (Cortissos); Oswestry, 1930 (Hignett); Bromfield, 1955 (Norton); Whixall Moss, 1981–87 (Hardwick and McWilliam) and Wyre Forest, 1981–87 (Plant).

650. *Esperia oliviella* **Fabricius** Wyre Forest, 1981–87 (Plant).

652. *Alabonia geoffrella* **Linnaeus** Oswestry, 1930 (Hignett); Craven Arms, June 1985 (Pugh) and Wyre Forest, 1981–87 (Plant).

654. *Pleurota bicostella* **Clerck** Whixall Moss, 1930 (Hignett), 1981–85 (Hardwick) and 30.v.1987 (Langmaid and Pelham-Clinton).

657. *Hypercallia citrinalis* **Scopoli** One unconfirmed record from Clee St. Margaret, 22.viii.1984 (Denman).

658. *Carcina quercana* **Fabricius** Haughmond, 1898 (Cortissos); Oswestry, 1930 (Hignett); Dothill, 11.vii.1976 (Riley); Shrewsbury, 30.vii.1986 and Whixall Moss, 31.vii.1986 (Pelham-Clinton and Langmaid) and Wyre Forest, 1981–87 (Plant).

659. *Amphisbatis incongruella* **Stainton** Whixall Moss, 1930 (Hignett).

663. *Diurnea fagella* **Denis & Schiffermüller** Prees Heath (Burrows, per Fielding, 1974b); Haughmond Hill, 1898 (Cortissos); Oswestry, 1930 (Hignett); Wyre Forest, 1949 (Smith); Hopedale, October 1974 (Langmaid); Whixall Moss, 11.iv.1987 (Langmaid and Pelham-Clinton) and Preston Montford, 1986, 1987 and 1988 (R.I.S. trap, det. Riley).

664. *Diurnea phryganella* **Hübner** Candy Wood, November 1931 (Hignett).

666. *Semioscopis avellanella* **Hübner** Candy Wood, 1929 (Hignett).

667. *Semioscopis steinkellneriana* **Denis & Schiffermüller** Preston Montford, April 1987 (two) and February 1988 (one) (R.I.S. trap, det. Riley).

670. *Depressaria daucella* **Denis & Schiffermüller** Oswestry, July 1932 (Hignett) and Preston Montford, 16.viii.1982 (Finch).

672. *Depressaria pastinacella* **Duponchel Parsnip Moth** Prees Heath (Burrows, per Fielding, 1974b); Oswestry, 1930 (Hignett); Shrawardine army training ground, pupal cases in *Heracleum sphondylium*, 18.viii.1984 (Finch); Harley, 9.viii.1986, larvae on *H. sphondylium* (Langmaid and Pelham-Clinton); Preston Montford, 16.vii.1982 (Finch), 11.iv.1986 (one) and May 1988 (one) (R.I.S. trap, det. Riley) and Wem, 10.vii.1990, spinnings common on *H. sphondylium* (Palmer).

674. *Depressaria badiella* **Hübner** One at Preston Montford, April 1987 (R.I.S. trap, det. Riley).

676. *Depressaria pulcherrimella* **Stainton** Church Stretton, larvae on *Chenopodium* (Langmaid).

677. *Depressaria douglasella* **Stainton** Oswestry, 1929 (Hignett).

681. *Depressaria olerella* **Zeller** Bromfield, 30.viii.1952 (Norton).

682. *Depressaria chaerophylli* **Zeller** Oswestry, August 1931 (Hignett).

687. *Exaeretia allisella* **Stainton** Bromfield, 16.viii.1952 and Haughmond Hill, 16.viii.1952 (Norton) and Preston Montford, 18.viii.1982 (Finch).

688. *Agonopterix heracliana* **Linnaeus** Common at Preston Montford (Finch; Riley). Other records: Prees Heath (Burrows, per Fielding, 1974b); Oswestry, 1930 (Hignett); Church Stretton, larvae on *Chenopodium*, 28.vi.1979 and *Chaerophyllum*, 27.vi.1979 (Langmaid) and Colemere, 30.v.1987, a few larvae on *Anthriscus* (Langmaid and Pelham-Clinton).

689. *Agonopterix ciliella* **Stainton** Bromfield, 30.viii.1954 (Norton) and Preston Montford, 16.viii.1982 (Finch).

691. *Agonopteryx purpurea* **Haworth** Wolfshead, 1948 (Hignett).

695. *Agonopterix alstromeriana* **Clerck** Whixall Moss, August 1931 (Hignett) and Preston Montford, March 1987 (R.I.S. trap, det. Riley).

696. *Agonopterix propinquella* **Treitschke** Oswestry, August 1931 (Hignett); Bromfield, 17.v.1953 (Norton); Craven Arms, 17.iv.1983 (Michaelis) and Preston Montford, April 1987, one (R.I.S. trap, det. Riley).

697. *Agonopterix arenella* **Denis & Schiffermüller** Oswestry, 1930 (Hignett) and Preston Montford, June and November, 1986 (two), August and September 1987 (four) and May (two), August (one) and September (three) 1988 (R.I.S. trap, det. Riley).
698. *Agonopterix kaekeritziana* **Linnaeus** Llanymynech Quarry, 19.viii.1984 (Finch).
701. *Agonopterix ocellana* **Fabricius** Oswestry, 1930 (Hignett).
702. *Agonopterix assimilella* **Treitschke** Bromfield, 1955 (Norton) and Pontesbury, larvae on *Cytisus scoparius*, 2.v.1973 (Langmaid).
703. *Agonopterix atomella* **Denis & Schiffermüller** Nesscliffe, 1931 (Hignett) and Bromfield, 1955 (Norton).
705. *Agonopteryx ulicetella* **Stainton** Oswestry, 1949 (Hignett).
706. *Agonopterix nervosa* **Haworth** Oswestry, 1931 (Hignett); Ercall Woods, 17.viii.1976 (Riley) and Whixall Moss, 1981–85 (Hardwick).
708. *Agonopterix carduella* **Hübner** Oswestry, 1931 (Hignett).
709. *Agonopterix liturosa* **Haworth** Oswestry, 1931 (Hignett) and Wyre Forest, 1981–87 (Plant).
714. *Agonopterix yeatiana* **Fabricius** Oswestry, 1934 (Hignett).
715. *Agonopterix capreolella* **Zeller** Llanymynech Hills, 1929 (Hignett).
720. *Ethmia bipunctella* **Fabricius** One unconfirmed record from Clee St. Margaret, 21.viii.1984 (Denman).

FAMILY: GELECHIIDAE

726. *Metzneria metzneriella* **Stainton** One at Preston Montford, June 1987 (R.I.S. trap, det. Dunn).
729. *Isophrictis striatella* **Denis & Schiffermüller** Dolgoch, 1946 (Hignett).
732. *Eulamprotes unicolorella* **Duponchel** Wyre Forest, 1981–87 (Plant, det. Bradford).
735. *Monochroa tenebrella* **Hübner** Llanymynech Hills, 8.vii.1932 (Hignett); Knockin, 1944 (Hignett) and Whixall Moss, 28.vi.1958 (Warren).
741. *Monochroa suffusella* **Douglas** Alston, 1930 (Hignett) and Whixall Moss, 20.vi.1954 (Warren).
747. *Chrysoesthia sexguttella* **Thunberg** Mile House, 1944 (Hignett) and Ludlow, 11.vii.1990, mines on *Chenopodium* (Palmer).
752. *Aristotelia ericinella* **Zeller** Whixall Moss, 1930 (Hignett), 1981–85 (Hardwick) and 31.vii.1986, several (Langmaid and Pelham-Clinton).
760. *Exoteleia dodecella* **Linnaeus** One record from Knockin, 1948 (Hignett).
763. *Xenolechia aethiops* **Humphreys & Westwood** Whixall Moss (Burrows, per Fielding, 1974a) and Oswestry, 1930 (Hignett).
764. *Pseudotelphusa scalella* **Scopoli** Wyre Forest, 1981–87 (Plant, det. Bradford).
766. *Teleiodes scriptella* **Hübner** Llanforda, 1930, noted as being very local (Hignett, 1931).
768. *Teleiodes notatella* **Hübner** Whixall Moss, June 1931 (Hignett).
770. *Teleiodes proximella* **Hübner** Rednal, 1948 (Hignett); Hopley Coppice, 4.vi.1974 (Pelham-Clinton) and Whixall Moss, 1931 (Hignett), 15.ix.1981, larvae on *Betula* and *Alnus* (Langmaid), 3.vii.1976 (Warren), 1981–85 (Hardwick) and 30.v.1987 and 1.viii.1988 (Langmaid and Pelham-Clinton).
771. *Teleiodes alburnella* **Zeller** Whixall Moss, 3.vii.1976 (Warren).
773. *Teleiodes paripunctella* **Thunberg** Whixall Moss, 1981–85 (Hardwick) and 30.v.1987, one (Langmaid and Pelham-Clinton).
774. *Teleiodes luculella* **Hübner** Mile House, 1944 (Hignett) and Wyre Forest, 1981–87 (Plant, det. Bradford).
775. *Teleiodes sequax* **Haworth** Llanforda, 1929 (Hignett) and Preston Montford, July 1987 (R.I.S. trap, det. Dunn).
776. *Teleiopsis diffinis* **Haworth** Candy Wood, 1929 (Hignett); Whixall Moss, 13.ix.1981 (Langmaid) and 1981–85 (Hardwick) and Preston Montford, 19.viii.1984 (Finch) and 1987 (R.I.S. trap, det. Dunn).
778. *Bryotropha umbrosella* **Zeller** One unconfirmed record of this usually coastal species from Whixall Moss, August 1931 (Hignett). This record seems unlikely and should be treated with caution.

779. *Bryotropha affinis* **Haworth**   Oswestry, 1930 (Hignett).
780. *Bryotropha similis* **Stainton**   Candy Wood, 1929 (Hignett) and Preston Montford, June and August 1987 (R.I.S. trap, det. Dunn).
782. *Bryotropha senectella* **Zeller**   Wyre Forest, 1981–87 (Plant, det. Bradford).
786. *Bryotropha desertella* **Douglas**   Whixall Moss, 1981–85 (Hardwick). This usually coastal species is only occasionally recorded inland.
787. *Bryotropha terrella* **Dennis & Schiffermüller**   Candy Wood, 1930 (Hignett); Wyre Forest, 1981–87 (Plant, det. Bradford) and Preston Montford, July 1986, 1987 and 1988 (R.I.S. trap, det. Dunn).
788. *Bryotropha politella* **Stainton**   Llanforda, 1929 (Hignett).
792. *Mirificarma mulinella* **Zeller**   Preston Montford July (two) and August (one) 1986 (R.I.S. trap, det. Dunn).
794. *Lita virgella* **Thunberg**   Whixall Moss, 1931 (Hignett).
796. *Aroga velocella* **Zeller**   Polebank area of Longmynd, one on afternoon of 5.v.1990 (Riley, det. conf. P. A. Sokoloff).
797. *Neofaculta ericetella* **Geyer**   Prees Heath (Burrows, per Fielding, 1974b); Wem Moss, 7.vii.1963 (Warren); Whixall Moss (Burrows, per Fielding, 1974a), 1930 (Hignett) and 1981–87 (Hardwick, McWilliam, Langmaid and Pelham-Clinton); Wyre Forest, 1981–87 (Plant, det. Bradford) and Ashes Hollow, Longmynd, 5.v.1990, common (Riley and Townsend).
802a. *Gelechia sororculella* **Hübner**   Whixall Moss, 1981–85 (Hardwick).
819. *Scrobipalpa costella* **Humphreys & Westwood**   Whixall Moss, 1930 (Hignett) and Preston Montford, August to October 1987, five (R.I.S. trap, det. Dunn).
832. *Caryoculum blandella* **Douglas**   Preston Montford, August (two) and September (one) 1988 (R.I.S. trap, det. Dunn).
834. *Caryocolum tricolorella* **Haworth**   One at Preston Montford, August 1987 (R.I.S. trap, det. Dunn).
841. *Sophronia semicostella* **Hübner**   Prees Heath (Burrows, per Fielding 1974b); Knockin, 1948 (Hignett) and Wyre Forest, 1981–87 (Plant, det. Bradford).
844. *Syncopacma larseniella* **Gozmány**   Wyre Forest, 1981–87 (Plant, det. Bradford).
847. *Syncopacma taeniolella* **Zeller**   Llanymynech Quarry, 19.viii.1984 (Finch).
849. *Syncopacma cinctella* **Clerck**   Dolgoch, 1946 (Hignett).
853. *Anacampsis populella* **Clerck**   Hopley Coppice, 4.vi.1974, larva on *Populus tremula* (Pelham-Clinton) and Whixall Moss, 15.ix.1984 (Langmaid) and 31.vii.1986 (Langmaid and Pelham-Clinton).
854. *Anacampsis blattariella* **Hübner**   Whixall Moss, 31.vii.1986 (Langmaid and Pelham-Clinton) and Brown Moss, 1986 and 1987 (McWilliam) and 25.vii.1987 (Lancs and Chesh. Ent. Soc.).
855. *Acompsia cinerella* **Clerck**   Llanforda, 1930 (Hignett).
858. *Hypatima rhomboidella* **Linnaeus**   Oswestry, 1930 (Hignett) and Brown Moss, 9.ix.1989 (Hardwick).
866. *Brachmia blandella* **Fabricius**   Oswestry, 1930 (Hignett).
868. *Brachmia rufescens* **Haworth**   Wyre Forest, 1981–87 (Plant, det. Bradford) and Preston Montford, July & August 1986, 1987 and 1988 (R.I.S. trap, det. Riley and Dunn).
870. *Oegoconia quadripuncta* **Haworth**   Preston Montford, August 1986 (R.I.S. trap, det. Riley).

FAMILY: BLASTOBASIDAE
873. *Blastobasis lignea* **Walsingham**   Shrewsbury, 30.vii.1986, two at M.V. (Langmaid and Pelham-Clinton).

FAMILY: MOMPHIDAE
878. *Batrachedra praeangusta* **Haworth**   Rednal, 1934 (Hignett).
879. *Batrachedra pinicolella* **Zeller**   Knockin, 1948 (Hignett). This species appears to have been recorded as far north as Herefordshire (Meyrick, 1927) but as there is no confirmatory specimen for Hignett's record we must treat it with caution.

883. *Mompha raschkiella* **Zeller** Candy Wood and Aston, 1948 (Hignett); Bromfield, 1952, 1954, 1955 and 1971 (Norton); Earl's Hill, 20.viii.1984, larvae on *Epilobium angustifolium* (Finch); Wyre Forest, 1981–88, mines common in *E. angustifolium* (Plant); Whixall Moss, 15.iv.1981, larvae on *E. angustifolium* and 31.viii.1986 and 1.vii.1988, mines in *E. angustifolium* (Langmaid and Pelham-Clinton); Harley, 9.viii.1986, mines in *E. angustifolium* (Langmaid and Pelham-Clinton) and Brown Moss and Ironbridge, 11.vii.1990, mines in *E. angustifolium* (Palmer).

884. *Mompha miscella* **Denis & Schiffermüller** Llanymynech, 1929 (Hignett).

885. *Mompha conturbatella* **Hübner** Wyre Forest, 1981–87 (Plant) and Whixall Moss, 30.v.1987, one larva on *E. angustifolium* (Langmaid and Pelham-Clinton).

886. *Mompha ochraceella* **Curtis** Whixall, 1930 (Hignett) and Preston Montford, June 1987 (R.I.S. trap, det. Dunn).

887. *Mompha lacteella* **Stephens** Oswestry, 1930 (Hignett).

893. *Mompha epilobiella* **Denis & Schiffermüller** Oswestry, 1930 (Hignett) and Whixall Moss, 1981–85 (Hardwick).

FAMILY: COSMOPTERIGIDAE

898. *Limnaecia phragmitella* **Stainton** Ellesmere, 1930 (Hignett), Brown Moss, 1986–88 (McWilliam) and Whixall Moss, 21.v.1988 (McWilliam; Hardwick).

902. *Glyphipteryx lathamella* **Fletcher** Whixall Moss, 28.vi.1951 (Warren).

904. *Spuleria flavicaput* **Haworth** Oswestry, 1929 (Hignett).

905. *Spuleria hellerella* **Duponchel** Preston Montford, June and July 1986, 1987 and 1988 (R.I.S. trap, det. Dunn).

906. *Blastodacna atra* **Haworth** Oswestry, 1930 (Hignett).

FAMILY: SCYTHRIDIDAE

911. *Scythris grandipennis* **Haworth** Prees Heath (Burrows, per Fielding 1974b) and Llynclys, 1948 (Hignett).

912. *Scythris fuscoaenea* **Haworth** Llanymynech, 22.viii.1931 (Hignett).

FAMILY: TORTRICIDAE

925. *Phtheochroa rugosana* **Hübner** Seven at Preston Montford, May and June 1987 (R.I.S. trap, det. Riley).

934. *Phalonidia curvistrigana* **Stainton** One record from Llynclys, 1947 (Hignett).

936. *Stenodes straminea* **Haworth** Llanforda, 1930 (Hignett).

937. *Agapeta hamana* **Linnaeus** Common at Preston Montford during July and August (R.I.S. trap, det. Riley). Other records from: Shrewsbury, 1897 (Cortissos); Oswestry, 1930 (Hignett); Bromfield, 3.viii.1964 (Norton); Ercall Woods, 3.vii.1976 (Riley); Wyre Forest, 1981–87 (Plant) and Wem, 10.vii.1990 (Palmer).

938. *Agapeta zoegana* **Linnaeus** Shrewsbury, 1897 (Cortissos); Broseley, 1898 (Potts); Oswestry, 1930 (Hignett); Bucknell, 1972 (Shephard); Shrawardine army training grounds, 25.vii.1981 and Llanymynech Quarry, 19.viii.1984 (Finch); Preston Montford, 10.vii.1979 and July 1986 (R.I.S. trap, det. Riley) and Wyre Forest, 1981–87 (Plant).

942. *Aethes piercei* **Obraztov** Llynclys, 1947 (Hignett). However, as the specimen is not available for examination the record must be treated with caution. There is considerable taxonomic confusion between this species and *A. hartmanniana* Clerck. Some authors believe that the two are merely ecological forms of one species (Bradley, *et al.*, 1973).

945. *Aethes cnicana* **Westwood** Candy Wood, 1930 (Hignett).

946. *Aethes rubigana* **Treitschke** Whixall Moss, 1931 (Hignett) and Preston Montford, 1986 (four), 1987 (two) and 1988 (one) (R.I.S. trap, det. Riley).

947. *Aethes smeathmanniana* **Fabricius** Preston Montford, August 1988, three (R.I.S. trap, det. Riley).

951. *Aethes beatricella* **Walsingham** Preston Montford, one in July 1986 (R.I.S. trap, determined by genitalia examination, Riley).

954. *Eupoecilia angustana* **Hübner** Whixall Moss, 1930 (Hignett) and 1981–85 (Hardwick) and 31.vii.1986 (Langmaid and Pelham-Clinton) and Preston Montford, June 1988, one (R.I.S. trap, det. Dunn).

960. *Falseuncaria ruficiliana* **Haworth** Llanforda, 1930 (Hignett).

965. *Cochylis hybridella* **Hübner** Llanymynech, 1948 (Hignett) and Harley, 9.viii.1986, three (Langmaid and Pelham-Clinton).

968. *Cochylis nana* **Haworth** Whixall Moss, 1930 (Hignett) and 30.v.1987, a few (Langmaid and Pelham-Clinton).

969. *Pandemis corylana* **Fabricius** **Chequered Fruit-tree Tortrix** Shrewsbury, 1897 (Cortissos); Oswestry, 1930 (Hignett); Bucknell, 1972 (Shephard); Whixall Moss, 28.viii.1979 (Warren); Wyre Forest, 1981–87 (Plant) and Preston Montford, 16.viii.1982 (Finch) and August 1987 and July and August 1988 (R.I.S. trap, det. Riley).

970. *Pandemis cerasana* **Hübner** **Barred Fruit-tree Tortrix** Oswestry, 1930 (Hignett); Cuckoopen Coppice, July 1963 (Warren); Ercall Woods, June 1975 (Riley); Hawk Lake, 1981–85 (Hardwick); Wyre Forest, 1981–87 (Plant); Whixall Moss, 1981–85 (Hardwick) and 30.v.1987, larvae on *Frangula*, *Betula* and *Quercus* (Langmaid and Pelham-Clinton) and 16.vii.1988 (Riley); Brown Moss, 21.v.1988 (Hardwick) and Preston Montford, 9.vii.1979 and July and August 1986, 1987 and 1988 (R.I.S. trap, det. Riley).

971. *Pandemis cinnamomeana* **Treitschke** Candy Wood, 1930 (Hignett) and Cuckoopen Coppice, 10.vii.1963 (Warren).

972. *Pandemis heparana* **Denis & Schiffermüller** **Dark Fruit-tree Tortrix** Oswestry, 1930 (Hignett); Bucknell, July 1971 (Shephard); Preston Montford, 18.viii.1982 and 31.vii.1984 (Finch); Wyre Forest, 1981–87 (Plant) and Whixall Moss, 1981–85 (Hardwick) and 30.v.1987, larvae on *Frangula* (Langmaid and Pelham-Clinton).

974. *Argyrotaenia ljungiana* **Thunberg** Common on the Longmynd at Ashes Hollow, 5.v.1990 (Riley and Townsend). Also recorded from Whixall Moss, 1930 (Hignett); 22.vii.1934 (Warren) and 1981–85 (Hardwick).

977. *Archips podana* **Scopoli** Oswestry, 1930 (Hignett); Wyre Forest, 1981–87 (Plant); Preston Montford, June 1987 (three) and June (one) and July (one) 1988 (R.I.S. trap, det. Riley) and Brown Moss, 21.v.1988 (Hardwick).

979. *Archips crataegana* **Hübner** **Brown Oak Tortrix** Shrewsbury, 30.vi.1988, one at M.V. (Langmaid and Pelham-Clinton).

980. *Archips xylosteana* **Linnaeus** **Variegated Golden Tortrix** Oswestry, 1930 (Hignett); Clee St. Margaret, 14.vii.1984 (Denman); Wyre Forest, 1981–87 (Plant); Colemere 30.v.1987, one larva on *Salix* (Langmaid and Pelham-Clinton) and Preston Montford, July 1987, one (R.I.S. trap, det. Riley).

981. *Archips roseana* **Linnaeus** **Rose Tortrix** Oswestry, 1930 (Hignett) and Bromfield, 28.vi.1953 (Norton).

982. *Choristoneura diversana* **Hübner** Shrewsbury, 1897 (Cortissos, per Pendlebury, 1950).

983. *Choristoneura hebenstreitella* **Müller** Whixall Moss, 1930 (Hignett).

986. *Syndemis musculana musculana* **Hübner** Oswestry, 1930 (Hignett); Whixall Moss, 28.v.1939 (Warren), 30.v.1987, several (Langmaid and Pelham-Clinton) and 1981–88 (Hardwick and McWilliam) and Brown Moss, 21.v.1988 (Hardwick).

987. *Ptycholomoides aeriferanus* **Herrich-Schäffer** Whixall Moss, 1981–85 (Hardwick).

988. *Aphelia viburnana* **Denis & Schiffermüller** **Bilberry Tortrix** Whixall Moss, 1930 (Hignett), 27.vii.1981 (Finch), 1981–85 (Hardwick) and 30.v.1987, larvae on *Betula* (Langmaid and Pelham-Clinton).

989. *Aphelia paleana* **Hübner** **Timothy Tortrix** Whixall Moss, 1981–85 (Hardwick).

991. *Clepsis senecionana* **Hübner** Oswestry, 15.vi.1932 (Hignett).

993. *Clepsis spectrana* **Treitschke** **Cyclamen Tortrix** Frequent at Preston Montford, 1979–86 (R.I.S. light trap, det. Riley). Other records from: Oswestry, 1930 (Hignett); Shrewsbury, 21.ii.1981, one larva on *Artemisia vulgaris* (Langmaid and Pelham-Clinton); Brown Moss, 1981–87 (McWilliam) and Wyre Forest, 1981–87 (Plant).

994. *Clepsis consimilana* **Hübner** Oswestry, 1930 (Hignett); Preston Montford, 1987

and 1988, several (R.I.S. trap, det. Riley) and Shrewsbury, 30.vi.1988, two at M.V. (Langmaid and Pelham-Clinton).

1000. *Ptycholoma lecheana* **Linnaeus** Hopley Coppice, one pupa 4.vi.1974 (Pelham-Clinton); Shrewsbury, larvae on *Salix caprea* May 1976 (Langmaid); Clee St. Margaret, July and August 1984, five (Denman); Whixall Moss, 26.vi.1931 (Hignett) and 1981–85 (Hardwick) and Wyre Forest, 1981–87 (Plant).

1001. *Lozotaeniodes formosanus* **Geyer** Oswestry, 1930 (Hignett); Bucknell, July 1971 (Shephard) and Shrewsbury, 30.vi.1988, one at M.V. (Langmaid and Pelham-Clinton).

1002. *Lozotaenia forsterana* **Fabricius** Shrewsbury, 1897 (Cortissos); Broseley, 1898 (Potts); Oswestry, 1930 (Hignett) and Preston Montford, 11.vii.1979, July 1986 (several), June 1987 (four) and June 1988 (two) (R.I.S. trap, det. Riley).

1006. *Epagoge grotiana* **Fabricius** Preston Montford, 12.vii.1979 (two) and July 1986 (six) (R.I.S. trap, det. Riley) and Whixall Moss, 1930 (Hignett), 1981–85 (Hardwick) and 1.vii.1988 (Langmaid and Pelham-Clinton).

1007. *Capua vulgana* **Frölich** Whixall Moss, 1932 (Hignett); Pontesbury, 16.v.1976 and Colemere, 30.v.1987 several (Langmaid and Pelham-Clinton).

1008. *Philedone gerningana* **Denis & Schiffermüller** Whixall Moss, 2.vii.1931 (Hignett); Wem Moss, 4.vii.1963 (Warren) and the Stiperstones, 27.vii.1981, flying in bright sunshine (Finch).

1010. *Ditula angustiorana* **Haworth Red-barred Tortrix** Oswestry, 1930 (Hignett); Preston Montford, 28.vii.1981, one female at M.V. (Finch); Shrewsbury, 30.vii.1986 and Whixall Moss, 31.vii.1986 (Langmaid and Pelham-Clinton) and Wem, 10.vii.1990, common in a yew hedge (Palmer).

1011. *Pseudargyrotoza conwagana* **Fabricius** Oswestry, 1930 (Hignett); Llanymynech, 6.vii.1963 and Cuckoopen Coppice, July 1963 (Warren); Hawk Lake, 1981–85 (Hardwick); Brown Moss, 1986–87 (McWilliam) and Wyre Forest, 1981–87 (Plant).

1015. *Eulia ministrana* **Linnaeus** Oswestry, 1930 (Hignett); Wyre Forest, 1981–87 (Blunt; Plant) and Whixall Moss, 28.v.1938 (Warren), 1983 and 1984 (Blunt), 30.v.1987, several (Langmaid and Pelham-Clinton) and 1981–87 (Hardwick and McWilliam).

1018. *Cnephasia communana* **Herrich-Schäffer** Whixall Moss, 1981–85 (Hardwick).

1020. *Cnephasia stephensiana* **Doubleday Grey Tortrix** Whixall Moss, 1981–85 (Hardwick); Preston Montford, June 1986, two (R.I.S. trap, determined by genitalia examination, Riley); Shrewsbury, 30.vii.1986, one (Langmaid and Pelham-Clinton) and Wyre Forest, 1981–87 (Plant).

1021. *Cnephasia asseclana* **Denis & Schiffermüller Flax Tortrix** Clarepool Moss, 2.vii.1963 (Warren); Whixall Moss, 1981–85 (Hardwick) and 1.vii.1988 (Langmaid and Pelham-Clinton); Preston Montford, frequent in 1986 and 1987 at R.I.S. trap (determined by genitalia examination, Riley); Wyre Forest, 1981–87 (Plant) and Shrewsbury, 30.vi.1988, one at M.V. (Langmaid and Pelham-Clinton).

1022. *Cnephasia pasiuana* **Hübner** Oswestry, 1930 (Hignett).

1024. *Cnephasia incertana* **Treitschke Light Grey Tortrix** Shrewsbury, 1905 (Melvill); Oswestry, 1930 (Hignett) and Whixall Moss, 31.vii.1986 (Langmaid and Pelham-Clinton).

1025. *Tortricodes alternella* **Denis & Schiffermüller** Oswestry, 1930 (Hignett) and Clee St. Margaret, 20.vii.1984 (Denman).

1026. *Exapate congelatella* **Clerck** Preston Montford, two in November 1986 and one in October 1987 (R.I.S. trap, det. Riley).

1027. *Neosphaleroptera nubilana* **Hübner** Oswestry, 1930 (Hignett) and Preston Montford, 11.vii.1979 (R.I.S. trap, det. Riley).

1029. *Eana osseana* **Scopoli** Oswestry, 1930 (Hignett) and Preston Montford, 1979 and 1987 (R.I.S. trap, det. Riley and Dunn).

1030. *Eana incanana* **Stephens** Clee St. Margaret, 20.viii.1984 (Denman).

1032. *Aleimma loeflingiana* **Linnaeus** Nesscliffe, July 1931 (Hignett); Cuckoopen Coppice, July 1963 (Warren); Wyre Forest, 1981–85 (Plant); Whixall Moss, 1981–85 (Hardwick), 30.v.1987, larvae on *Quercus* and 1.vii.1988 (Langmaid and Pelham-Clinton) and Preston Montford, June 1987 (five) and June 1988 (one) (R.I.S. trap, det. Riley).

1033.	*Tortrix viridana* **Linnaeus** **Green Oak Tortrix** Common throughout the county near oaks. Often abundant in the Ercall Woods, 1970–87 (Riley).

1035.	*Croesia bergmanniana* **Linnaeus** Shrewsbury, 1905 (Melvill); Oswestry, 1930 (Hignett); Bucknell, 1972 (Shephard); Clee St. Margaret, 25.vii.1979 and 19.vii.1984 (Denman) and Preston Montford, 11.vii.1979 and July 1986 (R.I.S. trap, det. Riley).

1036.	*Croesia forsskaleana* **Linnaeus** Oswestry, 1930 (Hignett); Preston Montford, 29.vii.1981 (R.I.S. trap, det. Riley) and Clee St. Margaret, 26.viii.1984 (Denman).

1037.	*Croesia holmiana* **Linnaeus** Prees Heath (Burrows, per Fielding, 1974b); Oswestry, 1930 (Hignett); Clee St. Margaret, 23.viii.1984 (Denman) and Preston Montford, 5.viii.1979, 29.vii.1981 and August 1986, 1987 and 1988 (Finch; Riley).

1038.	*Acleris laterana* **Fabricius** Clee St. Margaret, 22 & 28.viii.1984 (Denman); Whixall Moss, 1981–85 (Hardwick) and Wyre Forest, 1981–87 (Plant).

1039.	*Acleris comariana* **Lienig & Zeller** **Strawberry Tortrix** Prees Heath (Burrows, per Fielding, 1974b).

1041.	*Acleris sparsana* **Denis & Schiffermüller** Oswestry, 1930 and Whixall Moss, 1932 (Hignett) and Preston Montford, October (one) and November (one) 1988 (R.I.S. trap, det. Riley).

1042.	*Acleris rhombana* **Denis & Schiffermüller** **Rhomboid Tortrix** Oswestry, 1930 (Hignett); Pontesbury, 12.x.1974 (Langmaid); Clee St. Margaret, 21.vii.1984 (Denman); Whixall Moss, 1981–85 (Hardwick) and Preston Montford, 16.viii.1982 (Finch), September 1986 and 1987 and October to December 1988 (R.I.S. trap, det. Riley).

1043.	*Acleris aspersana* **Hübner** Prees Heath (Burrows, per Fielding, 1974b); Llanymynech Quarry, one female 19.viii.1984 (Finch) and Wyre Forest, 1981–87 (Plant).

1044.	*Acleris ferrugana* **Denis & Schiffermüller** Prees Heath (Burrows, per Fielding, 1974b) and Oswestry, 1930 (Hignett).

1045.	*Acleris notana* **Donovan** Bromfield, 12.vii.1955 (Norton); Whixall Moss, 1981–85 (Hardwick) and Preston Montford, two 16.viii.1982 (Finch) and several in 1987 (R.I.S. trap, det. Riley).

1047.	*Acleris schalleriana* **Linnaeus** Oswestry, 1930 (Hignett) and Whixall Moss, 27.vii.1981 and 19.vii.1984 (Finch).

1048.	*Acleris variegana* **Denis & Schiffermüller** **Garden Rose Tortrix** Common at the R.I.S. trap at Preston Montford, 1986 & 1987 (Riley). Other records from: Press Heath (Burrows, per Fielding, 1974b); Oswestry, 1930 (Hignett); Ercall Woods, 1975 (Riley); Cosford, 29.vii.1976 and Wellington, 29.vii.1976 (Riley); Clee St. Margaret, July and August 1984, six (Denman) and Wyre Forest, 1981–87 (Plant).

1049.	*Acleris permutana* **Duponchel** Recorded from Oswestry in 1930 by Hignett. This local and uncommon species feeds on Burnet Rose (*Rosa pimpinellifolia* L.) which is known to occur in SJ22 near Oswestry. Unfortunately the specimen is no longer available for confirmation. As *A. permutana* is mainly a coastal species, this record should be regarded with extreme caution.

1054.	*Acleris cristana* **Denis & Schiffermüller** Wyre Forest, 1981–87 (Plant).

1055.	*Acleris hyemana* **Haworth** Common on the Longmynd at Ashes Hollow, 5.v.1990 (Riley and Townsend). Also recorded from Prees Heath (Burrows, per Fielding, 1974b) and Whixall Moss, 10.iv.1931 (Hignett).

1061.	*Acleris literana* **Linnaeus** Oswestry, 1930 (Hignett) and Ludlow, 1948 (Allen).

1062.	*Acleris emargana* **Fabricius** Prees heath (Burrows, per Fielding, 1974b); Llanymynech Hills, 1930 (Hignett); Whixall Moss (Burrows, per Fielding 1974a), 1930 (Hignett) and 1981–85 (Hardwick); Wyre Forest, 1981–87 (Plant); Preston Montford, August 1988, two (R.I.S. trap, det. Riley) and Brown Moss, 9.ix.1989 (Hardwick).

1062i.	*Olindia schumacherana* **Fabricius** Oswestry, 1934 (Hignett); Wyre Forest, 1981–87 (Plant) and Hodnett, 30.vi.1988, two (Langmaid and Pelham-Clinton).

1062ii.	*Isotrias rectifasciana* **Haworth** Oswestry, 1930 (Hignett) and Wyre Forest, 1981–87 (Plant).

1063.	*Celypha striana* **Denis & Schiffermüller** Abundant at Preston Montford (R.I.S. trap, det. Riley). Other records from: Oswestry, 1930 (Hignett); Prees Heath, 24.vii.1938 (Warren); Shrewsbury, 29.vii.1986 and Harley, 9.viii.1986 (Langmaid and Pelham-Clinton); Wyre Forest, 1981–87 (Plant) and Wem, 10.vii.1990 (Palmer).

1064. *Celypha rosaceana* **Schläger** Cuckoopen Coppice, July 1963 (Warren).
1068. *Olethreutes rivulana* **Scopoli** Whixall Moss, 18.viii.1982 (Finch).
1073. *Olethreutes schulziana* **Fabricius** Whixall Moss, 1930 (Hignett), 2.vii.1977 and 28.viii.1979 (Warren) and 1981–85 (Hardwick).
1075. *Olethreutes olivana* **Treitschke** Wem Moss, 4.vii.1963 (Warren) and Whixall Moss, 1981–85 (Hardwick).
1076. *Olethreutes lacunana* **Denis & Schiffermüller** Common in lowland areas throughout the county.
1079. *Olethreutes bifasciana* **Haworth** Knockin, 1948 (Hignett, per Pendlebury, 1950). Although this species is nationally rather uncommon, it has previously been recorded from several of Shropshire's bordering counties. (Bradley *et al.*, 1979).
1082. *Hedya pruniana* **Hübner Plum Tortrix** Shrewsbury, 1905 (Melvill); Oswestry, 1930 (Hignett); Wyre Forest, 1981–87 (Plant) and common at Preston Montford, 1986, 1987 and 1988 (R.I.S. trap, det. Riley).
1083. *Hedya dimidioalba* **Retzius Marbled Orchard Tortrix** Widely and generally distributed throughout the county and often common.
1084. *Hedya ochroleucana* **Frölich** Oswestry, 1948 (Hignett).
1085. *Hedya atropunctana* **Zetterstedt** Whixall Moss, 1931 (Hignett), 28.v.1939 (Warren) and 1981–85 (Hardwick).
1086. *Hedya salicella* **Linnaeus** Shrewsbury, larvae on *Salix fragilis*, May 1976 (Langmaid); Preston Montford, July 1987, one (R.I.S. trap, det. Riley) and Button Bridge, Wyre Forest, 7.viii.1990, one (Blunt, confirmed Riley).
1087. *Orthotaenia undulana* **Denis & Schiffermüller** Oswestry, 1930 (Hignett) and Whixall Moss, 1.vii.1988, a few (Langmaid and Pelham-Clinton).
1089. *Apotomis semifasciana* **Haworth** Whixall Moss, 31.vii.1954 (Warren).
1091. *Apotomis lineana* **Denis & Schiffermüller** Whixall Moss, one 1930 (Hignett).
1092. *Apotomis turbidana* **Hübner** Wyre Forest, 1981–87 (Plant) and Whixall Moss, 1981–85 (Hardwick) and 1.vii.1988, one (Langmaid and Pelham-Clinton).
1093. *Apotomis betuletana* **Haworth** Whixall Moss, 1930, common (Hignett), 31.vii.1986, several (Langmaid and Pelham-Clinton) and 1981–85 (Hardwick) and Wyre Forest, 1981–87 (Plant).
1099. *Endothenia marginana* **Haworth** Whixall Moss, 1930 (Hignett); Sturt Common, 18.vii.1971 (Warren) and Wyre Forest, 1981–87 (Plant).
1102. *Endothenia nigricostana* **Haworth** Wyre Forest, 1981–87 (Plant).
1104. *Endothenia quadrimaculana* **Haworth** Three at Preston Montford, June and July 1987 (R.I.S. trap, det. Riley).
1106. *Lobesia reliquana* **Hübner** Wyre Forest, 1981–87 (Plant).
1110. *Bactra furfurana* **Haworth** This species was recorded by the Lancs and Chesh. Ent. Soc. on a field meeting to Brown Moss on 25.vii.1987. There are no other records.
1111. *Bactra lancealana* **Hübner** Llanforda, 1930 (Hignett); Whixall Moss, 1981–85 and Hawk Lake, 1986 and 1987 (Hardwick); Brown Moss, 23.viii.1984, flying around *Juncus* in bright sunshine (Finch) and 1986 and 1987 (McWilliam); Wyre Forest, 1981–87 (Plant); All Stretton, 29.v.1987 (Langmaid and Pelham-Clinton); the Longmynd, May 1988 (Riley) and Preston Montford, June 1986, 1987 and 1988 (R.I.S. trap, det. Riley and Dunn).
1113. *Eudemis profundana* **Denis & Schiffermüller** Wyre Forest, 1981–87 (Plant).
1115. *Ancylis achatana* **Denis & Schiffermüller** Several at Preston Montford, June and July 1987 (R.I.S. trap, det. Riley).
1118. *Ancylis uncella* **Denis & Schiffermüller** Whixall Moss (Burrows, per Fielding, 1974a), 1930 (Hignett), 28.v.1938 (Warren), 1981–85 (Hardwick) and 30.v.1987 (Langmaid and Pelham-Clinton) and Brown Moss, 21.v.1988 (Hardwick).
1119. *Ancylis geminana* **Donovan** Whixall Moss, 10.vi.1932 (Hignett) and 15.ix.1981, larvae on *Salix atrocinerea* (Langmaid).
1119a. *Ancylis diminutana* **Haworth** Whixall Moss (Burrows, per Fielding, 1974a).
1120. *Ancylis mitterbacheriana* **Denis & Schiffermüller** Wyre Forest, 1981–87 (Plant).
1122. *Ancylis obtusana* **Haworth** Wyre Forest, 1981–87 (Plant).
1125. *Ancylis unculana* **Haworth** Wyre Forest, 1981–87 (Plant).

1126. *Ancylis badiana* **Denis & Schiffermüller** Oswestry, 1930 (Hignett); Harley, 9.viii.1986, several (Langmaid and Pelham-Clinton); Whixall Moss, 1981–87 (Hardwick and McWilliam) and Wyre Forest, 1981–87 (Plant).

1129. *Ancylis apicella* **Denis & Schiffermüller** Bradley *et al.* (1979) pp. 98-99 and Whixall Moss, 1931 (Hignett) and 30.v.1987, one (Langmaid and Pelham-Clinton).

1133. *Epinotia bilunana* **Haworth** Whixall Moss, 1981–85 (Hardwick); Wyre Forest, 1981–87 (Plant) and Preston Montford, June 1988, one (R.I.S. trap, det. Riley).

1134. *Epinotia ramella* **Linnaeus** Whixall Moss, 1930 (Hignett), 22.vii.1934 (Warren), and 1981–85 (Hardwick) and Wyre Forest, 1981–87 (Plant).

1135. *Epinotia demarniana* **Fischer von Röslerstamm** Whixall Moss, 1930 (Hignett) and just over the county border into Flintshire on Fenn's Moss and Bettisfield (Bradley *et al.* (1979) pp. 105-106).

1136. *Epinotia immundana* **Fischer von Röslerstamm** Whixall Moss, May 1931 (Hignett), 1981–85 (Hardwick) and 30.v.1987, one (Langmaid and Pelham-Clinton).

1137. *Epinotia tetraquetrana* **Haworth** Hopley Coppice, 4.vi.1974 (Pelham-Clinton); Whixall Moss, May 1931 (Hignett), 1981–85 (Hardwick) and 30.v.1987 and 1.vii.1988, several (Langmaid and Pelham-Clinton) and Brown Moss, 21.v.1988 (Hardwick).

1138. *Epinotia nisella* **Clerck** Haughmond Hill, 16.viii.1982 and Shrawardine army training ground, 20.viii.1984 (Finch) and Whixall Moss, 1930 (Hignett) and 1981–85 (Hardwick).

1139. *Epinotia tenerana* **Denis & Schiffermüller** **Nut Bud Moth** Candy Wood and Llanymynech Hills, 1930 (Hignett); Whixall Moss, 1981–85 (Hardwick) and 31.vii.1986, one (Langmaid and Pelham-Clinton) and Preston Montford, July 1988, three (R.I.S. trap, det. Dunn).

1142. *Epinotia tedella* **Clerck** Candy Wood, 1930 (Hignett); Minsterley, 27.iv.1985 (Jardine); Preston Montford, July 1986, one (R.I.S. trap, det. Dunn) and Wyre Forest, 1981–87 (Plant).

1146. *Epinotia rubiginosana* **Herrich-Schäffer** Wyre Forest, 1981–85 (Plant).

1147. *Epinotia cruciana* **Linnaeus** **Willow Tortrix** Whixall Moss, 1931 (Hignett), 1981–85 (Hardwick) and 31.vii.1986, one (Langmaid and Pelham-Clinton).

1150. *Epinotia abbreviana* **Fabricius** Oswestry, 1930 (Hignett); Shrewsbury, larvae on *Ulmus glabra*, May 1976 (Langmaid) and 1981–85 (Hardwick).

1151. *Epinotia trigonella* **Linnaeus** Whixall Moss, 1930 (Hignett), 15.ix.1981 (Langmaid) and 1981–85 (Hardwick); Preston Montford, 1986 (R.I.S. trap, det. Riley) and Wyre Forest, 1981–87 (Plant).

1152. *Epinotia maculana* **Fabricius** Prees Heath (Burrows, per Fielding, 1974b) and Rednal, 1932 (Hignett).

1153. *Epinotia sordidana* **Hübner** Prees Heath (Burrows, per Fielding, 1974b) and Whixall Moss, June 1931 (Hignett).

1154. *Epinotia caprana* **Fabricius** Whixall Moss, June 1931; Rednal, 1948 (Hignett) and Wem Moss, 24.vii.1977 (Warren).

1155. *Epinotia brunnichana* **Linnaeus** Oswestry, 1931 (Hignett); Whixall Moss, 1981–85 (Hardwick) and 31.vii.1986, one (Langmaid and Pelham-Clinton) and Wyre Forest, 1981–87 (Plant).

1156. *Epinotia solandriana* **Linnaeus** Oswestry, 1930 (Hignett); Whixall Moss, 1981–85 (Hardwick); Wyre Forest, 1981–87 (Plant); Brown Moss, 9.ix.1989 (Hardwick) and Brown Moss and Ironbridge, 11.vii.1990, larva on *Betula* sp. (Palmer).

1159. *Rhopobota naevana* **Hübner** **Holly Tortrix** Oswestry, 1930, common amongst *Ilex* (Hignett) and Shrewsbury, 29.vii.1986 (one at M.V.) and Whixall Moss, 30.v.1987, many larvae on *Vaccinium myrtillus* (Langmaid and Pelham-Clinton).

1162. *Griselda myrtillana* **Humphreys & Westwood** Whixall Moss, 28.v.1938 (Warren).

1163. *Zeiraphera ratzeburgiana* **Ratzeburg** Candy Wood and Llanymynech Hills, 1930 (Hignett).

1165. *Zeiraphera isertana* **Fabricius** Oswestry, 1930 (Hignett); Wyre Forest, 1981–87 (Plant) and Brown Moss, 25.vii.1987 (per Hancock).

1167. *Gypsonoma aceriana* **Duponchel** Rednal, 1948 (Hignett).

1168. *Gypsonoma sociana* **Haworth** Candy Wood, 1936 and Rednal, 1948 (Hignett) and Shrewsbury, May 1976, larvae on *Salix caprea* (Langmaid).

1169. *Gypsonoma dealbana* **Frölich** Candy Wood, 1930 (Hignett); Whixall Moss, 1981–85 (Hardwick); Wyre Forest, 1981–87 (Plant) and Wem, 10.vii.1990, common around White Poplar (Palmer).

1170. *Gypsonoma opressana* **Treitschke** Rednall, 1948 (Hignett). Nationally this is a very local species but it has previously been recorded from nearby Gloucestershire and Herefordshire (Bradley *et al.*, 1979). Hignett's record may, therefore, be valid.

1174. *Epiblema cynosbatella* **Linnaeus** Shrewsbury, 1897 (Cortissos); Oswestry, 1930 (Hignett); Wyre Forest, 1981–87 (Plant) and Preston Montford, June 1988 (R.I.S. trap, det. Riley).

1175. *Epiblema uddmanniana* **Linnaeus** **Bramble Shoot Moth** Benthall, 1904, (Potts); Oswestry, 1934(Hignett); Whixall Moss, 1981–85 (Hardwick); Wyre Forest, 1981–87 (Plant) and Preston Montford, 26.viii.1981 (Finch) and 1986, 1987 and 1988 (R.I.S. trap, det. Riley).

1176. *Epiblema trimaculana* **Haworth** Candy Lane and Oswestry, 1930 (Hignett); Bromfield, 12.viii.1955 (Norton) and the Longmynd, 8.vii.1963 (Warren).

1177. *Epiblema rosaecolana* **Doubleday** Oswestry, 1930 (Hignett); and Wyre Forest, 1981–87 (Plant).

1178. *Epiblema roborana* **Denis & Schiffermüller** Two at Preston Montford, June and August 1987 and 1988 (R.I.S. trap, det. Riley).

1179. *Epiblema incarnatana* **Hübner** Preston Montford, July and August 1986, two (R.I.S. trap, det. Riley).

1180. *Epiblema tetragonana* **Stephens** Oswestry, 1930 (Hignett).

1183. *Epiblema foenella* **Linnaeus** Shrewsbury, 1906 (Melvill) and one at Preston Montford, 15.vii.1986 (R.I.S. trap, det. Riley).

1184. *Epiblema scutulana* **Denis & Schiffermüller** Llanymynech Hills, 1930 (Hignett); Hawk Lake, 1981–85 (Hardwick) and Wyre Forest, 1981–87 (Plant).

1186. *Epiblema sticticana* **Fabricius** Oswestry, 1930 (Hignett); Harley, 9.viii.1986, one (Langmaid and Pelham-Clinton) and Llanymynech, 29.v.1989 (Townsend).

1187. *Epiblema costipunctana* **Haworth** Oswestry, 1930 (Hignett) and Llanymynech, 23.vii.1989 (Townsend, det. confirmed Riley).

1190. *Eucosma aspidiscana* **Hübner** Bradley *et al.* (1979) pp. 178-179.

1197. *Eucosma campoliliana* **Denis & Schiffermüller** Oswestry, 1930 (Hignett) and Llanymynech Quarry, larvae on *Senecio jacobaea* 19.viii.1984 (Finch).

1200. *Eucosma hohenwartiana* **Denis & Schiffermüller** Llynclys, 1929 (Hignett) and Wyre Forest, 1981–87 (Plant).

1200a. *Eucosma fulvana* **Stephens** Wyre Forest, 1981–87 (Plant).

1201. *Eucosma cana* **Haworth** Llanymynech Hills, 1930 (Hignett); Prees Heath, 24.vi.1936 and Sweat Mere, 3.vii.1963 (Warren); Whixall Moss, 1981–85 (Hardwick); Wyre Forest, 1981–87 (Plant) and Preston Montford, 6.vii.1979 (two) and common in June and July 1986, 1987 and 1988 (R.I.S. trap, det. Riley).

1205. *Spilonota ocellana* **Denis & Schiffermüller** Oswestry, 1930 (Hignett); Earl's Hill, 20.viii.1984 (Finch) and Wyre Forest, 1981–87 (Plant).

1210. *Rhyacionia buoliana* **Denis & Schiffermüller** **Pine Shoot Moth** Oswestry, 1935 (Hignett).

1211. *Rhyacionia pinicolana* **Doubleday** Candy Wood, 1930, amongst firs (Hignett).

1212. *Rhyacionia pinivorana* **Lienig & Zeller** **Spotted Shoot Moth** Knockin, 1948 (Hignett), and Wyre Forest, 1981–87 (Plant). Also stated by Bradley *et al.* (1979) to occur on Fenn's Moss and at Bettisfield on the Shropshire-Flintshire border.

1216. *Enarmonia formosana* **Scopoli** **Cherry-bark Moth** Oswestry, 1930 (Hignett).

1217. *Eucosmomorpha albersana* **Hübner** Oswestry, 15.vii.1931 (Hignett).

1219. *Lathronympha strigana* **Fabricius** Prees Heath (Burrows, per Fielding, 1974b); Llanforda, 1929 and 1930, common (Hignett); Preston Montford, July and August 1986 (two) and 1987 (one) (R.I.S. trap, det. Riley) and Wyre Forest, 1981–87 (Plant).

1221. *Strophedra weirana* **Douglas** Wyre Forest, 1981–87 (Plant).

1222. *Strophedra nitidana* **Fabricius** Wyre Forest, 1981–87 (Plant).

1223. *Pammene splendidulana* **Guenée** Oswestry, 19.v.1931 (Hignett).

1229. *Pammene albuginana* **Guenée** Oswestry, 1930 and Candy Wood, 1948 (Hignett).

1231. *Pammene spiniana* **Duponchel** Kinnerley, 1946 (Hignett).

1232. *Pammene populana* **Fabricius**   Whixall Moss and Oswestry, 1930 (Hignett).
1234. *Pammene regiana* **Zeller**   Frankton, 1932 (Hignett).
1236. *Pammene fasciana* **Linnaeus**   Llynclys, 1930 (Hignett).
1239. *Pammene rhediella* **Clerck   Fruitlet-mining Tortrix**   Oswestry, 1933 (Hignett).
1241. *Cydia compositella* **Fabricius**   Oswestry, 1934 (Hignett) and Harley, 9.viii.1986, several (Langmaid and Pelham-Clinton).
1242. *Cydia internana* **Guenée**   Llanymynech Hills, 1930 (Hignett).
1245. *Cydia janthinana* **Duponchel**   Oswestry, 1935 (Hignett).
1246. *Cydia tenebrosana* **Duponchel**   Oswestry, 1941, larvae in rose hips (Hignett).
1247. *Cydia funebrana* **Treitschke   Plum Fruit Moth**   Bromfield, 1952, 1953 and 1955 (Norton); Preston Montford, July 1982 (R.I.S. trap, det. Riley) and Clee St. Margaret, 1984, two (Denman).
1251. *Cydia jungiella* **Clerck**   Whixall Moss, 1981–87 (Hardwick and McWilliam) and 30.v.1987, one (Langmaid and Pelham-Clinton).
1254. *Cydia strobilella* **Linnaeus**   Candy Wood, 1930 (Hignett).
1255. *Cydia succedana* **Denis & Schiffermüller**   Llanymynech Hills, 1930 (Hignett); Hopley Coppice, 4.vi.1974 (Pelham-Clinton); Whixall Moss, 21.v.1988 (McWilliam) and Brown Moss, 21.v.1988 (Hardwick).
1256. *Cydia servillana* **Duponchel**   Wyre Forest, 1981–87 (Plant).
1257. *Cydia nigricana* **Fabricius   Pea Moth**   Wyre Forest, 1981–87 (Plant).
1260. *Cydia splendana* **Hübner**   Whixall Moss and Llynclys, larvae in acorns, 1930 (Hignett); Haughmond Hill, 16.viii.1982 (Finch) and Wyre Forest, 1981–87 (Plant).
1261. *Cydia pomonella* **Linnaeus   Codling Moth**   Shrewsbury, 1898 (Cortissos); Albynes, 1918 (Pitt); Oswestry, 1930 (Hignett); Wellington, 1971 and the Ercall Woods, June 1975 (Riley).
1271. *Cydia gallicana* **Guenée**   Hignett recorded larvae in carrot heads at Llanymynech in 1948 (Pendlebury, 1950).
1272. *Cydia aurana* **Fabricius**   Oswestry, 15.vii.1931 (Hignett); Ellesmere, 3.vii.1963 (Warren) and Preston Montford, July 1988 (R.I.S. trap, det. Riley).
1273. *Dichrorampha petiverella* **Linnaeus**   Llanymynech Hills, 1929 (Hignett) and 6.vii.1963 (Warren) and Preston Montford, 19.viii.1987 (R.I.S. trap, det. Riley).
1276. *Dichrorampha plumbagana* **Treitschke**   Oswestry, 1930 (Hignett).
1278. *Dichrorampha sequana* **Hübner**   West Felton, June 1932 (Hignett).
1279. *Dichrorampha acuminatana* **Lienig & Zeller**   Hawk Lake, 1981–85 (Hardwick) and Llanymynech, 23.vii.1989 (Townsend, det. confirmed Riley).
1283. *Dichrorampha montanana* **Duponchel**   Oswestry, 1930 (Hignett) and Llany-mynech, 23.vii. 1989 (Townsend, det. confirmed Riley).
1284. *Dichrorampha gueneeana* **Obraztov**   Whixall Moss, 1930 (Hignett).
1285. *Dichrorampha plumbana* **Scopoli**   Oswestry, 1930 and Llanymynech, 1933 (Hignett) and Wem, 19.vi.1977 (Warren).
1287. *Dichrorampha aeratana* **Pierce & Metcalfe**   Llanymynech, 6.vii.1963 (Warren, det. Bradley).

FAMILY: ALUCITIDAE

1288. *Alucita hexadactyla* **Linnaeus   Twenty-plume Moth**   Shrewsbury, 1898 (Cortissos); Oswestry, 1930 (Hignett); Bromfield, 1.viii.1952 and 6.iv.1953 (Norton); Bucknell, 1972 (Shephard); Hopton Titterhill, 4.viii.1982 (Hicks); Wyre Forest, 1988 (Plant) and Preston Montford, 1986, 1987 and 1988 (R.I.S. trap, det. Riley).

FAMILY: PYRALIDAE

1290. *Chilo phragmitella* **Hübner**   Aston Lock, 1933 (Hignett) and Brown Moss, 1986 and 1987 (McWilliam).
1292. *Calamotropha paludella* **Hübner**   Bromfield, 1952 and 1.viii.1955 (Norton).
1293. *Chrysoteuchia culmella* **Linnaeus**   Recorded commonly from grassy localities throughout the county.
1294. *Crambus pascuella* **Linnaeus**   Llynclys, 1929 (Hignett); Dothill, 1976 (Riley); Wyre Forest, 1981–87 (Plant); Preston Montford, July 1987, one (R.I.S. trap, det. Riley)

and Whixall Moss, 1981–85 (Hardwick), 30.vii.1986 and 1.vii.1988, several (Langmaid and Pelham-Clinton).

1297. *Crambus uliginosellus* Zeller   Brown Moss, 24.vii.1938 (Warren).

1299. *Crambus hamella* Thunberg   Prees Heath (Burrows, per Fielding, 1974b).

1300. *Crambus pratella* Linnaeus   One unconfirmed record from Whixall Moss, 1930 (Hignett).

1301. *Crambus lathoniellus* Zincken   Oswestry, 1930 (Hignett); Whixall Moss, 1981–85 (Hardwick); Wyre Forest, 1981–87 (Plant) and Preston Montford, 1986, 1987 and 1988 (R.I.S. trap, det. Riley).

1302. *Crambus perlella* Scopoli   Shrewsbury, 1905 (Melvill); Whixall Moss, 1930 (Hignett) and 3.vii.1972 (Warren); Ercall Woods, 1976 and Wellington, 1977 (Riley); Clee St. Margaret, 19.vii.1984 (Denman) and Preston Montford, 1986, 1987 and 1988 (R.I.S. trap, det. Riley).

1303. *Agriphila selasella* Hübner   Bromfield, 2.viii. and 7.viii.1952 (Norton) and Wyre Forest, 1981–87 (Plant).

1304. *Agriphila straminella* Denis & Schiffermüller   Often abundant in grassy places throughout the county.

1305. *Agriphila tristella* Denis & Schiffermüller   Very common in grassy areas throughout the county.

1306. *Agriphila inquinatella* Denis & Schiffermüller   Prees Heath, (Burrows, per Fielding, 1974b); Llanymynech Hills, 1930 (Hignett), 4.vii.1963 (Warren) and 1984 (Finch); Earl's Hill, 20.viii.1984 (Finch); Whixall Moss, 1981–86 (Hardwick, Langmaid and Pelham-Clinton); Shrewsbury, 29.vii.1986 (Langmaid and Pelham-Clinton) and Wyre Forest, 1981–87 (Plant).

1307. *Agriphila latistria* Haworth   Clee St. Margaret, 28.vii.1984 (Denman) and Wyre Forest, 27.viii.1985 (Plant).

1309. *Agriphila geniculea* Haworth   Ercall Woods, 17.vii.1976 (Riley); Llanymynech, 1930 (Hignett) and 29.viii.1984 (Finch) and Wyre Forest, 1981–87 (Plant).

1313. *Catoptria pinella* Linnaeus   Prees Heath (Burrows, per Fielding, 1974b); Haughmond Hill, 16.viii.1982 and Preston Montford, 21.viii.1984 (Finch); Whixall Moss, 1981–86 (Hardwick, Finch, Langmaid and Pelham-Clinton); Wyre Forest, 1981–87 (Plant) and Llanymynech Hills, 1929 (Hignett) and 22.vii.1989 (Townsend).

1314. *Catoptria margaritella* Denis & Schiffermüller   Whixall Moss, 1930 (Hignett), 27.vii.1981 (Finch), 1981–85 (Hardwick) and 31.vii.1986 and 1.vii.1988 (Langmaid and Pelham-Clinton) and Preston Montford, August 1988, one (R.I.S. trap, det. Riley).

1316. *Catoptria falsella* Denis & Schiffermüller   Shrawardine army training ground, 20.viii.1984 (Finch) and Preston Montford, 10.vii.1979 (R.I.S. trap, det. Riley), 16.viii.1982 (Finch) and July and August, 1986 (nine), 1987 (eight) and June (six) and July (one) 1988 (R.I.S. trap, det. Riley).

1329. *Schoenobius forficella* Thunberg   Whixall Moss, 28.vi.1953 (Warren); Brown Moss, 1986–87 (McWilliam) and Preston Montford, June 1988, two (R.I.S. trap, det. Riley).

1332. *Scoparia subfusca* Haworth   Llanforda 1929 and 1930 (Hignett).

1333. *Scoparia pyralella* Denis & Schiffermüller   Llanymynech Hills, 1930 (Hignett); Ludlow, 7.vii.1945 (Allen); Longmynd, 8.vii.1963 (Warren); Bucknell, 1971 and 1973 (Shephard); Preston Montford, June 1987, two (R.I.S. trap, det. Riley); Whixall Moss, 1981–88 (Hardwick) and Shrewsbury, 30.vi.1988, one at M.V. (Langmaid and Pelham-Clinton).

1334. *Scoparia ambigualis* Treitschke   Common at Preston Montford (R.I.S. trap, det. Riley). Other records from: Oswestry, 1930 (Hignett); Ercall Woods, June 1975 (Riley); Whixall Moss and Hawk Lake, 1981–85 (Hardwick, Langmaid and Pelham-Clinton); Wyre Forest, 1981–87 (Plant) and Brown Moss, 21.v.1988 (Hardwick).

1338. *Eudonia lacustrata* Panzer   Oswestry, 1930 (Hignett); Wyre Forest, 6.viii.1988 (Plant) and Shrewsbury, 30.vi.1988, four at M.V. (Langmaid and Pelham-Clinton).

1340. *Eudonia truncicolella* Stainton   Whixall Moss, 1930 (Hignett) and 31.vii.1986 (Langmaid and Pelham-Clinton) and Wyre Forest, 1981–87, very common (Plant).

1342. *Eudonia angustea* Curtis   Oswestry, August 1931 (Hignett) and Lilleshall, 5.ix.1970 (Warren).

1344. *Eudonia mercurella* **Linnaeus** Oswestry, 1930 (Hignett); Dothill, 11.vii.1976 (Riley, det. genitalia); Whixall Moss, 2.vi.1939 (Warren), 1981–85 (Hardwick) and 31.vii.1986 (Langmaid and Pelham-Clinton); Wyre Forest, 1981–87 (Plant) and Shrewsbury, 29.vii.1986 and 31.vi.1988 (Langmaid and Pelham-Clinton).

1345. *Elophila nymphaeata* **Linnaeus** **Brown China-mark** Oswestry, 1930 (Hignett); Bromfield, 16.vii.1955 (Norton); Preston Montford, 16.viii.1982 (Finch); Whixall Moss, 1981–85 (Hardwick); Catherton Common, 1985 (Blunt); Wyre Forest, 1981–87 (Plant) and Brown Moss, 1986 and 1987 (McWilliam).

1348. *Parapoynx stratiotata* **Linnaeus** **Ringed China-mark** Oswestry, 1930 (Hignett) and Whixall Moss, 1981–85 (Hardwick) and 16.vii.1988 (Riley).

1350. *Nymphula stagnata* **Donovan** **Beautiful China-mark** Ellesmere, 23.vii.1932 (Hignett), and Whixall Moss (Burrows, per Fielding, 1974a), 21.vii.1934 and 28.vi.1953 (Warren).

1354. *Cataclysta lemnata* **Linnaeus** **Small China-mark** Whixall Moss (Burrows, per Fielding, 1974a); Llanforda, 1929 (Hignett); Bromfield, 1955 (Norton); Ercall Woods, 1976 (Riley); Wyre Forest, 1981–87 (Plant) and Preston Montford, 16.viii.1982 and 18.viii.1984 (Finch) and July 1986 (one), 1987 (two) and August 1988 (one) (R.I.S. trap, det. Riley).

1355i. *Acentria ephemerella* **Denis & Schiffermüller** **Water Veneer** Preston Montford, 19.viii.1984 (Finch); Whixall Moss (Burrows, per Fielding, 1974a), 1981–85 (Hardwick) and Wyre Forest, 1981–87 (Plant).

1356. *Evergestis forficalis* **Linnaeus** **Garden Pebble** Common throughout the county in gardens and allotments where *Brassica*'s are grown.

1358. *Evergestis pallidata* **Hufnagel** Bromfield, 1942 and 23.vii.1952 (Norton) and Wyre Forest, 1981–87 (Plant).

1361. *Pyrausta aurata* **Scopoli** Benthall, 1903 (Potts); Albynes, 1918 (Pitt); Bromfield, 1948 (Norton); Whitehaven, 1948 (Hignett) and Llanymynech, 22.vii.1989 (Townsend).

1362. *Pyrausta purpuralis* **Linnaeus** Bromfield, 1948 and Solway Dingle, 30.vii.1955 (Norton); Much Wenlock, (K.G.V. Smith, 1956) and Llanymynech, 1930 (Hignett), August 1980 and 19.viii.1984 (Finch) and 29.v. and 22.vii.1989 (Townsend).

1363. *Pyrausta ostrinalis* **Hübner** Recorded by K.G.V. Smith (1956) at Much Wenlock as *P. purpuralis* var. *ostrinalis* flying in company with *P. purpuralis*. Also recorded from Bromfield, 1948 (Norton) and Clee St. Margaret, 28.vii.1984 (Denman).

1364. *Pyrausta sanguinalis* **Linnaeus** Bromfield, 19.vii.1952 and Far Forest, 17.viii.1952 (Norton).

1365. *Pyrausta cespitalis* **Denis & Schiffermüller** Bromfield, 1955 (Norton); Wyre Forest, 1981–87 (Plant) and Llanymynech Hills, 1930 (Hignett), 4.vii.1963 (Warren) and 22.vii.1989 (Townsend).

1367. *Pyrausta cingulata* **Linnaeus** Bromfield, 1952 (Norton) and Llanymynech, 1930 (Hignett), August 1980 (Finch) and 22.vii.1989 (Townsend).

1371. *Sitochroa verticalis* **Linnaeus** Bromfield, 1948–55 (Norton); Bucknell, 1971–73 (Shephard); Clee St. Margaret, 3.viii.1984 (Denman) and Wyre Forest, 1981–87 (Plant).

1376. *Eurrhypara hortulata* **Linnaeus** **Small Magpie** Generally distributed and common throughout the county.

1377. *Perinephela lancealis* **Denis & Schiffermüller** Wyre Forest, 1981–88 (Blunt; Plant).

1378. *Phylctaenia coronata* **Hufnagel** Shrewsbury, 1897 (Cortissos); Broseley, 1898 and Benthall, 1904 (Potts); Oswestry, 1930 (Hignett); Much Wenlock, most years up to 1956 (K.G.V. Smith, 1956); Ercall Woods, 1975 (Riley) and Preston Montford, 11.vii.1979, 16.vii.1987 and June 1988 (R.I.S. trap, det. Riley).

1385. *Ebulea crocealis* **Hübner** Oswestry, 1949, larva on *Inula* (Hignett) and Preston Montford, September 1987 (R.I.S. trap, det. Riley).

1388. *Udea lutealis* **Hübner** Common on wasteground, rough pasture and overgrown gardens, allotments etc. throughout the county.

1390. *Udea prunalis* **Denis & Schiffermüller** Common at Preston Montford (R.I.S. trap, det. Riley). Also recorded from Benthall, 1903 (Potts); Shrewsbury, 1905

(Melvill); Oswestry, 1930 (Hignett); Ellesmere, 11.vii.1963 (Warren); Brown Moss, 1986 and 1987 (McWilliam); Wyre Forest, 1988 (Plant) and Llanymynech, 22.vii.1989 (Townsend).

1392. *Udea olivalis* **Denis & Schiffermüller** Widely distributed and common in woodlands, on rough ground and along hedgerows, throughout the county.

1395. *Udea ferrugalis* **Hübner** Oswestry, 1948 (Hignett) and Preston Montford, August 1987 (R.I.S. trap, det. Riley).

1398. *Nomophila noctuella* **Denis & Schiffermüller Rush Veneer** Prees Heath (Burrows, per Fielding, 1974b); Oswestry, 1930 (Hignett); Stoke-on-Tern, 1978 (Littlewood) and Preston Montford, 10.x.1986 (R.I.S. trap, det. Riley).

1402. *Diasemia reticularis* **Linnaeus** This scarce immigrant was recorded once in 1957 at Oakley Park (Norton).

1405. *Pleuroptya ruralis* **Scopoli Mother of Pearl** Very common throughout the county wherever stinging nettle grows.

1413. *Hypsopygia costalis* **Fabricius Gold Triangle** Common at Preston Montford (Riley; Finch). Other records from: Oswestry, 1930 (Hignett); Bromfield, 1952 and 1955 (Norton); Goldstone Common, 29.vii.1972 (Dawson); Dothill, 1976 (Riley); Earl's Hill, 1984 (Finch); Ercall Woods, 1979–85 (Riley); Whixall Moss, 1981–86 (Hardwick, Langmaid and Pelham-Clinton); Wyre Forest, 1981–87 (Plant) and Llanymynech, 22.vii.1989 (Townsend).

1415. *Orthopygia glaucinalis* **Linnaeus** Ercall Woods, 4.vii.1976 (Riley) and Preston Montford, July to September, 1986, 1987 and 1988 (R.I.S. trap, det. Riley).

1417. *Pyralis farinalis* **Linnaeus Meal Moth** Shrewsbury, 1897 (Cortissos); Oswestry, 1930 (Hignett); Ercall Woods, 1970 and Dothill, 11.vii.1976 (Riley) and Clee St. Margaret, 1984 (Denman).

1421. *Aglossa pinguinalis* **Linnaeus Large Tabby** Broseley, 1898 (Potts); Shrewsbury, 1913 (Pendlebury, 1915); Albynes, 1918 (Pitt); Oswestry, 1930 (Hignett) and Clee St. Margaret, 26.vi.1984 (Denman).

1426. *Achroia grisella* **Fabricius Lesser Wax Moth** Oswestry, 1949 (Hignett).

1428. *Aphomia sociella* **Linnaeus Bee Moth** Albynes, 1918 (Pitt); Benthall, 1902 and 1925 (Potts); Oswestry, 1930 (Hignett); Bromfield, 1952, 1953 and 1955 (Norton); Bucknell, 1971 (Shephard); Wyre Forest, 1981–87 (Plant); Preston Montford, June 1987 and 1988 (R.I.S. trap, det. Riley) and Shrewsbury, 30.vi.1988, one at M.V. (Langmaid and Pelham-Clinton).
Note: The order of species 1436 to 1483 have been arranged according to the original numbering system in Bradley & Fletcher (1979) as the order in Bradley & Fletcher (1986) is not numerical and would therefore appear confusing in the format of the present work.

1436. *Acrobasis repandana* **Fabricius** Wyre Forest, 1981–87 (Plant).

1437. *Acrobasis consociella* **Hübner** Wyre Forest, 6.viii.1988 (Goater, per Plant).

1439. *Numonia advenella* **Zincken** Rednal, 1948, common (Hignett) and Preston Montford, July and August 1987 (R.I.S. trap, det. Riley) and July 1988 (R.I.S. trap, det. Dunn).

1440. *Numonia marmorea* **Haworth** Preston Montford, 18.viii.1979, two (R.I.S. trap, det. Riley).

1442. *Pempelia palumbella* **Denis & Schiffermüller** Whixall Moss, 1981–85 (Hardwick).

1450. *Metriostola betulae* **Goeze** Whixall Moss, 1930 (Hignett), 1981–85 (Hardwick) and 30.v.1987, many larvae on *Betula* and 1.vii.1988, a few pupae on *Betula* (Langmaid and Pelham-Clinton).

1451. *Pyla fusca* **Haworth** Whixall Moss, 10.vii.1931 (Hignett) and Wellington, 29.vii.1976 (Riley).

1452. *Phycita roborella* **Denis & Schiffermüller** Whixall Moss, 1981–85 (Hardwick) and Wyre Forest, 1981–87 (Plant).

1454. *Dioryctria abietella* **Denis & Schiffermüller** Bucknell, 1972 (Shephard).

1457. *Hypochalcia ahenella* **Denis & Schiffermüller** All Stretton, 29.v.1987, one at M.V. (Langmaid and Pelham-Clinton).

1462. *Pempeliella dilutella* **Hübner** Wyre Forest, 1986 (Plant).

1469. *Euzophera cinerosella* **Zeller** Wyre Forest, 1981–87 (Plant).

1470. *Euzophera pinguis* **Haworth**   Preston Montford, 16.viii.1982 (Finch).
1473. *Ephestia elutella* **Hübner**   **Cacao Moth**   Oswestry, 1930 (Hignett) and Wellington, 29.vii.1976 (Riley).
1475. *Ephestia kuehniella* **Zeller**   **Mediterranean Flour Moth**   Oswestry, 27.x.1932 (Hignett).
1480. *Homoeosoma nebulella* **Denis & Schiffermüller**   One unconfirmed record from Whixall Moss, 1929 (Hignett). There are several other superficially similar species which are more widespread and common than *H. nebulella*. Therefore Hignett's record must be treated with caution.
1483. *Phycitodes binaevella* **Hübner**   Preston Montford, July 1986 (four) and June 1987 (two) (R.I.S. trap, det. Riley).

FAMILY: PTEROPHORIDAE

1487. *Agdistis staticis* **Millière**   There is an unconfirmed record from Whixall Moss, 1930 (Pugh, per Pendlebury, 1950). This is almost certainly erroneous as the nearest colony of this coastal species is on the Gower Peninsula (Emmet, pers. comm.).
1494. *Capperia britanniodactyla* **Gregson**   Prees Heath (Burrows, per Fielding 1974b) and Preston Montford, July 1987, one (R.I.S. trap, det. Riley).
1497. *Amblyptilia acanthadactyla* **Hübner**   Prees Heath (Burrows, per Fielding 1974b); Whixall Moss (Burrows, per Fielding, 1974a, 1930 (Hignett), 2.vii.1939 (Warren), 15.ix.1981 (Langmaid), 1981–85 (Hardwick) and 1.vii.1988, one (Langmaid and Pelham-Clinton) and Preston Montford, July 1986 (one) and June 1988 (one) (R.I.S. trap, det. Dunn).
1498. *Amblyptilia punctidactyla* **Haworth**   Wyre Forest, 6.viii.1988, larvae and pupae common on Hedge Woundwort (*Stachys sylvatica*) (Dyke, Goater and Plant).
1501. *Platyptilia gonodactyla* **Denis & Schiffermüller**   Shrewsbury, 1899 (Cortissos); Oswestry, 1930 (Hignett) and Clee St. Margaret, 11.vi.1984 (Denman).
1502. *Platyptilia isodactylus* **Zeller**   Whixall Moss, 1930 (Hignett).
1503. *Platyptilia ochrodactyla* **Denis & Schiffermüller**   Meole Brace, 1918 (Melvill) and Preston Montford, July 1987, three (R.I.S. trap, det. Riley).
1504. *Platyptilia pallidactyla* **Haworth**   Whixall Moss, 2.vii.1977 (Warren) and Wyre Forest, 1981–87 (Plant).
1508. *Stenoptilia* **Group.** *S. bipunctidactyla* Scop. has been recorded from Llynclys, 1930 (Hignett) and Preston Montford, 1986 and 1988 (R.I.S. trap, det. Dunn) and *S. pterodactyla* L. has been recorded from Prees Heath (Burrows, per Fielding, 1974b) and Preston Montford, 1988 (R.I.S. trap, det. Dunn) but due to the taxonomic complexities of this group, these records must be treated with caution.
1510. *Pterophorus tridactyla* **Linnaeus**   Llanymynech, 1930 (Hignett, 1931).
1513. *Pterophorus pentadactyla* **Linnaeus**   **White Plume**   Shrewsbury, 1897 (Cortissos); Oswestry, 1930 (Hignett); Wellington, 20.v.1968 and 22.v.1973 (Riley); Whixall Moss, 1981–85 (Hardwick) and Preston Montford June 1987 (R.I.S. trap, det. Riley).
1517. *Adaina microdactyla* **Hübner**   A single unconfirmed record from Melverley, 1948 (Pugh, per Pendlebury, 1950).
1520. *Leioptilus osteodactylus* **Zeller**   A single specimen was caught at Llanymynech on 23.vii.1989 by M. C. Townsend (det. confirmed Riley).
1523. *Oidaematophorus lithodactyla* **Treitschke**   A single specimen (which cannot be traced) was recorded at Llanymech in 1930 by Hignett. It was a larva found on Goldenrod and was apparently reared through to the adult (Hignett, 1931). Pendlebury (1950) questioned the likelihood of this species feeding on *Solidago*; the usual foodplants are *Pulicaria dysenterica* and *Inula conyza* (Emmet, 1979). Considering this anomaly and the taxonomic difficulties of this group, we must regard Hignett's record as doubtful.
1524. *Emmelina monodactyla* **Linnaeus**   Shrewsbury, 1905 (Melvill); Oswestry, 1930 (Hignett); Whixall Moss, 1981–85 (Hardwick) and Wyre Forest, 1981–87 (Plant).

Appendix II — Butterfly Distribution Maps

The Shropshire Trust for Nature Conservation expressed the desire for 2 km tetrad distribution maps to be included in this work.

Unfortunately the majority of records are based on localities (e.g. ". . . Longmynd . . ." or ". . . Church Stretton . . .") and are not accompanied by the grid references which are necessary to enable translation into the format required for a mapping exercise. This is a particular problem with historical moth records such as those cited by Newnham (1908). However, due mainly to the success of the butterfly recording scheme organised by the Biological Records Centre at Ludlow Museum, it was felt that sufficient suitable data were available to provide maps for this particular group.

A few of the butterfly species are extremely localised in their distribution (e.g. *Plebejus argus*) and these are not included in the series of maps in order to avoid possible pressure

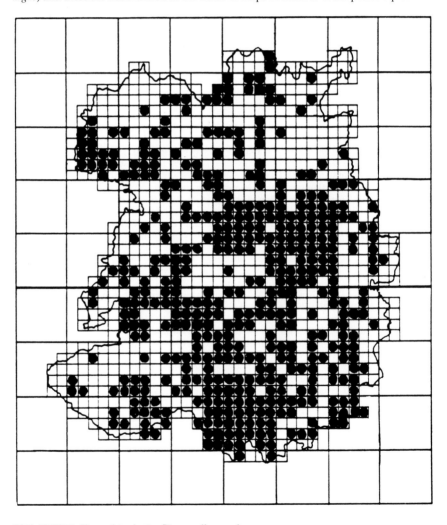

FIG. EIGHT. Shropshire butterflies — all records.

from collectors. Also omitted are those migrant species which occur so sporadically in the county (e.g. *Colias croceus*) that maps would be of little use.

The majority of these maps are based on records received since 1970. This date was chosen to conform with Sinker *et al.* (1985) which also uses 2 km tetrads for Shropshire's flora. However, where the distribution of a particular species has appeared to contract, the known pre–1970 range is indicated by open circles. In one species (*Strymonidia w-album*) a contraction of range has become apparent since 1970. In this case 1970–1980 records are represented by open circles and those for 1980–1989 are shown as solid circles. *Argynnis adippe* has declined so dramatically in recent years that three separate maps have been used to show its distribution over three time periods. It is evident from records received that no butterfly species has increased its range over the period 1970–1989.

Great care must be taken in interpreting these maps as the recording coverage is highly concentrated in some areas (e.g. Telford, Shrewsbury and Ludlow and popular collecting sites such as Whixall Moss, Wyre Forest and Wenlock Edge) and very sparse in others (e.g. the Clun Forest Uplands) (Fig. 8). It is hoped that publication of the distribution maps will encourage readers to visit under-recorded localities, record the Lepidoptera they find there and consequently help to complete our understanding of Shropshire's butterflies.

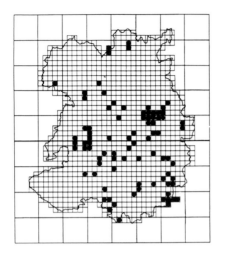

a. *Thymelicus sylvestris* Poda

b. *Ochlodes venata* Brem. & Grey

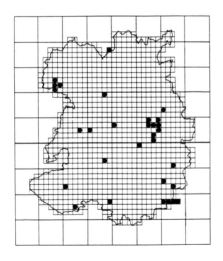

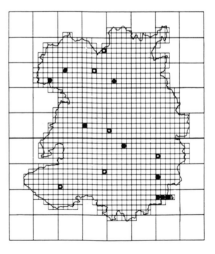

c. *Erynnis tages* Linn.

d. *Pyrgus malvae* Linn.:
○ = pre 1970; ● = post 1970

FIG. NINE

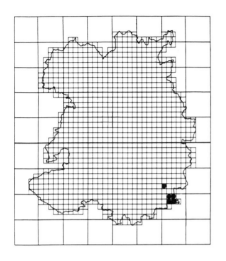

a. *Leptidea sinapis* Linn.

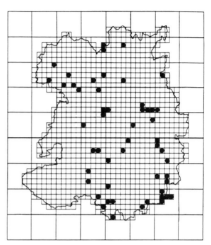

b. *Gonepteryx rhamni* Linn.

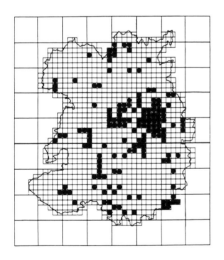

c. *Pieris brassicae* Linn.

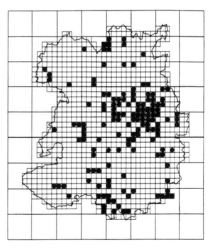

d. *Pieris rapae* Linn.

FIG. TEN

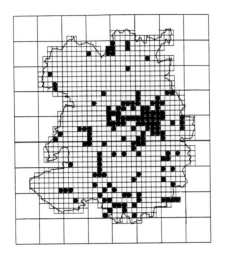

a. *Pieris napi* Linn.

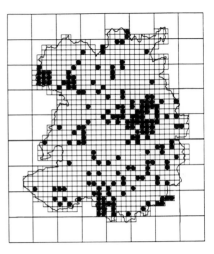

b. *Anthocharis cardamines* Linn.

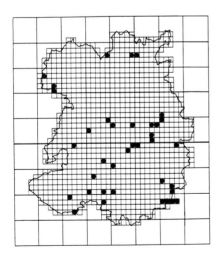

c. *Callophrys rubi* Linn.

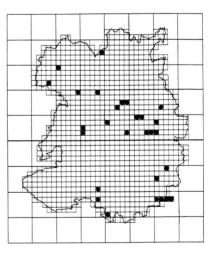

d. *Quercusia quercus* Linn.

FIG. ELEVEN

174

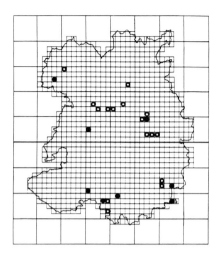

a. *Strymonidia w-album* Knoch:
○ = pre 1980; ● = post 1980

b. *Lycaena phlaeas* Linn.

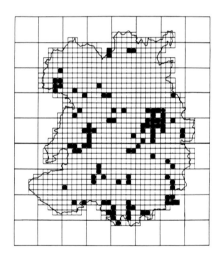

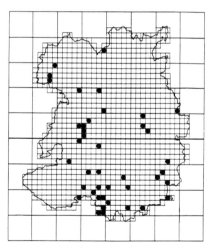

c. *Polyommatus icarus* Rott.

d *Celastrina argiolus* Linn.

FIG. TWELVE

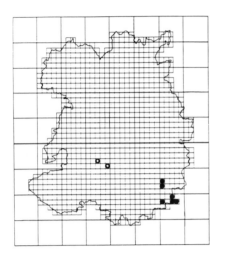

a. *Ladoga camilla* Linn.:
○ = pre 1970;   ● = post 1970

b. *Vanessa atalanta* Linn.

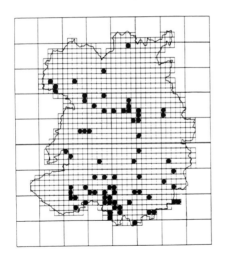

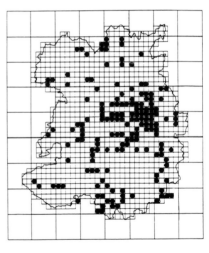

c. *Cynthia cardui* Linn.

d. *Aglais urticae* Linn.

FIG. THIRTEEN

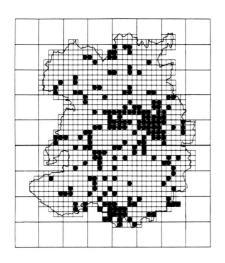

a. *Inachis io* Linn.

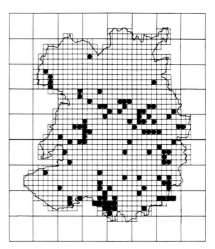

b. *Polygonia c-album* Linn.

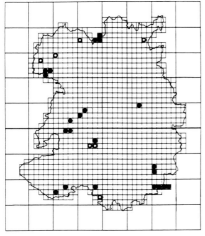

c. *Boloria selene* D. & S.
○ = pre 1970; ● = post 1970

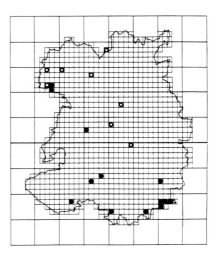

d. *Boloria euphrosyne* Linn.:
○ = pre 1970; ● = post 1970

FIG. FOURTEEN

177

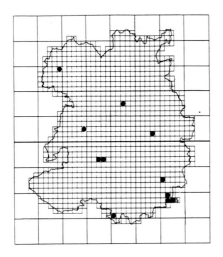

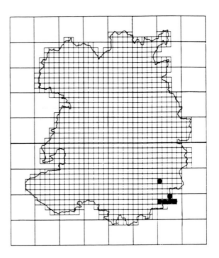

a. *Argynnis adippe* D. & S.: pre 1970

b. *Argynnis adippe* D. & S.: 1970–1985

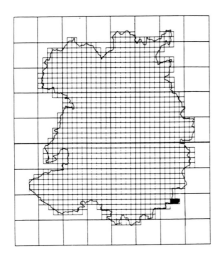

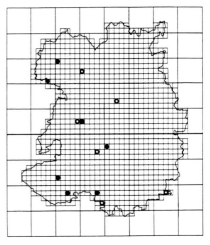

c. *Argynnis adippe* D. & S.: 1985–1988

d. *Argynnis aglaja* Linn.:
○ = pre 1970;   ● = post 1970

FIG. FIFTEEN

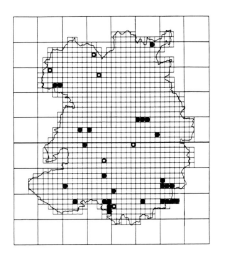
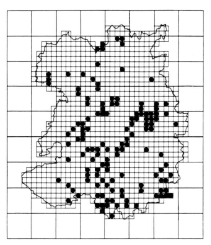

a. *Argynnis paphia* Linn.:
○ = pre 1970;   ● = post 1970

b. *Pararge aegeria* Linn.

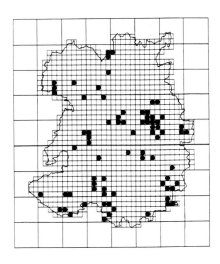
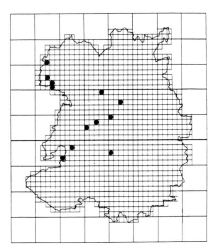

c. *Lasiommata megera* Linn.

d. *Hipparchia semele* Linn.

FIG. SIXTEEN

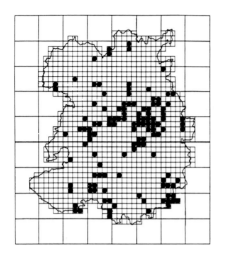

a. *Pyronia tithonus* Linn.

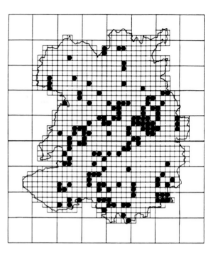

b. *Maniola jurtina* Linn.

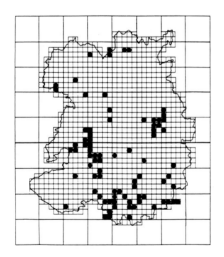

c. *Coenonympha pamphilus* Linn.

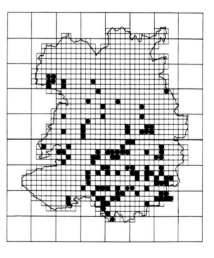

d. *Aphantopus hyperantus* Linn.

FIG. SEVENTEEN

Acknowledgements

Special thanks are due to Clive Tate whose enthusiastic persuit of funds has enabled publication of this work.

The author is indebted to D. J. Denman for his research into the geography of the county and for collating the Lepidoptera records held at Ludlow Museum.

A list of the many recorders who are mentioned in the text of this work is given below. However, special thanks are extended to John Norton for his advice and help in collating the Shropshire Biological Records Centre data and for allowing free access to the reference collections at Ludlow Museum; Brian Eversham and the late John Heath for their help in gleaning information from the files of the Institute for Terrestrial Ecology (National Biological Recording Scheme) at Huntingdon, Cambs.; Adrian Bayley and his staff at Preston Montford Field Centre for continued and valued co-operation in operating the Rothamsted Insect Survey light trap there and L.J. Evans and C.W. Plant for their extensive lists and notes on the Wyre Forest.

The author is extremely grateful for the kindness and generosity of Richard Warren (county Lepidoptera recorder for Staffordshire) for donating his unique copy of Pendlebury's manuscript (Pendlebury, 1950). This contained many valuable notes and is a useful summary of the Lepidoptera records published in *The Record of Bare Facts*.

J. J. Tucker and T. Kohler (Shropshire Wildlife Trust); C.W. Rolfe (Nat. Trust); A. Hearle (N.C.C.); R. Rogers (Forestry Commission) and N. Jones (Shropshire County Council) contributed valuable information on habitat management in Shropshire. Their expertise and help is greatly appreciated.

Several of the photographs of the geographical areas for Plates One to Ten were kindly supplied by D.J. Smith and B. Brazier. Photographs of butterflies were supplied by the B.B.C.S. Their generosity is hereby gratefully acknowledged.

Thanks are extended to the Trustees of the British Museum (Natural History) for permission to examine and borrow specimens from the national Lepidoptera collection. Particular thanks are expressed to David Carter thereof for valuable correspondence.

The Trustees of the Royal Scottish Museum kindly allowed access to the diaries of the late E. C. Pelham-Clinton.

It would have been infeasible to produce the appended inventory of microlepidoptera without the lists kindly submitted by K.P. Bland, E. Hancock, W. Hardwick, J. Langmaid, S. McWilliam, E.C. Pelham-Clinton, C. Plant and R.G. Warren. The author is also grateful to E. Bradford for confirming the identification of Plant's Wyre Forest Gelichidae and T.C. Dunn M.B.E. for his help in identifying microleopdoptera collected from the Rothamsted Insect Survey light trap at Preston Montford Field Centre.

M.C. Clark (Editor of the Proc. Birm. Nat. Hist. Soc.), D. Emley, A.M. Emmett, I.F.G. McLean (N.C.C.) and C.I. Rutherford (Lancs. & Chesh. Ent. Soc.) were instrumental in passing on requests for records to prospective contributors. Their help is hereby gratefully acknowledged.

Thanks are also extended to Joan Johnson (Rothamsted Library) and A.M. Carr (Local Studies Dept., Shropshire Libraries) for tracing old and obscure literature; Lynda Alderson for helping to collate the microlepidoptera contributions; Jackie Fountain for typing, and A.M. Emmett, B.R. Kerry, S.C. Littlewood, J. Norton, C.W. Plant, D.K. Riley, B. Skinner, D. Smith, R. Whitney, M. Williams and I.P. Woiwod for checking the manuscript.

Alphabetical list of contributors referred to in the text.

Abbot, P.W.; Allan, W.D.; Bailey, J.A.; Baker, M.R.; Ball, N.A.; Barnett, D.W.; Beckett, A.; Bingham, J.; Bland, K.P.; Blunt, A.G.; Bradburne; Bretherton, R.F.; Brice, N.; Briggs, J.; Broadhurst, J.J.; Broome, M.; Burkhill, H.J.; Burrows, H.L.; Butler, S.; Bythell; Carles; Carlier, S.E.W.; Carson, M.; Casebourne, W.C.; Christie, L.; Cheung; Clapham, F.A.; Coates, D.L.; Coleshaw, T.; Cooper, S.; Cortissos, C.; Crewdson, R.C.; Crump ; D'Arcy, J.N.; Darling, D.; Davis, J.; Dawson, D.A.; Denman, D.; Derry, N.; Dobré-Fox, E.C.; Downes, M.; Dunn, T.C.; Dyer, A.; Dyke, R.; Edwards, W.H.; Elliot, J.C.; Ellis, H.A.; Emmett, A.M.; Evans, L.J.; Fairclough, R.; Faulkner, P.; Feeste, A.; Fielding, E.H.; Finch, A.; Frazer, J.F.D.; Garrett, A.B.; Gladman, J.C.; Goater, B.; Good, P.A.; Graham, P.; Green, J.E.; Harding, M.J.; Hardwick, W.; Harwood; Hastings, C.; Hayward; Heath, J.; Henstock, H.; Hewitt, S.; Hicks; Hignett, J.; Holdsworth, B.K.; Hope, F.W.; Horsefall; Hughes, H.H.; Hull, M.; Ingrams, A.D.; Ingrams, W.S.; Jacques, A.T.; James, A.H.; Jappy; Jardine, D.; Jones, C.M.; Jones, R.B.; Jones, W.; Joy, E.C.; Joy, J.; King, G.J.; Kirk, W.; Knill-Jones, R.P.; Knill-Jones, S.A.; Lamb, R.; Langmaid, J.; Lavin, J.C.; Leonard, R.E.; Lewis, E.S.; Lewis, K.; Littlewood, S.C.; Lorimer; Mason, D.; Matthews; McWilliam, S.; Meacock, N.; Melvill, J.C.; Michaelis, H.N.; Minshall, S.; Minton, M.; Morgan, M.J.; Moseley, K.A.; Newnham, F.B.; Nicholson, H.; Nicklen, J.; Noble, M.; Norton, J.; Oram, O.; Owen, J.H.; Paddock, G.H.; Palmer, K.; Palmer, R.M.; Parr, J.; Peake, H.E.; Peed, J.; Pelham-Clinton, E.C.; Pendlebury, H.; Pendlebury, M.; Pendlebury, W.J.; Pitt, F.; Plant, C.W.;Platts; Plymley, K.; Pons, M.A.; Potts, G.; Powell; Poynton, D.; Price, R.; Pringle, G.; Pugh, C.H.W.; Pugh, S.; Pugh, W.; Rea, C.; Reid, J.; Riley, D.K.; Roberts, W.; Rutherford, C.I.; Rutter, E.; Rylands; Sanky, D.; Scott, D.W.; Sequera, E.R.; Shephard, H.; Skare-Jennings, J.A.; Skinner, B.; Smith D.J.; Smith, G.; Smith, J.M.; Smith, K.G.V.; Smith, M.; Smith, W.; Steer, M.; Sutton, G.P.; Tanner, G.; Tatton, H.; Taylor, M.J.; Thompson, A.A.; Thompson, J.A.; Thornewill, C.F.; Townsend, M.C.; Turner, H.J.; Turner, J.R.G.; Turner, N.; Uttley; Wallace, I.D.; Warren, R.G.; Watson, B.; Wheeler, J.R.; White, A.; Whitney, R.; Williams, M.; Wint, W.; Woodforde, F.C.; Woodward, G.C.; Young, M.

The initials of some of these recorders can unfortunately no longer be traced.

Many other recorders have contributed through the butterfly recording scheme operated by the Shropshire Biological Records Centre. Although space does not permit a complete list here, thanks are extended to all those participants who submitted records.

Gazetteer of localities mentioned in the text

Abdon Burf SO5986
Acton Burnell SJ5302
Acton Scott SO4589
Adderley SJ6639
Admaston SJ6313
Albrighton SJ8104
Albynes SO6997
Alcaston SO4482
All Stretton SO4695
Allscott SJ6102
Alveley SO7583
Angel Bank SO5776
Annescroft SJ4507
Ashes Hollow SO4392
Ashes Valley SO4392
Ashford SO5270
Ashford Carbonel SO5272
Asteley Abbots SO7096
Aston SJ6109
Aston Lock SJ2623
Aston-on-Clun SO3981
Attingham Park SJ5509
Aymestry SO4265

Babbinswood SJ3033
Badger SO7695
Banks Wood SO4087
Baschurch SJ4523
Bayston Hill SJ4804
Bedstone SO3576
Beggarhill Brook Coppice SO69
Benthall SJ6602
Betton SJ3102
Betton Dingle SJ3102
Bewdley SO77
Bicton Heath SJ4513
Billingsley SO7185
Bitterley SO5776
Blackhill SO3278
Blakeway Coppice SO5998
Blist SJ5903
Boiling Well SO4294
Bomere SJ4719
Bonningale SJ8108
Boreatton SJ4024
Botvyle SO4796
Breidden SJ2914
Bridgnorth SO7193
Broadwood Hall SO3876
Bromfield SO4876
Broseley SJ6702
Brown Clee SO5984
Brown Moss SJ5639
Bucknell SO3573
Buildwas SJ6502

Burwarton SO6185
Bury Ditches SO3183
Button Oak SO7578
Bwlch SJ2525

Callow SO5979
Calverhall SJ6037
Candy SJ2528
Candy Wood SJ3129
Caradoc SO4795
Cardingmill SO4494
Catherton Common SO6378
Caybrook SO5373
Caynton SJ7021
Chelmarsh Reservoir SO7287
Chelton SO6791
Chetton SO6890
Chetwynd Heath SJ7419
Chirbury SO2698
Chirk SJ23
Chorley Coppice SO7084
Church Stretton SO4593
Clarepool Moss SJ4334
Claverley Park SJ6137
Clee Downton SO5880
Clee St. Margaret SO5684
Cleobury Mortimer SO6775
Cloverley SJ6137
Clun SO3080
Clungunford SO3978
Clunton SO3381
Coachroad Coppice SO7076
Coalport SJ6902
Cold Hatton SJ6221
Colemere SJ4333
Colly Brook SO5774
Colstey SO3083
Condover SJ4905
Cookeridge SO4607
Cosford SJ7905
Cound SJ5504
Craven Arms SO4382
Cressage SJ5904
Crickheath SJ2327
Criftin SJ5513
Crosemere SJ4330
Crosshouses SJ5806
Cuckoopen Coppice SO5380
Culmington SO4982
Cwm Clunton SO2590

Dale Coppice SJ6704
Dawley SJ6907
Diddlebury SO5085
Ditton Priors SO6289

Dolgoch Quarry SJ2724
Donnington SJ7115
Donnington Wood SJ7113
Dorrington SJ7102
Doseley SJ6706
Dothill SJ6412
Dowles Brook SO77
Dudgeley SO4696
Dudmaston SO7488
Dukes Wood SJ4333

Earl's Hill SJ4004
Easthope Wood SO6099
East Hamlet SO5175
Edgerley SJ3418
Edgmond SJ4219
Ellesmere SJ4034
Ercall Heath SJ6823
Ercall Wood SJ62

Far Forest SO7274
Farley Dingle SJ3807
Farnden SO5775
Fenemere SJ4423
Fenn's Moss SJ4936
Ford SJ4113
Forton SJ7521
Frankton SJ3631

Gallow Bank SO5274
Gippols SO5858
Glazeley SO78
Gobowen SJ3032
Goldstone Common SJ7029
Gorsley Rough SO5975
Grinshill SJ5223

Hadley SJ6711
Halston SJ3431
Harley SJ6000
Haughmond Hill SJ5414
Hawk Lake SJ5730
Hawkhurst SO4187
Hawkstone SJ5729
Hayton's Bent SO5180
Hazler Hill SO4692
Helmeth Wood SO4794
Highley SO7483
Hinstock SJ6926
Hodnet SJ5827
Holmer SO7080
Holmer Lake SJ7085
Hopedale SO4887
Hopesay SO3986
Hope Valley SJ3501

183

Hopley Coppice SJ5826
Hopton Cangeford SO5180
Hungary Hill SO7075

Ightfield SJ5938
Ireland Cottage SO4687
Ironbridge SJ6703

Ketley SJ6611
Kingsland SJ4811
Knockin SJ3322
Knowbury SO5775
Knowle SO5973

Lactone SO5779
Lawley Bank SJ6608
Ledwyche SO5374
Lebotwood SO4798
Leintwardine SO4074
Lilleshall SO5796
Little Hereford SO5568
Little Stretton SJ4491
Little Weston SO5871
Llanforda SJ2927
Llansantffraid SJ2220
Llanymynech SJ2722
Llanymynech Quarry SJ2621
Llynclys Common SJ2824
Llynclys Hill SJ2327
Lodge Hill SO5199
Longdon-on-Tern SJ6215
Longmynd SO49
Ludford SO5073
Ludlow SO5175
Lyth Hill SJ4606

Madeley SJ6803
Maesbrook SJ2130
Maesbury SJ3025
Mary Knowll Valley SO4873
Market Drayton SJ6633
Marsh Brook SO5287
Melverley SJ3316
Meole Brace SJ4810
Middleton SO2999
Middleton Priors SO6290
Mile House Lane SJ3029
Millen Heath SJ5835
Minsterley SJ3605
Moelydd SJ2425
Mogg Forest SO59
Monkhopton SO6293
Moreton SJ5722
Mortimer SO4873
Morton Mill SJ5722
Morville SO6694
Mounds SO6199

Much Wenlock SO6299
Munslow SO5287
Myddlewood SJ4523

Neenton SO6587
Nesscliffe SJ3819
Netley Hall SJ4701
New Hall SO4989
Newport SJ7419
Nordley SJ6297
Novers SO5974
Nubold SJ4710

Oakengates SJ7010
Oakley SO4876
Oakley Park SO4875
Oswestry SJ2929
Overley SJ6111

Pant SJ2722
Peatoe SO5384
Pennerley SO3598
Petton Park SJ4426
Pike's End Moss SJ4431
Plealey SJ4206
Plough Hill SO5373
Pontesbury SJ4006
Pradoe SO3524
Prees Heath SJ5636
Preston Montford SJ4314
Preston-on-the-Weald SJ6815
Pulley Common SJ4809

Quat SO7588
Quatford SO7491

Ragleth Wood SO4592
Ratlinghope SO4096
Rednal SJ3426
Redwood SO3183
Richard's Castle SO4969
Rindleford SO7395
Ritton Castle SJ3497
Roden SJ5716
Rodington SJ5814
Rorrington Wood SO3099
Rowton SJ6119
Rudge Common SO7996
Rue Wood SJ4928
Rushbury SO5191

Sallow Coppice SO4282
Selattyn SJ2633
Sharpstones SJ5007
Shavington SJ6339
Shawbury SJ5722
Sheinton SJ5904

Shelton SJ4513
Shelve SO3399
Sherriffhales SJ7413
Shirlett SO6698
Shrawardine SJ3816
Shrewsbury SJ41
Silvington Common SO6379
Sokewood SO4281
Solway Dingle SO4876
Spoon Hill SO6095
Springs SJ8307
Stanton Lacey SO5281
Stapleton SJ4704
Stiperstones SO3698
Stockton Moor SJ7716
Stoke-on-Tern SJ6228
Stoke St. Milborough SO5980
Stoneyhill SJ6606
Stottesdon SO7083
Stow Hill SO3174
Sturt Common SO7477
St. George's SJ7010
St. Martin's SJ3236
Sunny Dingle SO4873

Targrove SO5271
Temeside SO5174
Tenbury SO5967
Tesmore SJ22
Thatcher's Wood SO7090
Ticklerton SO4890
Tiger Hall SO49
Tilsbrook SJ5433
Tong SJ7907
Trefonen SJ2526
Trench SJ6913
Twemlows SJ5737

Uffington SJ5213
Upper Galdeford SO5174
Upton SO6592
Upton Magna SJ5512

Walcott SO3585
Wellington SJ6511
Wem SJ5129
Wem Industrial Estate
    SJ5203
Wem Moss SJ4734
Wenlock Edge SO59
West Felton SJ3426
Westbury SJ3507
Westhope SO4786
Weston-under-Lizard
    SJ8011
Westwood SO6990

Whattall Moss SJ4331
Wheathill SJ5008
Whitchurch SJ5442
Whitchurch Heath SJ5637
Whitcliffe SO5174
Whitehaven SJ2426
Whixall Moss SJ4835
Wigmore SO4069
Wigmore Rolls SO3968
Wilderhope SO5493

Wilderley SO69
Willey SO6798
Wimperhill Wood SO7180
Winstanton SO5385
Withington SJ5714
Wolfshead SJ3620
Woodcote SO49
Woore SJ7242
Worfield SO7396
World's End SO4493

Worthen SJ3204
Wrekin SJ6208
Wrockwardine SJ6212
Wrockwardine Wood SJ6111
Wroxeter SJ5608
Wyre Forest SO77 & SO78

Yeld SO5683
Yetchleys SJ33

References and Bibliography

Journal abbreviations

Entom.	The Entomologist.
Ent. Rec. J. Var.	Entomologist's Record and Journal of Variation.
Ent. Gaz.	Entomologist's Gazette.
Ent. Mon. Mag.	Entomologist's Monthly Magazine.
Ent. Obozr.	Entomologicheskoe Obozrenie.
Proc. Trans. Br. Ent. Nat. Hist. Soc.	Proceedings and Transactions of the British Entomological and Natural History Society.
J. South Staffs. Nat. Soc.	Journal of the South Staffordshire Naturalist's Society.
Proc. Ent. Soc. Lond.	Proceedings of the Entomological Society of London.
Rec. Bare Facts	Record of Bare Facts.
Rep. Proc. Trans. Manchr. Ent. Soc.	Report, Proceedings and Transactions of the Manchester Entomological Society.
Tijd. Ent.	Tijdschrift Entomologie.
Trans. C. & S.V.F.C.	Transactions of the Caradoc and Severn Valley Field Club.

Agassiz, D.J.L. (1988)   Recorder's Log Book or Label List of British Butterflies and Moths. Addenda and Corrigenda. Harley, Colchester.

Allan, P.B.M. (1980)   Leaves from a Moth-hunter's Notebook. Classey, Oxon.

Anon. (1931)   English examples of *Lasiommeta maera* L. Proc. Ent. Soc. Lond. **6**: 71.

Anon. (1978)   Illustrated papers on British Microlepidoptera. B.E.N.H.S., London.

Bankes, E.R. (1889)   Extract from unpublished diary. Held at the British Museum (Nat. Hist.).

Blackie, J.E.H. (1948)   History, status and prospects in England of *Coenonympha tullia* Müller. Entom. **81**: 229–230.

Blackie, J.E.H. (1949)   *Coenonympha tullia* Müller. A postscript. Entom. **82**: 83.

Blatch, W.G. (1886)   Lepidoptera. In: Hughes, W.H. *et al.* (eds.) Handbook to Birmingham, pp. 301–304. British Association, Birmingham.

Bradley, J.D. & Fletcher, D.S. (1979)   A Recorder's Log Book or Label List of British Butterlies and Moths. Curwen, London.

Bradley, J.D. & Fletcher, D.S. (1987)   Indexed List of British Butterflies and Moths. Kedleston Press, Kent.

Bradley, J.D., Tremewan, W.G. and Smith, A. (1973)   British Tortricoid Moths, Tortricidae: Tortricinae. Ray Society, London.

Bradley, J.D., Tremewan, W.G. and Smith, A. (1979)   British Tortricoid Moths, Tortricidae: Olethreutinae. Ray Society, London.

Brookes, M. & Knight, C. (1982)   Complete Guide to British Butterflies. Cape, London.

Carter, C.I. & Anderson, M.A. (1987) Enhancement of lowland forest ridesides and roadsides to benefit wild plants and butterflies. Research Information Note 126. Forestry Commission, Farnham.

Christie, L. (1952) *Cucullia absinthii* (Pale Wormwood Shark) Linn. in Shropshire. Ent. Gaz. **3**: 44.

Cortissos, C. (1898) Lepidoptera records for 1897. Rec. Bare Facts. **7**: 25–27.

Cortissos, C. (1899) Lepidoptera records for 1898. Rec. Bare Facts. **8**: 20–23.

Cortissos, C. (1900) Lepidoptera records for 1899. Rec. Bare Facts. **9**: 32–33.

Dannreuther, T. (1950) Migration Records, 1949. Entom. **83**: 131.

Emmet, A.M. (1979) Field Guide to the Smaller British Lepidoptera. B.E.N.H.S., London.

Emmet, A.M. (1987) Addenda and Corrigenda to the British List of Lepidoptera. Ent. Gaz. **38**: 31–52.

Emmet, A.M. & Heath, J. (eds.) (1989) The Moths and Butterflies of Great Britain and Ireland, Vol. 7(1). Harley, Essex.

Fielding, E.H. (1974a) Whixall Moss: description of locality and list of Lepidoptera taken by H.L. Burrows. Rep. Proc. Trans. Manchr. Ent. Soc. 1966–73: 14–16.

Fielding, E.H. (1974b) Prees Heath: description of locality and list of Lepidoptera taken by H.L. Burrows. Rep. Proc. Trans. Manchr. Ent. Soc. 1966–73: 17–18.

Fitter, R., Fitter, A. & Blamey, M. (1978) Wild Flowers of Britain and Northern Europe. Collins, London.

Frohawk, F.W. (1886) *Melitaea aurinia* in Shropshire. Ent. **19**: 41.

Frohawk, F.W. (1924) Natural History of British Butterflies. Vol. 1: 108–113. Hutchinson, London.

Goater, B. (1986) British Pyralid Moths. Harley, Colchester.

Hardcourt-Bath, W. (1887a) *Aporia crataegi* in the Wyre Forest. Entom. **20**: 39–40.

Hardcourt-Bath, W. (1887b) Abundance of diurni in the midlands. Entom. **20**: 209.

Harding, M.J. (1883) Notes from Shrewsbury and North Wales. Entom. **16**: 253.

Harding, M.J. (1884) *Melitaea artemis* in Shropshire. Entom. **17**: 182–183.

Harding, M.J. (1885) Butterflies of Church Stretton. In: Windsor, G.R.. Handbook . . . of Church Stretton, pp. 84–86. Windsor, Church Stretton.

Harding, M.J. (1906) *Chrysophanus phlaeas*, var. Entom. **39**: 235.

Harding, M.J. (1914) Gynandrous *P. icarus*. Entom. **47**: 277.

Harding, M.J. (1915) Aberrations of *Pyrameis atalanta*. Entom. **48**: 284–285.

Harding, M.J. (1917) Abundance of *Polygonia c-album* in Shropshire. Entom. **50**: 237.

Heath, J. (1976) Moths and Butterflies of Great Britain and Ireland, Vol. 1. Curwen, London.

Heath, J. (1979) Moths and Butterflies of Great Britain and Ireland, Vol. 9. Curwen, London.

Heath, J. (1983) Moths and Butterflies of Great Britain and Ireland, Vol. 10. Harley, Essex.

Heath, J. (1985) Moths and Butterflies of Great Britain and Ireland, Vol. 2. Harley, Essex.

Heath, J., Pollard, E. & Thomas, J. (1984) Atlas of Butterflies in Britain and Ireland. Viking, Harmondsworth.

Hickin, N.E. (1972) The Natural History of an English Forest. Country Book Club, Newton Abbot.

Higgins, L. & Riley, N. (1970) Field Guide to the Butterflies of Britain and Europe. Collins, London.

Hignett, J. (1931) Lepidoptera records for 1930. Rec. Bare Facts **40**: 17–30.

Hignett, J. (1932) Lepidoptera records for 1931. Rec. Bare Facts **41**: 15–17.

Howarth, T.G. (1973) South's British Butterflies. Warne, London.

Howarth, T.G. (1984) Colour Identification Guide to Butterflies of the British Isles. Viking, Harmondsworth.

Ingrams, W.S. (1917) Lepidoptera records for 1916. Rec. Bare Facts **26**: 23.

Ingrams, W.S. (1918) Lepidoptera records for 1917. Rec. Bare Facts **27**: 22.

Ingrams, W.S. (1919) Lepidoptera records for 1918. Rec. Bare Facts **28**: 19–20.

Ingrams, W.S. (1920) Lepidoptera records for 1919. Rec. Bare Facts **29**: 20–22.

Ingrams, W.S. (1921) Lepidoptera records for 1920. Rec. Bare Facts **30**: 24–25.

Ingrams, W.S. (1922) Lepidoptera records for 1921. Rec. Bare Facts **31:** 27–29.
Ingrams, W.S. (1923) Lepidoptera records for 1922. Rec. Bare Facts **32:** 29–30.
Ingrams, W.S. (1924) Lepidoptera records for 1923. Rec. Bare Facts **33:** 12.
Ingrams, W.S. (1925) Lepidoptera records for 1924. Rec. Bare Facts **34:** 31–33.
Ingrams, W.S. (1926) Lepidoptera records for 1925. Rec. Bare Facts **35:** 19–20.
Ingrams, W.S. (1927) Lepidoptera records for 1926. Rec. Bare Facts **36:** 20.
Ingrams, W.S. (1928) Lepidoptera records for 1927. Rec. Bare Facts **37:** 19–20.
Ingrams, W.S. (1929) Lepidoptera records for 1928. Rec. Bare Facts **38:** 9–10.
Ingrams, W.S. (1930) Lepidoptera records for 1929. Rec. Bare Facts **39:** 17–18.
Ingrams, W.S. (1933) Lepidoptera records for 1932. Rec. Bare Facts **42:** 16–17.
J.C.C.B.I. (1972) A code for insect collecting. Ent. Mon. Mag. **107:** 193–195; Entom. **105:** 110–112; Ent. Gaz. **23:** 135–137; Ent. Rec. J. Var. **84:** 94–96; Proc. Trans. Br. Ent. Nat. Hist. Soc. **5:** 80–83.
Jordan, M.J.R. (1986) The genitalia of the species pair *Mesapamea secalis* (L.) and *M. secalella* Remm (Lep.: Noctuidae). Ent. Rec. J. Var. **98:** 41–44.
Lempke, B.J. (1951) Catalogus der Nederlandes Macrolepidoptera. Tijd. Ent. **94:** 255–256.
Lewis, T.L. & Taylor, L.R. (1967) Introduction to Experimental Ecology, pp. 107–109. Academic Press, London.
Meyrick, E. (1927) Revised Handbook of British Lepidoptera. Watkins & Doncaster, London.
Morris, Rev. F.O. (1895) A History of British Butterflies. Nimmo, London.
Newman, E. (1869) Natural History of British Moths. Tweedie, London.
Newman, L. & Leeds, H. (1913) Textbook of British Butterflies and Moths. Gibbs & Bamforth, St. Albans.
Newnham, F.B. (1890–91) Vars. of *Anthocharis cardamines*. Ent. Rec. J. Var. **1:** 242.
Newnham, F.B. (1891) Varieties of *Saturnia pavonia*. Ent. Rec. J. Var. **2:** 198.
Newnham, F.B. (1892a) Assembling (. . . on the Longmynds). Ent. Rec. J. Var. **3:** 254.
Newnham, F.B. (1892b) Foodplant of *Odonestis potatoria*. Ent. Rec. J. Var. **3:** 268.
Newnham, F.B. (1893) *Chelomia plantaginis* ab. *hospita*. Ent. Rec. J. Var. **4:** 295.
Newnham, F.B. (1894a) Aberrations of various butterflies. Ent. Rec. J. Var. **5:** 12–13.
Newnham, F.B. (1894b) Larvae of *Macroglossa stellatarum*. Ent. Rec. J. Var. **5:** 14.
Newnham, F.B. (1894c) A probable new species of *Euchloe*. Ent. Rec. J. Var. **5:** 97.
Newnham, F.B. (1894d) Further notes on *Euchloe hesperidis*. Ent. Rec. J. Var. **5:** 219–220.
Newnham, F.B. (1895a) *Dicanura bifida* ab. *aurata*. Ent. Rec. J. Var. **6:** 15–16.
Newnham, F.B. (1895b) Some unusual foodplants. Ent. Rec. J. Var. **6:** 33.
Newnham, F.B. (1896) Notes on the season — Church Stretton, Salop. Ent. Rec. J. Var. **7:** 185–186.
Newnham, F.B. (1897a) The Lepidoptera of Church Stretton in 1896. Ent. Rec. J. Var. **9:** 65–67.
Newnham, F.B. (1897b) *Choerocampa celerio* in Shropshire. Ent. Rec. J. Var. **9:** 332–333.
Newnham, F.B. (1901a) Catalogue of the macrolepidoptera of Church Stretton. In: Campbell-Hyslop, C.W. (1901). Church Stretton, Vol. 1: 119–178. Shrewsbury.
Newnham, F.B. (1901b) *Argynnis adippe* male paired with *A. paphia* female. Ent. Rec. J. Var. **13:** 298.
Newnham, F.B. (1902a) Aberration of *Argynnis aglaia*. Ent. Rec. J. Var. **14:** 342.
Newnham, F.B. (1902b) Aberration of *Brenthis euphrosyne*. Ent. Rec. J. Var. **14:** 342.
Newnham, F.B. (1908) Victoria County History of Shropshire, Vol. 1: 108–135.
Parker, T.E.C. (1969) Entomological Report. J. South Staffs. Nat. Soc., 1969: 14–17.
Peake, H. (1897) Historical Guide to Ellesmere, p. 15. C. Roberts, Ellesmere.
Pendlebury, H.M. (1915) Lepidoptera records for 1914. Rec. Bare Facts **24:** 19–21.
Pendlebury, H.M. & Pendlebury, M.M. (1914) Lepidoptera records for 1913. Rec. Bare Facts **23:** 26–36.
Pendlebury, M.M. (1915) Butterflies and Moths at Shrewsbury. Trans. C. & S.V.F.C. **6:** 16–28.
Pendlebury, W.J. (1934) Lepidoptera records for 1933. Rec. Bare Facts **43:** 15–16.
Pendlebury, W.J. (1935) Lepidoptera records for 1934. Rec. Bare Facts **44:** 15–16.
Pendlebury, W.J. (1936) Lepidoptera records for 1935. Rec. Bare Facts **45:** 14.

Pendlebury, W.J. (1938)   Lepidoptera records for 1937. Rec. Bare Facts **47**: 15.
Pendlebury, W.J. (1939)   Lepidoptera records for 1938. Rec. Bare Facts **48**: 20–21
Pendlebury, W.J. (1940)   Lepidoptera records for 1939. Rec. Bare Facts **49**: 26–27.
Pendlebury, W.J. (1941)   Lepidoptera records for 1940. Rec. Bare Facts **50**: 22.
Pendlebury, W.J. (1942)   Lepidoptera records for 1941. Rec. Bare Facts **51**: 6–7.
Pendlebury, W.J. (1943)   Lepidoptera records for 1942. Rec. Bare Facts **52**: 15.
Pendlebury, W.J. (1946)   Recorders report on entomology, 1945. Trans. C. & S.V.F.C. **12**: 107.
Pendlebury, W.J. (1950)   British Lepidoptera recorded in Shropshire (unpublished).
Pendlebury, W.J. (1956)   Recorders report on entomology, 1947–50. Trans. C. & S.V.F.C. **13**: 61–62.
Phillips, J. (1869)   Guide Book of Church Stretton. Sandford, Shrewsbury.
Plant, C.W. (1987)   Notes on *Hypena rostralis* L. Ent. Rec. J. Var. **99**: 276–277.
Plant, C.W. (1989)   A new aberration of *Gymnoscellis rufifasciata* (Haworth) (Lep.: Geometridae) — the Double-striped Pug. Ent. Rec. J. Var. **101**: 105.
Pollard, E., Hall, M.L. & Bibby, T.J. (1986)   Monitoring the Abundance of Butterflies. Inst. Terr. Ecol., Monkswood Exp. Stn., Cambs.
Potts, G. (1903)   Lepidoptera records for 1902. Rec. Bare Facts **12**: 42–44.
Potts, G. (1904)   Lepidoptera records for 1903. Rec. Bare Facts **13**: 38–40.
Potts, G. (1905)   Lepidoptera records for 1904. Rec. Bare Facts **14**: 39–40.
Potts, G. (1906)   Lepidoptera records for 1905. Rec. Bare Facts **15**: 32–36.
Potts, G. (1907)   Lepidoptera records for 1906. Rec. Bare Facts **16**: 32–33.
Potts, G. (1908)   Lepidoptera records for 1907. Rec. Bare Facts **17**: 34–38.
Potts, G. (1909)   Lepidoptera records for 1908. Rec. Bare Facts **18**: 26–27.
Potts, G. (1910)   Lepidoptera records for 1909. Rec. Bare Facts **19**: 33–34.
Potts, G. (1911)   Lepidoptera records for 1910. Rec. Bare Facts **20**: 24.
Potts, G. (1913)   Lepidoptera records for 1912. Rec. Bare Facts **22**: 24.
Remm, H. (1983)   New species of Noctuidae (Lepidoptera) from the U.S.S.R. Ent. Obozr. **62**: 596–600.
Riley, A.M. (1981)   Butterflies and Moths of Shropshire. Shropshire County Museums Services, Ludlow.
Riley, A.M. (1986a)   Review of the status of *Eupithecia goossensiata* Mab. (The Ling Pug) and *E. absinthiata* Cl. (The Wormwood Pug) (Lep.: Geometridae). Ent. Rec. J. Var. **98**: 85–89.
Riley, A.M. (1986b)   Suspected second brood of *Eupithecia lariciata* Freyer (Larch Pug). Ent. Rec. J. Var. **98**: 207–208.
Riley, A.M. (1986c)   *Hypena crassalis* (Lep.: Noctuidae), the beautiful snout, in Hertfordshire. Ent. Rec. J. Var. **98**: 213.
Riley, A.M. (1987)   A further diagnostic feature for the separation of *Eilema lurideola* Zincken and *E. complana* L. (Lep.: Arctiidae). Ent. Rec. J. Var. **99**: 28.
Riley, A.M. (1988)   *Horisme tersata* Dennis & Schiffermüller (Lep.: Geometridae) in Shropshire. Ent. Rec. J. Var. **100**: 84.
Riley, A.M. (1989a)   *Agriopis marginaria* Fab. (Lep.: Geometridae), the dotted border moth, caught in December. Ent. Rec. J. Var. **101**: 35.
Riley, A.M. (1989b)   Early emergence of *Thera britannica* Turner (Lep.: Geometridae). Ent. Rec. J. Var. **101**: 178.
Riley, A.M. & Southwood, J.E. (1988)   The presence and relative abundance of *Mesapamea secalella* Remm and *M. secalis* (L.) (Lep.: Noctuidae) at Preston Montford Field Centre, Shropshire, in 1986. Ent. Rec. J. Var. **100**: 257–258.
Shropshire Trust for Nature Conservation (1988)   A Concise Flora of the Church Stretton Area. S.T.N.C., Shrewsbury.
Sinker, C.A. *et al.* (1985)   Ecological Flora of the Shropshire Region. S.T.N.C., Shrewsbury.
Skinner, B. (1984)   Colour Identification Guide to the Moths of the British Isles. Viking, Harmondsworth.
Smith, K.G.V. (1952)   Notes on the macrolepidoptera of Central Shropshire, 1948–1951. Entom. **85**: 25–32.
Smith, K.G.V. (1954)   Further notes on the macrolepidoptera of Shropshire. Entom. **87**: 107–111.

189

Smith, K.G.V. (1956)   Concluding notes on the macrolepidoptera of Shropshire. Entom. **89:** 167–173.

South, R. (1924)   Butterflies of the British Isles. Warne, London.

South, R. (1961)   Moths of the British Isles. (2 Vols). Warne, London.

Stainton, H.T. (1854)   Insecta Britannica. Lepidoptera: Tineina, pp. 44–45. London.

Stainton, H.T. (1857)   A Manual of British Butterflies and Moths. London.

Stainton, H.T. (1859)   Natural History of the Tineina. Vol. IV. Van Voorst, London.

Thomas, J. (1986)   R.S.N.C. Guide to Butterflies of the British Isles. Country Life Books, Northants.

Thornewill, Rev. C.F. (1895)   *Xanthia gilvago* in Shropshire. Entom. **28:** 281.

Thornewill, Rev. C.F. (1896)   Notes on the season — Whitchurch, Salop. Ent. Rec. J. Var. **8:** 88.

Thornewill, Rev. C.F. (1899)   *Acherontia atropos* in Shropshire. Entom. **32:** 256.

Thornewill, Rev. C.F. (1900a)   Shropshire (. . .C. *edusa* in . . .). Entom. **33:** 278.

Thornewill, Rev. C.F. (1900b)   *Melanippe tristata* (at Church Stretton). Entom. **33:** 307.

Thornewill, Rev. C.F. (1901a)   *Acherontia atropos* and *Vanessa cardui* in Shropshire. Entom. **34:** 20.

Thornewill, Rev. C.F. (1901b)   *Thecla w-album* in Shropshire. Entom. **34:** 231.

Watts, W.W. (1938)   Shropshire. Wilding and Son, Shrewsbury.

Woodforde, F.C. (1892) *Colias edusa* in England — Shropshire. Entom. **25:** 307.

Woodforde, F.C. (1894)   Collecting at Market Drayton. Entom. **27:** 30.

Woodforde, F.C. (1895a)   *Acherontia atropos* in Shropshire. Entom. **28:** 280.

Woodforde, F.C. (1895b)   *Acherontia atropos* in Shropshire. Entom. **28:** 310.

Woodforde, F.C. (1895c)   Notes from Shropshire. Entom. **28:** 339.

Woodforde, F.C. (1900a)   Spring Lepidoptera — Market Drayton. Ent. Rec. J. Var. **12:** 188.

Woodforde, F.C. (1900b)   Lepidoptera at Market Drayton and in North Wales. Ent. Rec. J. Var. **12:** 269–271.

Woodforde, F.C. (1900c)   Autumnal Lepidoptera at Market Drayton. Ent. Rec. J. Var. **12:** 272–273.

Woodforde, F.C. (1900d)   Yellow aberration of *Noctua castanea*. Ent. Rec. J. Var. **12:** 297–298.

Woodforde, F.C. (1900e)   Lepidoptera at Market Drayton. Ent. Rec. J. Var. **12:** 301.

Woodforde, F.C. (1900f)   Lepidoptera at Market Drayton and Cannock Chase. Ent. Rec. J. Var. **12:** 337–338.

Woodforde, F.C. (1901a)   *Noctua castanea* Esp. var. *xanthe*, n. var. Ent. Mon. Mag. **37:** 116–117.

Woodforde, F.C. (1901b)   Notes on collecting — Market Drayton. Ent. Rec. J. Var. **13:** 249.

Woodforde, F.C. (1901c)   Habits of *Asthena sylvata*. Ent. Rec. J. Var., Vol. **13:** 276.

Woodforde, F.C. (1901d)   Variation of *Zonosoma pendularia*. Ent. Rec. J. Var. **13:** 296.

Woodforde, F.C. (1901e)   Some exceptional sizes in Lepidoptera. Ent. Rec. J. Var. **13:** 359.

Woodforde, F.C. (1902a)   Spring Lepidoptera at Market Drayton. Ent. Rec. J. Var. **14:** 110.

Woodforde, F.C. (1902b)   Notes on collecting — Market Drayton. Ent. Rec. J. Var. **14:** 220.

Woodforde, F.C. (1902c)   The late season for Lepidoptera in the Wyre Forest. Ent. Rec. J. Var. **14:** 249.

Woodforde, F.C. (1902d)   Lepidoptera at Market Drayton and in the New Forest. Ent. Rec. J. Var. **14:** 346–347.

Woodforde, F.C. (1903)   Lepidoptera at Market Drayton . . . Ent. Rec. J. Var. **15:** 25–27.

Woodward, Comm. J.C. (1922a)   *C. alchymista* in Shropshire. Ent. Rec. J. Var. **34:** 142.

Woodward, Comm. J.C. (1922b)   Notes on collecting in June, July and August in Shropshire. Ent. Rec. J. Var. **34:** 189–191.

Wood-Taylor, R. (1941)   The Lepidoptera of Bayston Hill. Trans. C. & S.V.F.C. **11:** 135–147.

Organisations, Societies and Field Clubs consulted

Birmingham Natural History Society.
British Butterfly Conservation Society.
British Entomological and Natural History Society.
Caradoc and Severn Valley Field Club.
Field Studies Council.
Forestry Commission.
Institute of Terrestrial Ecology.
Lancashire and Cheshire Entomological Society.
National Trust.
Nature Conservancy Council.
Rothamsted Insect Survey.
Shropshire County Council.
Shropshire Wildlife Trust.
South Staffordshire Naturalists' Society.
Worcestershire Naturalist's Club.

Societies to join

Amateur Entomologists' Society, 355 Hounslow Road, Feltham, Middlesex, TW13 5JH.
British Butterfly Conservation Society, Tudor House, Quorn, nr. Loughborough,
    Leicestershire, LE12 8AD.
British Entomological and Natural History Society, 74 South Audley St., London,
    W1Y 5FF.
Caradoc and Severn Valley Field Club, Bear Steps Office, St. Alkmunds Square,
    Shrewsbury, Shropshire, SY1 1UH.
Royal Entomological Society, 41 Queen's Gate, London, SW7 5HU.
Shropshire Biological Recording Scheme, The Museum, Old Street, Ludlow,
    Shropshire SY8 1NW.
Shropshire Trust for Nature Conservation, Old St. George's School, New Street,
    Shrewsbury, Shropshire SY3 8JP.

Index of Scientific Names

App. = Appendix

abbreviana Fabr., Epinotia App. 1150
abbreviata Steph., Eupithecia 1852
abietella D. & S., Dioryctria App. 1454
abruptaria Thunb., Menophra 1936
absinthiata Cl., Eupithecia 1830
absinthii L., Cucullia 2211
acanthadactyla Hb., Amblyptilia App. 1497
aceriana Dup., Gypsonoma App. 1167
acerifoliella Zell., Phyllonorycter App. 362
achatana D. & S., Ancylis App. 1115
acuminatana Lein. & Zell., Dichrorampha App. 1279
acupaiae Frey. See nylandriella Tengst., App. 103
adippe D. & S., Argynnis 1606
adusta Esp., Blepharita 2250
adustata D. & S., Ligdia 1888
advenaria Hb., Cepphis 1901
advenella Zinck., Numonia App. 1439
aegeria L., Pararge 1614
aeratana Pier. & Metc., Dichrorampha App. 1287
aeriferanus H.-S., Ptychomoloides App. 987
aescularia D. & S., Alsophila 1663
aestivaria Hb., Hemithea 1669
aethiops Hump. & Westw., Xenolechia App. 763
affinis Haw., Bryotropha App. 779
affinis L., Cosmia 2316
affinitata Steph., Perizoma 1802
agathina Dup., Xestia 2135
agestis D. & S., Aricia 1572
aglaja L., Argynnis 1607
ahenella, D. & S., Hypochalcia App. 1457
albedinella Zell., Bucculatrix App. 271
albersana Hb., Eucosmomorpha App. 1217
albicillata Hb., Mesoleuca 1748
albicolon Hb., Sideridis 2152
albicosta Haw., Coleophora App. 544
albidella Nyl., Biselachista App. 630
albidella D. & S., Coleophora App. 532
albifasciella Hein., Ectoedemia App. 37
albifrontella Hb., Elachista App. 601
albimaculea Haw. See augustella Hb. App. 638
albipuncta Hufn., Cyclophora 1677
albistria Haw., Argyresthia App. 422
albuginana Guen., Pammene App. 1229
albulata Hufn., Asthena 1875
albulata D. & S., Perizoma 1807
alburnella Zell., Teleiodes App. 771
alchemillata L., Perizoma 1803
alchimiella Scop., Caloptilia App. 286
alchymista D. & S., Cetaphia 2464
allisella Stt., Exaeretia App. 687
alnetella Stt., Stigmella App. 115
alni L., Acronicta 2281
alniaria L., Ennomos 1913
alnifoliae Bar., Coleophora App. 498
alsines Brahm., Hoplodrina 2381
alstromeriana Cl., Agonopteryx App. 695
alternata Mull., Epirrhoe 1738
alternella D. & S., Tortricodes App. 1025
alticolella Zell., Coleophora App. 584
ambigualis Treits, Scoparia App. 1334
anatipennella Hb., Coleophora App. 533
anceps D. & S., Apamea 2333
anceps Geoze, Peridea 2005
anderidae Fletch., Phyllonorycter App. 347
anglicella Stt., Parornix App. 303
angulifasciella Stt., Ectoedemia App. 28
angustana Hb., Eupoecilia App. 954
angustea Curt., Eudonia App. 1342

angustiorana Haw., Ditula App. 1010
annulata Schulze, Cyclophora 1676
annulatella Curt., Rhingognostis App. 467
anomala Haw., Stilbia 2394
anomalella Goeze, Stigmella App. 92
antiqua L., Nymphalis 1596
antiqua L., Orgyia 2026
apicella D. & S., Ancylis App. 1129
apiformis Cl., Sesia 370
aprilina L., Dichonia 2247
aranella D. & S., Agonopterix App. 697
areola Esp., Xylocampa 2243
argentella D. & S., Elachista App. 610
argiolus L., Celastrina 1580
argus L., Plebejus 1571
argyropeza Zell., Ectoedemia App. 23
arion L., Maculinea 1581
aruncella Scop., Micropterix App. 4
aspersana Hb., Acleris App. 1043
aspidiscana Hb., Eucosma App. 1190
asseclana D. & S., Cnephasia App. 1021
assimilata Doubl., Eupithecia 1832
assimilella Treits., Agonopterix App. 702
atalanta L., Vanessa 1590
atomaria L., Ematurga 1592
atomella D. & S., Agonopterix App. 703
atra L., Acanthopsyche 191
atra Haw., Blastodacna App. 906
atrata L., Odezia 1870
atricapitella Haw., Stigmella App. 83
atricollis Stt., Ectoedemia App. 29
atricomella Stt., Elachista App. 597
atropos L., Acherontia 1973
atropunctana Zett., Hedya App. 1085
augur Fab., Graphiphora 2114
augustella Hb., Denisia App. 638
aurago D. & S., Xanthia 2272
aurana Fabr., Cydia App. 1272
aurantiaria Hb., Agriopis 1933
aurata Scop., Pyrausta App. 1361
aureatella Scop., Micropterix App. 3
aurella Fab., Stigmella App. 50
auroguttella Steph., Calybites App. 297
aurinia Rott., Eurodryas 1610
australis Ver., Colias 1543
autumnaria Wern., Ennomos 1911
autumnata Bork., Epirrita 1797
avellanella Hb., Semioscopis App. 666
aversata L., Idaea 1713

badiana D. & S., Ancylis App. 1126
badiata D. & S., Anticlea 1746
badiella Hb., Depressaria App. 674
baja D. & S., Xestia 2130
bajularia D. & S., Comibaena 1667
batis L., Thyatiris 1652
beatricella Wals., Aethes App. 951
bechsteinella Bech. & Scharf., Bucculatrix App. 275
bembeciformis Hb., Sesia 371
berbera Rungs., Amphipyra 2298
bergmanniana L., Croesia App. 1035
betulae Goeze, Metriostola App. 1450
betulae Stt., Parornix App. 301
betulae L., Thecla 1556
betularia L., Biston 1913
betuletana Haw., Apotomis App. 1093
betulicola Her., Caloptilia App. 283
betulicola Stt., Stigmella App. 110
betulinella Fabr., Nemaxera App. 223
bicolorata Hufn., Hecatera 2164

bicostella Cl., Pleurota App. 654
bicruris Hufn., Hadena 2173
bicuspis Bork., Furcula 1996
bidentata Cl., Odontopera 1920
bifaciata Haw., Perizoma 1804
bifasciana Haw., Olethreutes App. 1079
bifida Brahm., Furcula 1998
bilineata L., Camptogramma 1742
bilunana Haw., Epinotia App. 1133
bimaculata F., Lomographa 1957
binaevella Hb., Phycitodes App. 1483
binaria Hufn., Drepana 1646
bipunctaria D. & S., Scotopteryx 1731
bipunctella Fabr., Ethmia App. 720
bipunctidactyla Scop., Stenoptilia App. 1508
biren Geoze, Papestra 2162
biselata Hufn., Idaea 1702
bistortata Goeze, Ectropis 1947
bistrigella Haw., Phylloporia App. 128
blancardella Fabr., Phyllonorycter App. 326
blanda D. & S., Hoplodrina 2382
blandella Fabr., Brachmia App. 866
blandella Dougl., Caryoculum App. 832
blattariella Hb., Anacampsis App. 854
blomeri Curt., Discoloxia 1872
bombycina Hufn., Polia 2148
bonnetella L., Argyresthia App. 421
bractea D. & S., Autographa 2444
brassicae L., Mamestra 2154
brassicae L., Pieris 1549
britannica Turn., Thera 1769
britanniodactyla Gregs., Capperia App. 1494
brockeella Hb., Argyresthia App. 410
brongniardella Fabr., Acrocercops App. 313
brumata L., Operophtera 1799
brunnea D. & S., Diarsia 2122
brunnearia Vill., Selidosema 1938
brunnichana L., Epinotia App. 1155
brunnichella L., Stephensia App. 592
buoliana D. & S., Rhyacionia App. 1210
bucephala L., Phalera 1994

caeruleocephala L., Diloba 2020
caesiata D. & S., Entephria 1744
caesiella Hb., Swammerdamia App. 437
caespititiella Zell., Coleophora App. 587
cagnatella Hb., Yponomeuta App. 427
caja L., Arctia 2057
c-album L., Polygonia 1598
calthella L., Micropterix App. 5
cambrica Curt., Venusia 1873
camilla L., Ladoga 1584
campoliliana D. & S., Eucosma App. 1197
cana Haw., Eucosma App. 1201
canapennella Hb., Elachista App. 607
caprana Fabr., Epinotia App. 1154
capreolella Zell., Agonopterix App. 715
capucina L., Ptilodon 2008
cardamines L., Anthocharis 1553
carduella Hb., Agonopteryx App. 708
cardui L., Cynthia 1591
carpinata Bork., Trichopteryx 1881
casta Pall., Psyche App. 186
castanea Esp., Xestia 2132
cavella Zell., Phyllonorycter App. 338
celerio L., Hippotion 1993
centaureata D. & S., Eupithecia 1825
centifoliella Zell., Stigmella App. 93
centrago Haw., Atethmia 2269
cerasana Hb., Pandemis App. 970
cerasi Fabr., Orthosia 2187
cerusella Hb., Elachista App. 609
cervinalis Scop., Rheumaptera 1788
cespitalis D. & S., Pyrausta App. 1365

cespitis D. & S., Tholera 2177
chaerophyllella Goeze, Epermenia App. 483
chaerophylli Zell., Depressaria App. 682
chamomillae D. & S., Cucullia 2214
chenopodiata L., Scotopteryx 1732
chi L., Antitype 2254
chloerata Mab., Chloroclystis 1859
chlorosata Scop., Petrophora 1902
christyi Allen, Epirrita 1796
chrysitis L., Diachrysia 2434
chrysoprasaria Esp., Hemistola 1673
chryssorhoea L., Euproctis 2029
cidarella Zell., Bucculatrix App. 272
ciliella Stt., Agonopterix App. 689
cinctella Cl., Syncopacma App. 849
cinerella Cl., Acompsia App. 855
cineria D. & S., Agrotis 2084
cinerosella Zell., Euzophera App. 1469
cingulata L., Pyrausta App. 1367
cinnamomeana Treits., Pandemis App. 971
circellaris Hufn., Agrochola 2262
citrago L., Xanthia 2271
citrata L., Chloroclysta 1762
citrinalis Scop., Hypercallia App. 657
clathrata L., Semiothisa 1894
clavaria Haw., Larentia 1745
clavipalpis Scop., Caradrina 2389
clavis Hufn., Agrotis 2088
clematella Fabr., Nemapogon App. 220
clerkella L., Lyonetia App. 263
cloacella Haw., Nemapogon App. 216
clorana L., Earias 2418
cnicana Wests., Aethes App. 945
c-nigrum L., Xestia 2126
comariana Lien.& Zell., Acleris App. 1039
combinella Hb., Pseudoswammerdamia App. 436
comes Hb., Noctua 2109
comitata L., Pelurga 1749
comma Hb., Mythimna 2205
communana H.-S., Cnephasia App. 1018
complana L., Eilema 2047
compositella Fab., Cydia App. 1241
confusa Hufn., Hadena 2171
confusalis H.-S., Celama 2078
confusella Wood, Stigmella App. 117
congelatella Cl., Exapate App. 1026
conigera D. & S., Mythimna 2192
conjugella Zell., Argyresthia App. 418
consimilana Hb., Clepsis App. 994
consociella Hb., Acrobasis App. 1437
contigua D. & S., Lacanobia 2156
conturbatella Hb., Mompha App. 885
convolvuli L., Agrius 1972
conwagana Fabr., Pseudargyrotoza App. 1011
coracipennella Hb., Coleophora App. 494
coridon Poda, Lysandra 1575
coronata Haw., Phlyctaenia App. 1378
corylana Fabr., Pandemis App. 969
corylata Thun., Electrophaes 1773
coryli L., Calocasia 2425
coryli Nic., Phyllonorycter App. 342
corylifoiella Hb., Pyllonorycter App. 332
cossus L., Cossus 162
costaestrigalis Steph., Schrankia 2484
costalis Fabr., Hypsopygia App. 1413
costella Hum. & Westw., Scrobipalpa App. 819
costipunctana Haw., Epiblema App. 1187
crassalis Fabr., Hypena 2476
crataegana Hb., Archips App. 979
crataegella L., Scythropia App. 450
crataegella Klim., Stigmella App. 108
crataegi L., Aporia 1584
crataegi L., Trichiura 1632
crenata Hufn., Apamea 2326

crepuscularia D. & S., Ectropis 1948
crepsculella Zell., Opostega App. 121
cribraria L., Coscinia 2053
cristana D. & S., Acleris App. 1054
cristatella Zell., Bucculatrix App. 265
croceago D. & S., Jodia 2257
crocealis Hb., Ebulea App. 1385
croceus Geoff., Colias 1545
croesella Scop., Adela App. 151
cruciana L., Epinotia App. 1147
cruda D. & S., Orthosia 2182
cryptella Stt., Trifurcula App. 48
cucullatella L., Nola 2077
culiciformis L., Synanthedon 381
culmella L., Chrysoteuchia App. 1293
cultraria Fabr., Drepana 1647
cupriacella Hb., Nemophora App. 146
currucipennella Zell., Coleophora App. 534
curtula L., Clostera 2019
curvistrigana Stt., Phalonidia App. 934
cygnosbatella L., Epiblema App. 1174

dahlii Hb., Diarsia 2121
daplidice L., Pontia 1552
daucella D. & S., Depressaria App. 670
dealbana Fröl., Gypsonoma App. 1169
deauratella Zell., Coleophora App. 519
debiliata Hb., Chloroclystis 1861
decimalis Poda, Tholera 2178
defoliaria Cl., Erannis 1935
degeerella L., Nemophora App. 148
demarniana F.v.R., Epinotia App. 1135
denotata Hb., Eupithecia 1836
dentaria Fabr., Selenia 1917
dentella Fabr., Ypsolopha App. 453
denticulella Thunb., Callisto App. 310
depuncta L., Eugnorisma 2103
derivata D. & S., Anticlea 1747
desertella Dougl., Bryotropha App. 786
designata Hufn., Xanthorhoe 1722
devoniella Stt., Porornix App. 304
didymata L., Perizoma 1809
diffinis L., Cosmia 2317
diffinis Haw., Teleiopsis App. 776
diluta D. & S., Cymatophorima 1658
dilutata D. & S., Epirrita 1795
dilutella Hb., Pempeliella App. 1462
dimidiata Hufn., Idaea 1708
dimidioalba Retz., Hedya App. 1083
diminutana Haw., Ancylis App. 1119a
discordella Zell., Coleophora App. 547
dispunctella Dup., Elachista App. 615
dissoluta Treit., Achanaria 2317
distinctaria H.-S., Eupithecia 1843
ditrapezium D. & S., Xestia 2127
diversana Hb., Choristoneura App. 982
dodonaea D. & S., Drymonia 2014
dodoneata Guen., Eupithecia 1853
dolabraria L., Plagodis 1904
domestica Hufn., Cryphia 2293
douglasella Stt., Depressaria App. 677
dromedarius L., Notodonta 2000
dubitata L., Triphosa 1790
duplaris L., Ochropacha 1657

efformata Guen., Aplocera 1868
ekeblandella Bjerk., Tischeria App. 123
elinguaria L., Crocalis 1921
elongella L., Caloptilia App. 282
elpenor L., Deilephila 1991
elutella Hb., Ephestia App. 1473
emargana Fabr., Acleris App. 1062
emarginata L., Idaea 1712
emberizaepennella Bouché, Phyllonorycter App. 354

ephemerella D. & S., Acentria App. 1355i
epilobiella D. & S., Mompha App. 893
epiphron Knoch, Erebia 1617
epomidion Haw. Apamea 2327
eremita Fabr., Dryobotodes 2248
ericetella Gey., Neofaculta App. 797
ericinella Zell., Aristotelia App. 752
erosaria D. & S., Ennomos 1915
euphrosyne L., Boloria 1601
evonymella L., Yponomeuta App. 424
exanthemata Scop., Cabera 1956
exclamationis L., Agrotis 2089
exiguata Hb., Eupithecia 1819
expallidata Doubl., Eupithecia 1833
exsoleta L., Xylena 2242
extersaria Hb., Ectropis 1950

fabriciana L., Anthophila App. 385
fagana Fabr., Pseudoips 2422
fagaria Thunb., Dyscia 1969
fagata Scharf., Operophtera 1800
fagella D. & S., Diurnea App. 663
fagi L., Stauropus 1999
falcataria L., Drepana 1648
falsella D. & S., Catoptria App. 1316
farinalis L., Pyralis App. 1417
fasciana L., Pammene App. 1236
fasciaria L., Hylaea 1962
fasciuncula Haw., Oligia 2340
ferchaultella Steph., Luffia App. 185
ferrago Fabr., Mythimna 2193
ferrugalis Hb., Udea App. 1395
ferrugana D. & S., Acleris App. 1044
ferrugata Cl., Xanthorhoe 1725
ferruginea Esp., Rusina 2302
festaliella Hb., Schreckensteinia App. 485
festucae L., Plusia 2439
fibulella D. & S., Andelia App. 153
filigrammaria, H.-S., Epirrita 1798
filipendulae L., Zygaena 169
fimbriata Schreb., Noctua 2110
finitimella Zell., Parornix App. 308
firmata Hb., Thera 1767
flammea D. & S., Panolis 2179
flammeolaria Hufn., Hydrelia 1876
flavago D. & S., Gortyna 2364
flavicaput Haw., Spuleria App. 904
flavicincta D. & S., Polymixis 2252
flavicornis L., Achlya 1659
flavipennella Dup., Coleophora App. 492
flavofasciata Thunb., Perizoma 1808
flexula D. & S., Laspeyria 2473
floslactata Haw., Scopula 1693
floslactella Haw., Stigmella App. 75
fluctuata L., Xanthorhoe 1728
fluctuosa Hb., Tetheella 1656
foenella L., Epiblema App. 1183
follicularis Vallot, Coleophora App. 555
forficalis L., Evergestis App. 1356
forficella Thunb., Schoenobius App. 1329
formosana Scop., Enarmonia App. 1216
formosanus Gey., Lozotaeniodes App. 1001
forsskaleana L., Croesia App. 1036
forsterana Fabr., Lozotaenia App. 1002
fraxinata Cr., Eupithecia 1849
fraxini L., Catocala 2451
fraxinella Bjerk., Prays App. 449
freyerella Hb., Cosmiotes App. 631
froelichiella Zell., Phyllonorycter App. 358
fuciformis L., Hemaris 1983
fuliginaria L., Parascotia 2475
fuliginosa L., Phragmatobia 2064
fulvana Steph., Eucosma App. 1200a
fulvata Forst., Cidaria 1765
fulviguttella Zell., Phaulernis App. 478

fulvimitrella Sodof., Triaxomera App. 225
funebrana Treits., Cydia App. 1247
furcata Thunb., Hydriomena 1777
furcula Cl., Furcula 1997
furfurana Haw., Bactra App. 1110
furuncula D. & S., Mesoligia 2341
furva D. & S., Apamea 2329
fusca Haw., Pyla App. 1451
fusca Haw., Sterrhopterix App. 195
fuscantiaria Haw., Ennomos 1914
fuscatella Tengst., Lampronia App. 138
fuscella L., Niditinea App. 237
fuscescens Haw., Borkhausenia App. 644
fuscoaenea Haw., Scythris App. 912
fusconebulosa De G., Hepialus 18
fuscovenosa Goeze, Idaea 1705
fuscoviridella Haw., Glyphipterix App. 396

galathea L., Melanargia 1620
galiata D. & S., Epirrhoe 1740
gallicana Guen., Cydia App. 1271
gamma L., Autographa 2441
gangabella Zell., Elachista App. 620
geminana Don., Ancylis App. 1119
geniculea Haw., Agriphila App. 1309
geniculella Rag., Phyllonorycter App. 364
genistae Stt., Coleophora App. 546
geoffrella L., Alabonia App. 652
gerningana D. & S., Philedone App. 1008
gilvago D. & S., Xanthia 2275
glareosa Esp., Paradiarsia 2117
glaucata Scop., Cilix 1651
glaucicolella Wood, Coleophora App. 582
glaucinalis L., Orthopygia App. 1415
glutinosae Stt., Stigmella App. 114
glyphica L., Euclidia 2463
gnoma Fab., Pheosia 2006
goerdartella L., Argyresthia App. 411
gonodactyla D. & S., Platyptilia App. 1501
goossensiata Mab., Eupithecia absinthiata (f.) 1831
gothica L., Orthosia 2190
gracilis D. & S., Orthosia 2186
graminis L., Cerapteryx 2176
grandipennis Haw., Scythris App. 911
grisealis D. & S., Herminia 2492
griseata Peters, Timandra 1682
grisella Fab., Achroia App. 1426
griseola Hb., Eilema 2044
grossulariata L., Abraxas 1884
grotiana Fabr., Epagoge App. 1006
gryphipennella Hb., Coleophora App. 491
gueneeana Obraz., Dichrorampha App. 1284
gysselenia Zell., Cedestis App. 442

halterata Hufn., Lobophora 1879
hamana L., Agapeta App. 937
hamella Thunb., Crambus App. 1299
hammoniella Sor., Heliozela App. 157
harrisella L., Phyllonorycter App. 315
hartmanniana Cl., Aethes. See A. piercei Ob. App. 942
hastata L., Rheumaptera 1787
haworthana Steph., Glyphipterix App. 395
haworthiata Doubl., Eupithecia 1813
haworthii Curt., Celaena 2367
hebenstreitella Müll., Choristoneura App. 983
hecta L., Hepialus 16
heegeriella Zell., Phyllonorycter App. 317
hellerella Dup., Spuleria App. 905
helvola L., Agrochola 2265
hemargyrella Koll., Stigmella App. 81
heparana D. & S., Pandemis App. 972
hepatica Cl., see trimaculosa Esp. 2149
hepatica Cl., Lithophane Hufn. 2236
heracliana L., Agonopterix App. 688

heringi Toll., Ectoedemia App. 39
hexadactyla L., Alucita App. 1288
hilarella Zett., Phyllonorycter App. 337
hirtaria Cl., Lycia 1927
hispidaria D. & S., Apocheima 1925
hohenwartiana D. & S., Eucosma App. 1200
holmiana L., Croesia App. 1037
horridella Treits., Ypsolopha App. 456
hortulata L., Eurrhypara App. 1376
humidalis Doubl., Hypenodes 2485
humuli L., Hepialus 14
humilis Zell., Elachista App. 606
hyale L., Colias 1543
hybnerella Hb., Stigmella App. 99
hybridella Hb., Cochylis App. 965
hyemana Haw., Acleris App. 1055
hyperantus L., Aphantopus 1629

ibipennella Zell., Coleophora App. 536
icarus Rott., Polyommatus 1574
icterata Vill., Eupithecia 1838
icteritia Hufn., Xanthia 2274
ilicifolia L., Phyllodesma 1641
imitaria Hb., Scopula 1690
immundella Zell., Trifurcula App. 46
immundana F.v.R., Epinotia App. 1136
immutata L., Scopula 1692
impluviata D. & S., Hydriomena 1778
impura Hb., Mythimna 2198
incanana Steph., Eana App. 1030
incarnatana Hb., Epiblema App. 1179
incerta Hufn., Orthosia 2188
incertana Treits., Cnephasia App. 1024
incongruella Stt., Amphibastis App. 659
inconspicuella Stt., Dahlica App. 177
indigata Hb., Eupithecia 1844
inquinatella D. & S., Agriphila App. 1306
interjecta Hb., Noctua 2112
internana Guen., Cydia App. 1242
interrogationis L., Syngrapha 2447
intricata Frey., Eupithecia 1827
intimella Fell., Ectoedemia App. 25
inturbata Hb., Eupithecia 1812
io L., Inachis 1597
ipsilon Hufn., Agrotis 2091
iris L., Apatura 1585
irrorella L., Setina 2036
isertana Esp., Zeiraphera App. 1165
isodactylus Zell., Platyptilia App. 1502

jacobaeae L., Tyria 2069
janthina D. & S., Noctua 2111
janthinana Dup., Cydia App. 1245
jota L., Autographa 2443
juncicolella Stt., Coleophora App. 510
jungiella Cl., Cydia App. 1251
juniperata L., Thera 1771
jurtina L., Maniola 1626

kaekeritziana L., Agonopterix App. 698
kilmunella Stt., Ellachista App. 598
kleemannella Fabr., Phyllonorycter App. 360
kuehniella Zell., Ephestia App. 1475

laburnella Stt., Leucoptera App. 254
lacertinaria L., Falcaria 1645
lactearia L., Jodis 1674
lacteella Steph., Mompha App. 887
lacunana D. & S., Olethreutes App. 1076
lacustrata Panz., Eudonia App. 1338
laevigatella H.-S., Argyresthia App. 401
laevigella D. & S., Monopis App. 227
lambdella Don., Batia App. 641
lancealana Hb., Bactra App. 1111

195

lancealis D. & S., Perinephala App. 1377
lanestris L., Eriogaster 1633
lapponica Wocke, Stigmella App. 116
lariciata Frey., Eupithecia 1856
lariciella Hb., Coleophora App. 526
larseniella Goz., Syncopacma App. 844
laterana Fabr., Acleris App. 1038
lathamella Fletch., Glyphipteryx App. 902
lathoniellus Zinck., Crambus App. 1301
latistria Haw., Agriphila App. 1307
latruncula D. & S., Oligia 2339
lautella Zell., Phyllonorycter App. 351
legatella D. & S., Chesias 1864
lecheana L., Ptycholoma App. 1000
lemnata L., Cataclysta App. 1354
leporina L., Acronicta 2280
leucographa D. & S., Cerastis 2140
leucophaearia D. & S., Agriopis 1932
leucostigma Hb., Celaena 2368
libatrix L., Scoliopteryx 2469
lichenea Hb., Eumichtis 2255
lichenaria Hufn., Cleorodes 1945
ligula Esp., Conistra 2259
ligustri D. & S., Craniophora 2291
ligustri L., Sphinx 1976
limosipennella Dup., Coleophora App. 499
linariata D. & S., Eupithecia 1816
lineana D. & S., Apotomis App. 1091
linearia Hb., Cyclophora 1681
lineata Fab., Hyles 1990
lineolea Haw., Coleophora App. 522
literana L., Acleris App. 1061
literosa Haw., Mesoligia 2342
lithodactyla Treits., Oidaematophorus App. 1523
lithoxylaea D. & S., Apamea 2322
litura L., Agrochola 2266
liturata Cl., Semiothisa 1893
liturosa Haw., Agonopterix App. 709
lixella Zell., Coleophora App. 530
ljungiana Thunb., Argyrotaenia App. 974
loeflingiana L., Aleimma App. 1032
lonicerae Schev., Zygaena 171
lota Cl., Agrochola 2263
lubricipeda L., Spilosoma 2060
lucens Frey., Amphipoea 2359
lucernea L., Standfussiana 2104
lucina L., Hemearis 1582
lucipara L., Euplexia 2305
luculella Hb., Teleiodes App. 774
lunaris Haw., Batia App. 640
lunosa H., Omphaloscelis 2270
lunularia Hb., Selenia 1918
lupulinus L., Hepialus 17
luridata Hufn., Scotopteryx 1734
lurideola Zinck., Eilema 2050
lutarea Haw., Paraswammerdamia App. 441
lutealis D. & S., Udea App. 1388
luteella Stt., Stigmella App. 112
luteolata L., Opisthograptis 1906
luteum Hufn., Spilosoma 2061
luticomella Zell., Elachista App. 600
lutipennella Zell., Coleophora App. 490
lutosa Hb., Rhizedra 2375
lutulenta D. & S., Aporophyla 2231
lychnidis D. & S., Agrochola 2267

macilenta Hb., Agrochola 2264
maculana Fabr., Epinotia App. 1152
macularia L., Pseudopanthera 1909
maera L., Lasiommata 1616
maestingella Müll., Phyllonorycter App. 341
malella Stt., Stigmella App. 97
malifoliella Costa, Leucoptera App. 260
malvae L., Pyrgus 1534 .

margaritata L., Campaea 1961
margaritella D. & S., Catoptria App. 1314
marginana Haw., Endothenia App. 1099
marginaria Fabr., Agriopis 1934
marginata L., Lomaspilis 1887
marginea Haw., Tischeria App. 125
marginicolella Stt., Stigmella App. 63
marmorea Haw., Numonia App. 1440
masculella D. & S., Incurvaria App. 130
matura Hufn., Thalpophila 2303
maura L., Mormo 2300
mayrella Hb., Coleophora App. 518
mediopectinellus Haw., Ochsenheimeria App. 251
megacephala D. & S., Acronicta 2278
megera L., Lasiommata 1615
mellinata Fabr., Eulithis 1757
mendica Haw., Argyresthia App. 417
mendica Cl., Diaphora 2063
mendica Fabr., Diarsia 2120
menyanthidis Esp., Acronicta 2286
mercurella L., Eudonia 1344
mesomella L., Cybosia 2040
mespilella Hb., Phyllonorycter App. 325
messaniella Zell., Phyllonorycter App. 321
meticulosa L., Phlogophora 2306
metzneriella Stt., Metzneria App. 726
mi Cl., Callistege 2462
miata L., Chloroclysta 1761
micacea Esp., Hydraecia 2361
microdactyla Hb., Adaina App. 1517
microtheriella Stt., Stigmella App. 111
milvipennis Zell., Coleophora App. 496
miniata Forst., Miltochrista 2037
minima Haw., Photedes 2345
minimus Fuess., Cupido 1569
miniosa D. & S., Orthosia 2183
ministrana L., Eulia App. 1015
minorata Treits., Perizoma 1805
minutella L., Borkhausenia App. 645
miscella D. & S., Mompha App. 884
mitterbacheriana D. & S., Ancylis App. 1120
monacha L., Lymantria 2033
moneta Fabr., Polychrysia 2437
monilifera Geoff., Narycia App. 175
monodactyla L., Emmelina 1524
monoglypha Hufn., Apamea 2321
montanana Dup., Dichrorampha App. 1283
montanata D. & S., Xanthorhoe 1727
morpheus Hufn., Caradrina 2387
mucronata Scop., Scotopteryx 1733
muelleriella Zell., Phyllonorycter App. 322
mulinella Zell., Mirificarma App. 792
multistrigaria Haw., Colostygia 1775
munda D. & S., Othosia 2189
mundana L., Nudaria 2038
munitata Hb., Xanthorhoe 1723
muralis Forster, Cryphia 2295
muricata Hufn., Idaea 1698
murinata Scop., Minoa 1878
murinipennella Dup., Coleophora App. 578
musculana Hb., Syndemis App. 986
myllerana Fab., Choreutis App. 388
myrtillana Humph. & Westw., Griselda App. 1162
myrtillella Stt., Stigmella App. 72
myrtilli L., Anarta 2142

naevana Hb., Rhopobota App. 1159
nana Haw., Cochylis App. 968
nana Hufn., Hada 2147
nanata D. & S., Eupithecia 1846
napi L., Pieris 1551
nebulata Scop., Euchoeca 1874
nebulella D. & S., Homoeosoma App. 1480
nebulosa Hufn., Polia 2150

nemoralis Fabr. See grisealis D. & S. 2492
nemorella L., Ypsolopha App. 452
nervosa Haw., Agonopterix App. 706
neustria L., Malacosoma 1634
nicellii Stt., Phyllonorycter App. 359
nigra Haw., Aporophyla 2232
nigricana Fabr., Cydia App. 1257
nigricans L., Euxoa 2082
nigricomella Zell., Bucculatrix App. 266
nigrocostana Haw., Endothenia App. 1102
nigropunctata Hufn., Scopula 1684
nisella Cl., Epinotia App. 1138
nitidana Fabr., Strophedra App. 1222
noctuella D. & S., Nomophila App. 1398
notana Don., Acleris App. 1045
notata L., Semiothisa 1889
notatella Hb., Teleiodes App. 768
notha Hb., Achiearis 1662
nubilana Hb., Neosphaleroptera App. 1027
nupta L., Catocala 2452
nylandriella Tengst., Stigmella App. 103
nymphaeata L., Elophila App. 1345

obelisca D. & S., Euxoa 2080
obeliscata Hb., Thera 1768
obliquella Hein., Stigmella. App. 70
oblonga Haw., Apamea 2325
obscurata D. & S., Gnophos 1964
obscuratus D. & S. See obscurata D. & S., 1964
obscurella Stt. See pulchella Haw., App. 607
obscurepunctella Stt., Perittia App. 590
obstipata Fab., Orthonama 1720
obtusana Haw., Ancylis App. 1122
ocellana Fabr., Agonopterix App. 701
ocellana D. & S., Spilonota App. 1205
ocellata L., Cosmorhoe 1752
ocellata L., Smerinthus 1980
occulta L., Eurois 2137
occultella L., Ectoedemia App. 34
ochraceella Curt., Mompha App. 886
ochrodactyla D. & S., Platytilia App. 1503
ochroleuca D. & S., Eremobia 2352
ochroleucana Fröl., Hedya App. 1084
ocularis L., Tethea 1654
oculea L., Amphipoea 2360
oleracea L., Lacanobia 2160
olerella Zell., Depressaria App. 681
olivalis D. & S., Udea App. 1392
olivana Treits., Olethreutes App. 1075
olivata D. & S., Colostygia 1774
oliviella Fabr., Esperia App. 650
oo L., Dicycla 2315
ophiogramma Esp., Apamea 2336
opima Hb., Orthosia 2184
opressana Treits., Gypsonoma App. 1170
or D. & S., Tethea 1655
orbitella Zell., Coleophora App. 511
orbona Hufn., Noctua 2108
ornata Scop., Scopula 1687
ornitopus Hufn., Lithophane 2237
osseana Scop., Eana App. 1029
osteodactylus Zell., Leioptilus App. 1520
ostrinalis Hb., Pyrausta App. 1363
oxyacanthae L., Allophyes 2245
oxyacanthae Frey., Phyllonorycter App. 323
oxyacanthella Stt., Stigmella App. 100

pabulatricula Brahm., Apamea 2332
padella L., Yponomeuta App. 425
palaeana Hb., Aphelia App. 989
paleacea Esp., Enargia 2313
pallens L., Mythimna 2199
pallescentella Stt., Tinea App. 245
palliatella Zinc., Coleophora App. 537

pallidactyla Haw., Platyptilia App. 1504
pallidata Hufn., Evergestis App. 1358
palpina Cl., Pterostoma 2011
paludella Hb., Calamotropha App. 1929
palumbella D. & S., Pempelia App. 1442
pamphilus L., Coenonympha 1627
paphia L., Argynnis 1608
papilionaria L., Geometra 1666
parasitella Hb., Triaxomera App. 224
parenthesella L., Ypsolopha App. 460
paripennella Zell., Coleophora App. 560
paripunctella Thunb., Teleiodes App. 773
parthenias L., Archiearis 1661
pascuella L., Crambus App. 1294
pasiuana Hb., Cnephasia App. 1022
pastinacella Dup., Depressaria App. 672
pastinum Treits., Lygephila 2466
pavonia L., Saturnia 1643
pectinataria Knoch, Colostygia 1776
pellionella L., Tinea App. 240
pennaria Hb., Colotois 1923
pentadactyla L., Pterophorus App. 1513
perlella Scop., Crambus App. 1302
permutana Dup., Acleris App. 1049
perplexa D. & S., Hadena 2167
perpygmaeella Doubl., Stigmella App. 79
persicariae L., Melanchra 2171
petasitis Doubl., Hydraecia 2362
petiverella L., Dichrorampha App. 1273
pfeifferella Hb., Antispila App. 158
phasianipennella Hb., Calybites App. 296
phlaeas L., Lycaena 1561
phragmitella Hb., Chilo App. 1290
phragmitella Stt., Limnaecia App. 898
phragmitidis Hb., Arenostola 2377
phyganella Hb., Diurnea App. 664
piercei Ob., Aethes App. 942
pigra Hufn., Clostera 2017
pilosaria D. & S., Apocheima 1926
pinella L., Catoptria App. 1313
pinguinalis L., Aglossa App. 1421
pinguis Haw., Euzophera App. 1470
piniaria L., Bupalus 1954
piniariella Zell., Ocnerostoma App. 444
pinicolana Doubl., Rhyacionia App. 1211
pinivorana Lein. & Zell., Rhyacionia App. 1212
pisi L., Ceramica 2163
plagiata L., Aplocera 1867
plagicolella Stt., Stigmella App. 67
plantaginis L., Parasemia 2056
plecta L., Ochropleura 2102
plumbagana Treits., Dichrorampha App. 1276
plumbana Scop., Dichrorampha App. 1285
plumbella D. & S., Yponomeuta App. 430
podalirius Scop., Iphiclides 1540
podana Scop., Archips App. 977
politella Stt., Bryotropha App. 788
polychloros L., Nymphalis 1594
polycommata D. & S., Trichopteryx 1880
pomella Vaugh., Stigmella App. 78
pomonella L., Cydia App. 1261
populana Fabr., Pammene App. 1232
populata L., Eulithis 1756
populella Cl., Anacampsis App. 853
populeti Stt., Orthosia 2185
populetorum Zell., Caloptilia App. 281
populi L., Laothoe 1981
populi L., Poecilocampa 1631
porata L., Cyclophora 1679
porcellus L., Deilephila 1992
porphyrea D. & S., Lycophotia 2118
porrectella L., Plutella App. 465
potatoria L., Philudoria 1640
praeangusta Haw., Batrachedra App. 878

praecox L., Ochropleura 2009
prasina D. & S., Anaplectoides 2138
prasinana L., Bena 2421
pratella L., Crambus App. 1300
primaria Haw., Theria 1960
proboscidalis L., Hypena 2477
procellata D. & S., Melanthia 1784
profundana D. & S., Eudemis App. 113
pronuba L., Noctua 2107
propinquella Treits., Agonopterix App. 696
proximella Hb., Teleiodes App. 770
pruinata Hufn., Pseudoterpna 1665
prunalis D. & S., Udea App. 1390
prunaria L., Angerona 1924
prunata L., Eulithis 1754
pruni L., Strymonidia 1559
pruniana Hb., Hedya App. 1082
pseudospratella Stt., Hoffmannophila App. 647
psi L., Acronicta 2284
pudibunda L., Calliteara 2028
pudorina D. & S., Mythimna 2196
pulchellata Steph., Eupithecia 1817
pulcherrimella Stt., Depressaria App. 676
pulchrina Haw., Autographa 2442
pulveraria L., Plagodis 1903
pulverosella Stt., Bohemannia App. 19i
punctaria L., Cyclophora 1680
punctidactyla Haw., Amblyptilia App. 1498
punctinalis Scop., Serraca 1944
punctulata D. & S., Aethalura 1951
purpuralis L., Pyrausta App. 1362
purpurea Haw., Agonopteryx App. 691
pusaria L., Cabera 1995
pusillata D. & S., Eupithecia 1854
puta Hb., Agrotis 2092
putris L., Axylia 2098
pygarga Hufn., Lythacodia 2410
pygmaeella D. & S., Argyresthia App. 412
pygmina Haw., Photedes 2350
pyralella D. & S., Scoparia App. 1333
pyraliata D. & S., Eulithis 1758
pyralina D. & S., Cosmia 2319
pyramidea L., Amphipyra 2297
pyrella Vill., Swammerdamia App. 438
pyrina L., Zeuzera 161
pyritoides Hufn., Habrosyne 1653
pyrrhulipennella Zell., Coleophora App. 541

quadrifasiata Cl., Xanthorhoe 1726
quadrimaculana Haw., Endothenia App. 1104
quadrimaculella Boh., Bohemannia App. 19
quadripuncta Haw., Oegoconia App. 870
quadripunctaria Poda, Euplagia 2067
quercana Fab., Carcina App. 658
quercifolia L., Gastropacha 1642
quercifoliella Zell., Phyllonorycter App. 320
quercinaria Hufn., Ennomos 1912
quercus L., Lasiocampa 1637
quercus L., Quercusia 1557

rajella L., Phyllonorycter App. 345
ramella L., Epinotia App. 1134
rapae L., Pieris 1550
raschkiella Zell., Mompha App. 883
ratzeburgiana Ratz., Zeiraphera App. 1163
ravida D. & S., Spaelotis 2113
reaumurella L., Adelia App. 150
recens Hb., Orgyia 2025
rectangulata L., Chloroclystis 1860
rectifasciana Haw., Isotrias App. 1062ii
regiana Zell., Pammene App. 1234
reliquana Hb., Lobesia App. 1106
remissa Bh., Apamea 2330
repandana Fab., Acrobasis App. 1463

repandaria Hufn., Epione 1907
repandata L., Alcis 1941
resplendella Stt., Heliozela App. 156
reticularis L., Diasemia App. 1402
reticulata Geoze, Heliophobus 2153
retinella Zell., Argyresthia App. 415
retusa L., Ipimorpha 2311
revayana Scop., Nycteola 2423
rhamni L., Gonepteryx 1546
rhedella Cl., Pammene App. 1239
rhombana D. & S., Acleris App. 1042
rhomboidaria D. & S., Peribatodes 1937
rhomboidea Esp., Xestia 2131
rhomboidella L., Hypatima App. 858
ribeata Cl., Deileptenia 1940
ridens Fabr., Polyploca 1660
ripae Hb., Agrotis 2093
rivata Hb., Epirrhoe 1739
rivulana Scop., Olethreutes App. 1068
rivularis Fabr., Hadena 2166
roborana D. & S., Epiblema App. 1178
roboraria D. & S., Boarmia 1943
roborella D. & S., Phyctia App. 1452
roborella Joh., Stigmella App. 86
robustella Jäck., Caloptilia App. 287
rosaceana Schläg., Celypha App. 1064
rosaecolana Dbl., Epiblema App. 1177
roseana L., Archips App. 981
rostralis L., Hypena 2480
ruberata Frey., Hydriomena 1779
rubi L., Callophrys 1555
rubi View., Diarsia 2123
rubi L., Macrothylacia 1638
rubigana Treits., Aethes App. 946
rubiginata D. & S., Plemyria 1766
rubiginosana H.-S., Epinotia App. 1146
rubricollis L., Atolmis 2039
rubricosa D. & S., Cerastis 2139
rufa Haw., Coenobia 2379
rufata Fabr., Chesias 1865
rufescens Haw., Brachmia App. 868
ruficapitella Haw., Stigmella App. 84
ruficiliana Haw., Falseuncaria App. 960
ruficornis Hufn., Drymonia 2015
rufifasciata Haw., Gymnoscellis 1862
rufimatrella Scop., Adelia App. 152
rufocinerea Haw., Elachista App. 608
rugosana Hb., Phtheochroa App. 925
rumicis L., Acronicta 2289
ruralis Scop., Pleuroptya App. 1405

sacraria L., Rhodometra 1716
salaciella Treits., Opostega App. 119
salicata Bh., Coenotephria 1753
salicella L., Hedya App. 1086
salicicolella Sirc., Phyllonorycter App. 335
salicis L., Leucoma 2031
salicis Stt., Stigmella App. 68
salopiella Stt., Eriocrania App. 10
sambucaria L., Ourapteryx 1922
sangii Wood, Eriocrania App. 12
sanguinalis L., Pyrausta App. 1364
sannio L., Diacrisia 2059
sarcitrella L., Endrosis App. 648
satyrata Hb., Eupithecia 1828
saucia Hb., Peridroma 2119
saxicolella Dup., see vestianella L. App. 572
scabrella L., Ypsolopha App. 455
scabriuscula L., Dypterygia 2301
scalella Scop., Pseudotelphusa App. 764
schalleriana L., Acleris App. 1047
schreberella Fabr., Phyllonorycter App. 352
schulziana Fabr., Olethreutes App. 1073
schumacherana Fabr., Olindia App. 1062i

198

schwarziellus Zell., Nematopogon App. 141
scolopacina Esp., Apamea 2335
scopariella Zell., Phyllonorycter App. 340
scoticella Stt., Parornix App. 305
scriptella Hb., Teleiodes App. 766
scutulana D. & S., Epiblema App. 1184
secalella Remm, Mesapamea 2343a
secalis L., Mesapamea 2343
segetum D. & S., Agrotis 2087
sehestediana Fabr., Choreutis App. 387
selasella Hb., Agriphila App. 1303
selene D. & S., Boloria 1600
semele L., Hipparchia 1621
semibrunnea Haw., Lithophane 2235
semicostella Hb., Sophronia App. 841
semifasciana Haw., Apotomis App. 1089
semifulvella Haw., Tinea App. 246
semifusca Haw., Argyresthia App. 419
semipurpurella Steph., Eriocrania App. 13
semitestacella Curt., Argyresthia App. 423
senecionana Hb., Clepsis App. 991
senectella Zell., Bryotropha App. 782
senex Hb., Thumatha 2035
septembrella Stt., Fomoria App. 42
sequana Hb., Dichrorampha App. 1278
sequax Haw., Teleiodes App. 775
sequella Cl., Ypsolopha App. 462
seriata Sch., Idaea 1707
sericea Gregs., Eilema 2048
sericealis Scop., Rivula 2474
sericiella Haw., Heliozella App. 154
serratella L., Coleophora App. 493
servillana Dup., Cydia App. 1256
sexalata Retz. Pterapherapteryx 1882
sexguttella Thun., Chrysoesthia App. 747
sexstrigata Haw., Xestia 2133
silaceata D. & S., Ecliptopera 1759
similis Stt., Bryotropha App. 780
similis Feuss., Euproctis 2030
simpliciata Haw., Eupithecia 1842
simpliciella Steph., Glyphipteryx App. 391
simulans Hufn., Rhyacia 2105
sinapis L., Leptidea 1541
siterata Hufn., Chloroclysta 1760
smeathmanniana Fabr., Aethes App. 947
socia Hufn., see hepatica Cl. 2236
sociana Haw., Gypsonoma App. 1168
sociella L., Aphomia App. 1428
solandriana L., Epinotia App. 1156
solidaginis Hb., Lithomia 2233
solitariella Zell., Coleophora App. 525
sorbi Frey., Phyllonorycter App. 324
sorbiella Treits., Argyresthia App. 413
sordens Hufn., Apamea 2334
sordidana Hb., Epinotia App. 1153
sororculella Hb., Gelechia App. 802a
sororiata Hb., Carsia 1866
spadicearia D. & S., Xanthorhoe 1724
sparganella Thunb., Orthotaelia App. 470
sparsana D. & S., Acleris App. 1041
spartifoliella Hb., Leucoptera App. 256
spectrana Treits., Clepsis App. 993
spheciformis D. & S., Synanthedon 375
sphinx Hufn., Brachionycha 2227
spinella Schr., Coleophora App. 495
spiniana Dup., Pammene App. 1231
spinicolella Zell., Phyllonorycter App. 329
splendana Hb., Cydia App. 1260
splendidulana Guen., Pammene App. 1223
sponsa L., Catocala 2455
stabilis D. & S., see cerasi Fabr. 2187
stagnata Don., Nymphula App. 1350
statices L., Adscita 163
steinkellneriana D. & S., Semioscopis App. 667

stellatarum L., Macroglossum 1984
stephensiana Doubl., Cnephasia App. 1020
stettinensis Nic., Phyllonorycter App. 357
sticticana Fab., Epiblema App. 1186
stigmatella Fabr., Caloptilia App. 288
straminata Bork., Idaea 1715
straminea Treits., Mythimna 2197
straminea Haw., Stenodes App. 936
straminella D. & S., Agriphila App. 1304
strataria Hufn., Biston 1930
stratiotata L., Parapoynx App. 1348
striana D. & S., Celypha App. 1063
striatella Zell., Isophrictis App. 729
strigana Fabr., Lathronympha App. 1219
strigilis L., Oligia 2337
strigillaria Hb., Perconia 1970
strigillata L., Herminia 2488
strigulatella Zell., Phyllonorycter App. 344
strobilella L., Cydia App. 1254
suasa D. & S., Lacanobia 2159
subbimaculella Haw., Ectoedemia App. 38
subfasciella Steph., Cedestis App. 443
subfusca Haw., Scoparia App. 1332
subfuscata Haw., Eupithecia 1837
sublustris Esp., Apamea 2323
subocellea Steph., Elachista App. 613
subpurpurella Zell., Eriocrania App. 6
subsericeata Haw., Idaea 1709
subtusa D. & S., Ipimorpha 2312
succedana D. & S., Cydia App. 1255
succenturiata L., Eupithecia 1839
suffumata D. & S., Lampropteryx 1750
suffusella Dougl., Monochroa App. 741
sulphurella Fabr., Esperia App. 649
suspecta Hb., Parastichtis 2313i
svenssoni Johan., Stigmella App. 87
swammerdamella L., Nematopogon App. 140
sylvata Scop., Abraxas 1885
sylvata D. & S., Hydrelia 1817
sylvella L., Ypsolopha App. 459
sylvestris Poda, Thymelicus 1526
sylvina L., Hepialus 15
syringaria L., Apeira 1910
syringella Fabr., Caloptilia App. 293

taeniolella Zell., Syncopacma App. 847
taenialis Hb., Schrankia 2482
tages L., Erynnis 1532
tantillaria Boisd., Eupithecia 1857
tapezella L., Trichophaga App. 234
tarsipennalis Treits., Herminia 2489
tedella Cl., Epinotia App. 1142
temerata D. & S., Lomographa 1958
tenerana D. & S., Epinotia App. 1139
tenebrata Scop., Panemeria 2397
tenebrella Hb., Monochroa App. 735
tenebrosana Dup., Cydia App. 1246
tenuiata Hb., Eupithecia 1811
ternata Schr., Scopula 1694
terrella D. & S., Bryotropha App. 787
tersata D. & S., Horisme 1782
testata L., Eulithis 1755
tetragonana Steph., Epiblema App. 1180
tetralunaria Hufn., Selenia 1919
tetraquetrana Haw., Epinotia App. 1137
thalassina Hufn., Lacanobia 2158
tiliae L., Mimas 1979
tipuliformis Cl., Synanthedon 373
tithonus L., Pyronia 1625
tityrella Stt., Stigmella App. 77
tityus L., Hemaris 1982
togata Esp., Xanthia 2273
torquillella Zell., Parornix App. 309
tragopoginis Cl., Amphipyra 2299

transluscens Meyr., Tinea App. 242
transversa Hufn., Eupsilia 2256
transversata Hufn., Philereme 1792
trapezina L., Cosmia 2318
tremula Cl., Pheosia 2007
triangulum Hufn., Xestia 2128
triatomea Haw., Elachista App. 611
tricolorella Haw., Caryocolum App. 834
tridactyla L., Pterophorus App. 1510
tridens D. & S., Acronicta 2283
trifasciella Haw., Phyllonorycter App. 361
trifolii Curt., Coleophora App. 516
trifolii Hufn., Dicestra 2145
trifolii Esp., Zygaena 170
trigemina Werneb., Abrostola 2449
trigeminata Haw., Idaea 1711
trigonella L., Epinotia App. 1151
trigrammica Hufn., Charanyca 2380
trimaculana Haw., Epiblema App. 1176
trimaculella Haw., Stigmella App. 73
trimaculosa Esp., Polia 2149
tringipennella Zell., Aspilapteryx App. 294
trinotella Thunb., Tinea App. 247
triplasia L., Abrostola 2450
tripunctaria H.-S., Eupithecia 1835
trisignaria H.-S., Eupithecia 1826
tristata L., Epirrhoe 1737
tristella D. & S., Agriphila App. 1305
tristrigella Haw., Phyllonorycter App. 356
tritici L., Euxoa 2081
truncata Hufn., Chloroclysta 1764
tubulosa Retz., Taleporia App. 181
tullia Mull., Coenonympha 1628
tunbergella Fabr., Micropterix App. 1
turbidana Hb., Apotomis App. 1092
turca L., Mythimna 2191
typhae Thunb., Nonagria 2369
typica L., Naenia 2136

uddmanniana L., Epiblema App. 1175
ulicetella Stt., Agonopteryx App. 705
uliginosellus Zell., Crambus App. 1297
ulmella Zell., Bucculatrix App. 274
ulmifoliella Hb., Phyllonorycter App. 353
ulmivora Fol., Stigmella App. 80
umbra Hufn., Pyrrhia 2399
umbratica L., Cucullia 2216
umbrosella Zell., Bryotropha App. 778
unangulata Haw., Euphyia 1794
unanimis Hb., Apamea 2331
uncella D. & S., Ancylis App. 1118
unculana Haw., Ancylis App. 1125
undulana D. & S., Orthotaenia App. 1087
undulata L., Rheumaptera 1789
unicolorella Dup., Eulamprotes App. 732
unipunctella Steph., Phyllocnistis App. 368
unitella Hb., Batia App. 642

urticae L., Aglais 1593
urticae Esp., Spilosoma 2062
ustella Cl., Ypsolopha App. 461

vaccinii L., Conistra 2258
valerianata Hb., Eupithecia 1821
variata D. & S., Thera. See britannica Turn. 1769
variegana D. & S., Acleris App. 1048
v-ata Haw., Chloroclystis 1858
venata Brem. & Grey., Ochlodes 1531
venosata Fab., Eupithecia 1823
verbasci L., Cucullia 2221
versicolor Bork., Oligia 2338
versicolora L., Endromis 1644
verticalis L., Sitochroa App. 1371
vespiformis L., Synanthedon 374
vestianella L., Coleophora App. 572
vestigialis Hufn., Agrotis 2085
vetulata D. & S., Philereme 1791
vetusta Hb., Xylena 2241
v-flava Haw., Oinophila App. 250i
viburnana D. & S., Aphelia App. 988
villica L., Arctia 2058
viminalis Fabr., Brachylomia 2225
viminetella Zell., Coleophora App. 504
viminiella Sirc., Phyllonorycter App. 333
vinula L., Cerura 1995
viretata Hb., Acasis 1883
virgaureae Stt., Coleophora App. 564
virgaureata Doubl., Eupithecia 1851
virgella Thunb., Lita App. 794
viridana L., Tortrix App. 1033
viridaria Cl., Phytometra 2470
viridata L., Chlorissa 1670
viscerella Stt., Stigmella App. 95
vitalbata D. & S., Horisme 1781
vitellina Hb., Mythimna 2195
vittata Bork., Orthonama 1719
vittella L., Ypsolopha App. 463
vulgana Fröl., Capua App. 1007
vulgata Haw., Eupithecia 1834

w-album Knoch, Strymonidia 1558
wauaria L., Semiothisa 1897
weaverella Scott, Monopis App. 228
weirana Dougl., Strophedra App. 1221
w-latinum Hufn., Lacanobia 2157

xanthographa D. & S., Xestia 2134
xylosteana L., Archips App. 980
xylostella L., Plutella App. 464

yeatiana Fabr., Agonopteryx App. 714
ypsillon D. & S., Parastichtis 2314

ziczac L., Eligmodonta 2003
zoegana L., Agapeta App. 938

Index of English Names

Alchymist 2464
Alder 2281
Alder Kitten 1996
Angle Shades 2306
Angle-striped Sallow 2313
Annulet 1964
Anomalous Wainscot 2394
Antler 2176
Apple Fruit Moth App. 418
Apple Leaf Miner App. 263
Apple Pygmy App. 97
Archer's Dart 2085
Argent and Sable 1787
Ash Bud Moth App. 449
Ash Pug 1849
August Thorn 1912
Autumn Green Carpet 1761
Autumnal Moth 1797
Autumnal Rustic 2117

Barred Chestnut 2121
Barred Fruit-tree Tortrix App. 970
Barred Hook-tip 1647
Barred Red 1962
Barred Rivulet 1804
Barred Sallow 2272
Barred Straw 1758
Barred Tooth-striped 1880
Barred Umber 1903
Barred Yellow 1765
Bath White 1552
Beaded Chestnut 2267
Beautiful Brocade 2156
Beautiful Carpet 1748
Beautiful China-mark App. 1350
Beautiful Golden Y 2442
Beautiful Hook-tip 2473
Beautiful Snout 2476
Beatiful Yellow Underwing 2142
Bee Moth App. 1428
Beech Green Carpet 1774
Bilberry Pug 1861
Bilberry Tortrix App. 988
Birch Mocha 1677
Bird-cherry Ermine App. 424
Bird's Wing 2301
Black Arches 2033
Black Hairstreak 1559
Black Rustic 2232
Black-veined White 1548
Blackneck 2466
Bleached Pug 1833
Blomer's Rivulet 1872
Blood-vein 1682
Blossom Underwing 2183
Blotched Emerald 1667
Blue-bordered Carpet 1766
Bordered Beauty 1907
Bordered Gothic 2153
Bordered Grey 1938
Bordered Pug 1839
Bordered Sallow 2399
Bordered White 1954
Bramble Shoot Moth App. 1175
Brick 2262
Brimstone 1546
Brimstone Moth 1906
Brindled Beauty 1927
Brindled Green 2248
Brindled Pug 1852

Brindled White-spot 1950
Broad-barred White 2164
Broad-bordered Bee Hawk-moth 1983
Broad-bordered Yellow Underwing 2110
Broken-barred Carpet 1773
Broom 2163
Broom-tip 1865
Brown Argus 1572
Brown China-mark App. 1345
Brown Crescent 2368
Brown Hairstreak 1556
Brown House-moth App. 647
Brown Oak Tortrix App. 979
Brown Rustic 2302
Brown Scallop 1791
Brown Silver-lines 1902
Brown-line Bright-eye 2192
Brown-spot Pinion 2266
Brown-tail 2029
Brown-veined Wainscot 2371
Brussels Lace 1945
Bud Moth App. 1205
Buff Arches 1653
Buff Ermine 2061
Buff-tip 1994
Bulrush Wainscot 2369
Burnet Companion 2463
Burnished Brass 2434
Butterbur 2362
Buttoned Snout 2480

Cabbage 2154
Cacao Moth App. 1473
Camberwell Beauty 1596
Campanula Pug 1836
Campion 2166
Canary-shouldered Thorn 1913
Centre-barred Sallow 2269
Chalk Carpet 1731
Chalk Hill Blue 1575
Chamomile Shark 2214
Chequered Fruit-tree Tortrix App. 969
Cherry Bark Moth App. 1216
Chestnut 2258
Chevron 1755
Chimney Sweeper 1870
Chinese Character 1651
Chocolate-tip 2019
Cinnabar 2069
Clay Triple-lines 1681
Clay Wainscot 2193
Clifden Nonpariel 2451
Cloaked Minor 2341
Clouded Border 1887
Clouded Buff 2059
Clouded Brindle 2327
Clouded Drab 2188
Clouded Magpie 1885
Clouded Silver 1958
Clouded Yellow 1545
Clouded-bordered Brindle 2326
Cocksfoot Moth App. 391
Codling Moth App. 1261
Comma 1598
Common Blue 1574
Common Carpet 1738
Common Emerald 1669
Common Fat-foot 2488
Common Heath 1952
Common Lutestring 1657
Common Marbled Carpet 1764

Common Pug   1834
Common Quaker   2187
Common Rustic   2343
Common Swift   17
Common Wainscot   2199
Common Wave   1956
Common White Wave   1955
Confused   2329
Convolvulus Hawk-moth   1972
Copper Underwing   2297
Cork Moth   App. 216
Corn Moth   App. 215
Coronet   2291
Coxcomb Prominent   2008
Cream Wave   1693
Cream-bordered Green Pea   2418
Cream-spot Tiger   2058
Crescent Striped   2325
Currant Clearwing   373
Currant Pug   1832
Cyclamen Tortrix   App. 993

Dark Arches   2321
Dark Brocade   2250
Dark Chestnut   2259
Dark Crimson Underwing   2455
Dark Dagger   2283
Dark Fruit-tree Tortrix   App. 972
Dark Green Fritillary   1607
Dark Marbled Carpet   1762
Dark Spectacle   2449
Dark Spinach   1749
Dark Sword-grass   2091
Dark Umber   1792
Dark-barred Twin-spot Carpet   1725
Death's Head Hawk-moth   1973
December Moth   1631
Deep Brown Dart   2231
Delicate Wainscot   2195
Dew Moth   2036
Diamond-back Moth   App. 464
Dingy Footman   2044
Dingy Shell   1874
Dingy Skipper   1532
Dismal Shears   2314
Dog's Tooth   2159
Dot Moth   2155
Dotted Border   1934
Dotted Clay   2130
Dotted Rustic   2105
Double Dart   2114
Double Kidney   2311
Double Square-spot   2128
Double Line   2191
Double Lobed   2336
Double-striped Pug   1862
Drinker   1640
Duke of Burgundy   1582
Dun Bar   2318
Dusky Brocade   2330
Dusky Sallow   2352
Dusky Thorn   1914
Dusky-lemon Sallow   2275
Dwarf Cream Wave   1705
Dwarf Pug   1857

Ear Moth   2360
Early Grey   2243
Early Moth   1960
Early Thorn   1917
Early Tooth-striped   1881
Elephant Hawk-moth   1991
Emperor   1643
Engrailed   1947
Eyed Hawk-moth   1980

False Mocha   1679
Fan-foot   2489
Feathered Gothic   2178
Feathered Ranunculus   2255
Feathered Thorn   1923
Fen Wainscot   2377
Fern Carpet   1782
Figure of Eight   2020
Figure of Eighty   1654
Five-spot Burnet   170
Flame   2098
Flame Carpet   1722
Flame Shoulder   2102
Flax Tortrix   App. 1021
Flounced Chestnut   2265
Flounced Rustic   2353
Forester   163
Four-dotted Footman   2040
Fox Moth   1638
Foxglove Pug   1817
Freyer's Pug   1827
Frosted Green   1660
Frosted Orange   2364
Fruitlet-mining Tortrix   App. 1239

Galium Carpet   1740
Garden Carpet   1728
Garden Dart   2082
Garden Pebble   App. 1356
Garden Rose Tortrix   App. 1048
Garden Tiger   2057
Gatekeeper   1625
Gem   1720
Ghost Swift   14
Glaucous Shears   2162
Goat Moth   162
Gold Spangle   2444
Gold Spot   2439
Gold Swift   16
Gold Triangle   App. 1413
Golden Plusia   2437
Goldenrod Brindle   2233
Goldenrod Pug   1851
Gothic   2136
Grass Emerald   1665
Grass Rivulet   1807
Grass Wave   1970
Great Brocade   2137
Great Oak Beauty   1943
Great Oak Tortrix   App. 1033
Great Prominent   2005
Green Arches   2138
Green Carpet   1776
Green Hairstreak   1555
Green Pug   1860
Green Silver-lines   2422
Green-brindled Crescent   2245
Green-veined White   1551
Grey Arches   2150
Grey Birch   1951
Grey Chi   2254
Grey Dagger   2284
Grey Mountain Carpet   1744
Grey Pine Carpet   1768
Grey Pug   1837
Grey Scallop Bar   1969
Grey Shoulder-knot   2237
Grey Tortrix   App. 1020
Grizzled Skipper   1534

Haworth's Minor   2367
Haworth's Pug   1813
Hawthorn Moth   App. 450
Heart and Club   2088
Heart and Dart   2089

Heart Moth 2315
Heath Rivulet 1805
Heath Rustic 2135
Hebrew Character 2190
Hedge Rustic 2177
Herald 2469
High Brown Fritillary 1606
Holly Blue 1580
Holly Tortrix App. 1159
Honeysuckle Moth App. 453
Hornet Clearwing 370
Hummingbird Hawk-moth 1984

Ingrailed Clay 2120
Iron Prominent 2000

Jersey Tiger 2067
July Belle 1734
July Highflyer 1777
Juniper Carpet 1771
Juniper Pug 1854

Kentish Glory 1644

Laburnum Leaf Miner App. 254
Lace Border 1687
Lackey 1634
Lappet 1642
Larch Case-bearer App. 526
Larch Pug 1856
Large Blue 1581
Large Ear 2357
Large Emerald 1666
Large Fruit-tree Tortrix App. 977
Large Heath 1628
Large Nutmeg 2333
Large Ranunculus 2252
Large Red-belted Clearwing 381
Large Skipper 1531
Large Tabby App. 1421
Large Thorn 1911
Large Tortoiseshell 1594
Large Twin-spot Carpet 1726
Large Wainscot 2375
Large Wall 1616
Large White 1549
Large Yellow Underwing 2107
Latticed Heath 1894
Lead Belle 1733
Lead-coloured Drab 2185
Least Black Arches 2078
Least Yellow Underwing 2112
Leopard Moth 161
Lesser Broad-bordered Yellow Underwing 2111
Lesser Common Rustic, *see* Remm's Rustic 2343a
Lesser Cream Wave 1692
Lesser Lichen Case-bearer App. 177
Lesser Swallow Prominent 2006
Lesser Treble-bar 1868
Lesser Wax Moth App. 1426
Lesser-spotted Pinion 2316
Light Arches 2322
Light Brocade 2157
Light Emerald 1961
Light Grey Tortrix App. 1024
Light Knot Grass 2286
Light Orange Underwing 1662
Light Feathered Rustic 2084
Lilac Beauty 1910
Lime Hawk-moth 1979
Lime-speck Pug 1825
Ling Pug 1831
Little Emerald 1674
Little Thorn 1901

Lunar Hornet Clearing 371
Lunar Marbled Brown 2015
Lunar Thorn 1918
Lunar Underwing 2270
Lunar Yellow Underwing 2108
Lunar-spotted Pinion 2319
Lychnis 2173

Magpie 1884
Maiden's Blush 1680
Mallow 1745
Manchester Treble-bar 1866
Maple Pug 1812
Map-winged Swift 18
Marbled Beauty 2293
Marbled Brown 2014
Marbled Coronet 2171
Marbled Green 2295
Marbled Minor 2337
Marbled Orchard Tortrix App. 1083
Marbled White 1620
Marbled White-spot 2410
March Moth 1663
Marsh Fritillary 1610
Marsh Oblique-barred 2485
May Highflyer 1778
Meadow Brown 1626
Meal Moth App. 1417
Mediterranean Flour Moth App. 1475
Merveille du Jour 2247
Middle-barred Minor 2340
Miller 2280
Minor Shoulder-knot 2225
Mocha 1676
Monarch 1630
Mother of Pearl App. 1405
Mother Shipton 2462
Mottled Beauty 1941
Mottled Grey 1775
Mottled Pug 1819
Mottled Rustic 2387
Mottled Umber 1935
Mountain Ringlet 1617
Mouse Moth 2299
Mullein 2221
Muslin Moth 2063
Muslin Footman 2038

Narrow-bordered Bee Hawk-moth 1982
Narrow-bordered Five-spot Burnet 171
Narrow-winged Pug 1846
Neglected Rustic 2132
Netted Pug 1823
Northern Drab 2184
Northern Footman 2048
Northern Rustic 2104
Northern Spinach 1756
Northern Winter Moth 1800
November Moth 1795
Nut Bud Moth App. 1139
Nut Leaf Blister Moth App. 342
Nutmeg 2145
Nut-tree Tussock 2425

Oak Beauty 1930
Oak Eggar 1637
Oak Hook-tip 1646
Oak Lutestring 1658
Oak-tree Pug 1853
Oblique Carpet 1719
Ochreous Pug 1844
Old Lady 2300
Olive 2312
Orange Moth 1924

Orange Sallow   2271
Orange Swift   15
Orange Underwing   1661
Orange Upperwing   2257
Orange-tip   1553
Orchard Ermine   App. 425

Painted Lady   1591
Pale Brindled Beauty   1926
Pale Clouded Yellow   1543
Pale Mottled Willow   2389
Pale November Moth   1796
Pale Oak Beauty   1944
Pale Oak Eggar   1632
Pale Pinion   2236
Pale Prominent   2011
Pale Shining Brown   2148
Pale Tussock   2028
Pale-shouldered Brocade   2158
Parsnip Moth   App. 672
Pea Moth   App. 1257
Peach Blossom   1652
Peacock   1597
Peacock Moth   1889
Pear Leaf Blister Moth   App. 260
Pearl-bordered Fritillary   1601
Pearly Underwing   2119
Pebble Hook-tip   1648
Pebble Prominent   2008
Peppered Moth   1931
Phoenix   1754
Pine Beauty   2179
Pine Carpet   1767
Pine Shoot Moth   App. 1210
Pinion-streaked Snout   2484
Pink-barred Sallow   2273
Pistol Case-bearer   App. 533
Plain Clay   2103
Plain Golden Y   2443
Plain Pug   1842
Plain Wave   1715
Plum Fruit Moth   App. 1247
Plum Tortrix   App. 1082
Poplar Grey   2278
Poplar Hawk-moth   1981
Poplar Kitten   1998
Poplar Lutestring   1655
Portland Moth   2099
Powdered Quaker   2186
Pretty Chalk Carpet   1784
Privet Hawk-moth   1976
Purple Bar   1752
Purple Clay   2122
Purple Emperor   1585
Purple Hairstreak   1557
Purple Thorn   1919
Purple-bordered Gold   1698
Puss Moth   1995

Red Admiral   1590
Red Chestnut   2139
Red Northern Carpet   1723
Red Sword-grass   2241
Red Twin-spot Carpet   1724
Red Underwing   2452
Red-barred Tortrix   App. 1010
Red-green Carpet   1760
Red-line Quaker   2263
Red-necked Footman   2039
Reddish Light Arches   2323
Remm's Rustic   2343a
Rhomboid Tortrix   App. 1042
Riband Wave   1713
Ringed China-mark   1713

Ringlet   1629
Rivulet   1802
Rose Leaf Miner   App. 92
Rose Tortrix   App. 981
Rosy Footman   2037
Rosy Minor   2342
Rosy Rustic   2361
Round-winged Muslin Moth   2035
Ruby Tiger   2064
Ruddy Highflyer   1779
Rufous Minor   2338
Rush Veneer   App. 1398
Rustic   2382
Rustic Shoulder-knot   2334

Sallow   2274
Sallow Kitten   1997
Sandy Carpet   1808
Satellite   2256
Satin Beauty   1940
Satin Lutestring   1656
Satin Wave   1709
Satyr Pug   1828
Scalloped Hazel   1920
Scalloped Hook-tip   1645
Scalloped Oak   1921
Scalloped Shell   1789
Scarce Footman   2047
Scarce Silver Y   2447
Scarce Silver-lines   2421
Scarce Swallowtail   1540
Scarce Tissue   1788
Scarce Umber   1933
Scarce Vapourer   2025
Scorched Carpet   1888
Scorched Wing   1904
September Thorn   1915
Seraphim   1897
Setaceous Hebrew Character   2126
Shaded Broad-bar   1732
Shark   2216
Sharp-angled Carpet   1794
Shears   2147
Short-cloaked   2077
Shoulder-stripe   1746
Shoulder-striped Carpet   2205
Shuttle-shaped Dart   2092
Silver Arches   2149
Silver Y   2441
Silver-ground Carpet   1727
Silver-striped Hawk-moth   1993
Silver-studded Blue   1571
Silver-washed Fritillary   1608
Single-dotted Wave   1708
Six-spot Burnet   169
Six-striped Rustic   2133
Skin Moth   App. 227
Slender Brindle   2335
Slender Pug   1811
Sloe Pug   1859
Small Angle Shades   2305
Small Argent and Sable   1737
Small Autumnal Moth   1798
Small Blood-vein   1690
Small Blue   1569
Small Brindled Beauty   1925
Small China-mark   App. 1354
Small Chocolate-tip   2017
Small Clouded Brindle   2331
Small Copper   1561
Small Dotted Buff   2345
Small Dusty Wave   1707
Small Eggar   1633
Small Elephant Hawk-moth   1992

Small Emerald   1673
Small Engrailed   1948
Small Fan-foot   2492
Small Fan-footed Wave   1702
Small Grass Emerald   1670
Small Heath   1627
Small Lappet   1641
Small Magpie   App. 1376
Small Pearl-bodied Fritillary   1600
Small Phoenix   1759
Small Purple-barred   2470
Small Quaker   2182
Small Rivulet   1803
Small Rufous   2379
Small Seraphim   1882
Small Scallop   1712
Small Skipper   1526
Small Square-spot   2123
Small Tortoiseshell   1593
Smoky Wainscot   2350
Small Waved Umber   1781
Small White   1550
Small White Wave   1875
Small Yellow Underwing   2397
Small Yellow Wave   1876
Smoky Wainscot   2198
Smoky Wave   1694
Snout   2477
Southern Wainscot   2197
Speckled Footman   2053
Speckled Wood   1614
Speckled Yellow   1909
Spectacle   2450
Spinach   1757
Spindle Ermine   App. 427
Spotted Shoot Moth   App. 1212
Sprawler   2227
Spring Usher   1932
Spruce Carpet   1769
Square-spot Dart   2080
Square-spot Rustic   2134
Square-spotted Clay   2131
Stout Dart   2113
Straw Dot   2474
Straw Underwing   2303
Streak   1864
Streamer   1747
Striped Hawk-moth   1990
Striped Twin-spot Carpet   1753
Striped Wainscot   2196
Sub-angled Wave   1684
Suspected   2313i
Svensson's Copper Underwing   2298
Swallow Prominent   2007
Swallowtail Moth   1922
Sword Grass   2242

Tapestry Moth   App. 234
Tawny Marbled Minor   2339
Tawny Pinion   2235
Tawny Shears   2167
Tawny Speckled Pug   1838
Tawny-barred Angle   1893

Thyme Pug   1843
Timothy Tortrix   App. 989
Tissue   1790
Toadflax Pug   1816
Treble Brown Spot   1711
Treble Lines   2380
Treble-bar   1867
Treble-spotted Clay   2127
Triple-spotted Pug   1826
True Lover's Knot   2118
Turnip Moth   2087
Twenty-plume Moth   App. 1288
Twin-spot Carpet   1809
Twin-spot Quaker   2189

Uncertain   2381
Union Rustic   2332

Valerian Pug   1821
Vapourer   2026
Variegated Golden Tortrix   App. 980
Vestal   1716
V-moth   1897
V-Pug   1858

Wall   1615
Water Carpet   1750
Water Ermine   2062
Water Veneer   App. 1331
Waved Black   2475
Waved Carpet   1877
Waved Umber   1936
Welsh Wave   1873
White Admiral   1584
White Colon   2152
White Ermine   2060
White Plume   App. 1513
White Satin   2031
White-barred Clearwing   375
White-letter Hairstreak   1558
White-line Dart   2081
White-line Snout   2482
White-marked   2140
White-pinion Spotted   1957
White-shouldered House-moth   App. 648
White-spotted Pinion   2317
White-spotted Pug   1835
Willow Beauty   1937
Willow Tortrix   App. 1147
Winter Moth   1799
Wood Carpet   1739
Wood Tiger   2056
Wood White   1541
Wormwood Shark   2211
Wormwood Pug   1830

Yellow Horned   1659
Yellow Shell   1742
Yellow-barred Brindle   1883
Yellow-legged Clearwing   374
Yellow-line Quaker   2264
Yellow-tail   2030
Yellow V Moth   App. 277